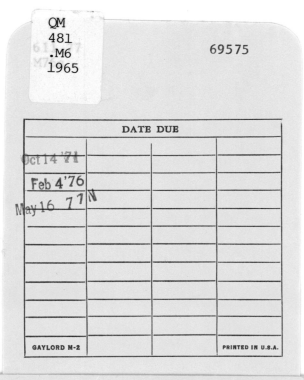

The Structure
and
Function of
SKIN

The Structure
and
Function of
SKIN

WILLIAM MONTAGNA

Brown University
Providence, Rhode Island

Second Edition

1962

ACADEMIC PRESS
New York and London

ACADEMIC PRESS INC.
111 FIFTH AVENUE
NEW YORK, NEW YORK 10003

United Kingdom Edition
Published by
ACADEMIC PRESS INC. (LONDON) LTD.
BERKELEY SQUARE HOUSE, LONDON W. 1

Library of Congress Catalog Card Number 56-6609

First Edition, 1956
Second Edition, 1962

Second Printing, 1965

PREFACE

This book, more than a simple revision of the volume published in 1956, has been largely rewritten to include as much of our more recent findings on the histology, cytology, histochemistry, ultrastructure, and function of the skin as is possible within manageable bounds. The book also deals with the known or presumptive functional significance of the cutaneous structures. Much of what is covered here is a gathering of studies carried out in our laboratory at Brown University and in the laboratories of many friends and colleagues in the United States and abroad. The book is written for those who are interested in the physiology, biochemistry, and anatomy of skin and for the dermatologist and the pathologist.

As in any endeavor of this magnitude, I have received the help of many. My collaborator and friend, Dr. Richard A. Ellis, has been enormously generous with his time, vigor, imaginativeness, and loyalty. The many friends in dermatology and pathology who have remained patient and indulgent for many years are, to a large measure, responsible for what progress I have made. There are too many of them to be named; I hope, therefore, that they will forgive me for expressing my particular gratitude to Dr. Herbert Fanger of the Rhode Island Hospital, Dr. Albert M. Kligman of the University of Pennsylvania Hospital, Dr. John S. Strauss of Boston University, and Dr. Tsuyoshi Aoki of Tohoku University. My various investigations on the biology of skin have, for years, been supported by the United States Public Health Service, without the help of which little of this work would have been accomplished. I express my thanks also to the Colgate-Palmolive Company and Chesebrough-Pond's, Inc. for their financial support, made liberally and without conditions.

All of the drawings were executed by Mrs. Margaret C. Gould. My assistant, Mrs. Jeung S. Yun, has been indispensable in every aspect of the preparation of the book. Finally, my secretary, Mrs. Elaine T. Grenier, has worked diligently, intelligently, and with enthusiasm. To all of these and the many unnamed ones my humble thanks and gratitude.

WILLIAM MONTAGNA

Brown University
Providence, Rhode Island
November, 1961

CONTENTS

INTRODUCTION

When the physiologist, the biochemist, and the biophysicist began to use the electron microscope, the study of form became important again. Although no study done well needs an apology, this trend of events has bestowed respectability on anatomy. Microscopy has today progressed so far that morphology is ever closer to the molecular level, and we are taking the first real step in beginning to read metabolic activity from structure. Structure and function are gradually, but surely, merging. "There is no difference between structure and function; they are the two sides of the same coin. If structure does not tell us anything about function, it means we have not looked at it correctly" (Szent-Györgyi, 1951). We must now become literate enough to read function out of design, for anatomy is the theater in which physiology takes place (Sherrington, 1950).

I had not begun to appreciate fully the extent of the recent advances of our knowledge of the biology of skin until I began to rewrite this book. Everything that one writes becomes progressively obsolete with each passing day; yet, basic truths do not change. Let us hope, therefore, that this book will become obsolete because of incompleteness rather than because of wrong information or of misinterpretation of facts.

It is difficult to resist the temptation to write long reviews of all that has been found during the last six years, particularly by the electron microscopist. There is, in this book, just enough consideration of fine structure to give the reader a general survey, orientation, and an appreciation of it. In most instances descriptions of fine structure have been woven with the descriptions of cytology and histochemistry.

The field of investigative dermatology has grown to such proportions that soon it will no longer be possible to gather all of the basic information in one single, manageable volume. The narrow horizons and the general ignorance of the author in 1956 made the writing of "The Structure and Function of Skin," a relatively easy task. There were few books in the English language at that time which covered the subject concisely. Since then, however, so much progress has been made on all fronts that one cannot cover adequately even a few of the more important aspects of normal skin. Electron microscopy of the skin, in its infancy in 1955, has improved enormously and has taught us much. In writing this book, therefore, I have had to use great discretion in deciding what to include and what to omit.

The publication of Rothman's book, "The Physiology and Biochemistry of Skin" in 1954, a landmark in modern dermatological science, and the subsequent publication of the first edition of "The Structure and Function of Skin" in 1956 gave us a capsule of knowledge of the biological properties of the skin. Now, aside from those books which deal with the pathology of the skin, and of these none is superior to Pillsbury *et al.* (1956), a number of basic books on skin have been published in English. The reader who wishes more information on some of the aspects of the biology of skin is referred to the following books:

1. Hamilton, J. B. (ed.) 1951. The Growth, Replacement, and Types of Hair. *Ann. N.Y. Acad. Sci.* **53**: 461-752.
2. Gordon, M. (ed.) 1953. "Pigment Cell Growth." Academic Press, New York.
3. Rothman, S. 1954. "Physiology and Biochemistry of the Skin." The University of Chicago Press, Chicago, Illinois.
4. Kuno, Y. 1956. "Human Perspiration." C. C Thomas, Springfield, Illinois.
5. Montagna, W. and R. A. Ellis (eds.) 1958. "The Biology of Hair Growth." Academic Press, New York.
6. Rothman, S. (ed.) 1959. "The Human Integument." American Association for the Advancement of Science, Washington, D.C.
7. Riley, J. F. 1959. "The Mast Cells." E. & S. Livingstone Ltd., Edinburgh and London, England.
8. Wolstenholme, G. E. W. and M. O'Connor (eds.) 1959. "Pain and Itch, Nervous Mechanisms," Ciba Foundation Study Group No. I. Little, Brown and Co., Boston, Massachusetts.
9. Hurley, H. J. and W. B. Shelley. 1960. "The Human Apocrine Sweat Gland in Health and Disease." C. C Thomas, Springfield, Illinois.
10. Montagna, W. (ed.) 1960. "Advances in the Biology of Skin," Vol. I: Cutaneous Innervation. Pergamon Press, New York.
11. Rook, A. (ed.) 1960. "Progress in the Biological Sciences in Relation to Dermatology." Cambridge Univ. Press, London and New York.
12. Winkelmann, R. K. 1960. "Nerve Endings in Normal and Pathologic Skin." C. C Thomas, Springfield, Illinois.

Never has so much foolishness been published together with so many good things on the biology of skin. There have been numerous assertions and denials of the positive action on the skin of carcinogens, vitamins, hormones, and other biologically active substances. The many clinical observations have often been too empirical to be taken entirely seriously. Most of these have suffered more from the difficulty of controlling the experiments on man than from bad experimental design. Those who have tested the effects of physicochemical agents upon the skin have often looked for changes when they did not understand normal structure. For example, recently someone brought to my laboratory a large number of histological preparations of the skin of hairless mice which had been treated with certain hormones. These preparations were of very poor quality, and the age and the sex of the animals used had not been recorded. What can be learned from such studies? Reports on "changes" due to the hormone in this and in similar cases are hardly valid.

Scientists are fond of constructing hierarchies of disciplines, placing their own specialty at the top. The biochemist, or worse still, the biochemically inclined morphologist, assumes that if an investigation is not quantitative it is of no consequence, since numbers in biology have a magic power. Yet, quantitative studies of substances in an organ as heterogeneous as skin is are scarcely significant if they ignore the area from which it was removed, the particular cutaneous appendages present, and the age, sex, and race of the individual. Such studies should be accepted on a qualitative basis, regardless of figures and charts. Histochemistry, with all of its faults and lack of refinements, is at least useful in demonstrating where a certain chemical entity is located; it could be found in the epidermis, sweat glands, sebaceous glands, hair follicles, or in the structures of the dermis. For example, we have known for some time that skin contains peptidase, and have assumed that the enzyme is mostly present in the lymphocytes pooled in the dermis (Fruton, 1946). Histochemical tests show us that the dermal papilla of hair follicles, the secretory coil of eccrine sweat glands and other cutaneous structures contain aminopeptidase (Adachi and Montagna, 1961). Since there are many more such examples, it is not a matter of which is the more elite, significant science for they are all significant and each complements the other.

Although the histologist usually recognizes a multitude of morphological imprints that reflect the different physiological states of an organ, he is seldom aware of these differences in skin. Still, skin is a heterogeneous organ, consisting of several suborgans, all of which have their peculiar patterns of growth, differentiation, and activity. To overlook these differences is to fail to understand the most fundamental feature of the anatomy of skin. Unfortunately, the histologist rarely knows the history of the human skin which comes to his laboratory. Progress will be slow as long as the rhythms of growth and quiescence, of activity and rest in epidermal appendages are overlooked. The investigative dermatologist must begin to look into the credentials of the skin he studies if his results are to be intelligible.

Few appreciate the many differences that exist in the skin from one part of the body to another. There is a peculiar topographic uniqueness in the skin of man. The scalp, the various regions of the face, the axilla, the abdomen are as different from each other as the skin of different species might be. Furthermore, even the same cutaneous appendages have different properties in the various areas of the body. Consider, for instance, that whereas the hair follicles of the scalp of men in certain circumstances undergo regressive aging changes in response to androgens, those over the rest of the body mostly grow larger under the same influence. The enormous species differences that exist in anatomy, physiology, and biochemistry of skin are far too poorly appreciated. For example, vitamin A, which readily passes through the intact skin of the rat and guinea pig, does not go through the skin of man in spite of heroic efforts. To understand certain things in the skin of laboratory animals makes us better informed about skin in general, but does not necessarily tell us what might be found in the skin of man. We must keep exploring the skin of all mammals, and particularly that of the primates to obtain a better perspective of the biological attributes of the skin of man.

The investigator who looks at skin with an interest in research finds, on the one hand, in textbooks, neat accounts of the structure and function of skin which rarely suggest the enormity of our ignorance and the tenuousness of even the most widely accepted concepts; on the other hand, he faces the vast and dissonant literature. Anatomical terminology is often meaningless. The appraisal of contradictory findings is difficult. For example, if one has decided to study the effect of vitamin A on skin, he is likely to gain the impression that deficiency of this vitamin causes extensive hyperkeratosis and an atrophy of hair follicles, and that on the contrary, excessive amounts of the vitamin cause epilation and a hypertrophy of the epidermis. Yet the skin of vitamin A-deficient animals is relatively normal although the hair follicles may not grow (Loewenthal, 1954). In laboratory animals large doses of vitamin A cause epilation of hairs from resting follicles but have no effect upon growing follicles or upon keratinization of the epidermis (Montagna, 1954; Rademacher and Montagna, 1956). It is important that the investigator understand first the normal biological potentialities of skin and the varieties of its modes of expression.

The cytologist has avoided the study of skin because it is hard to prepare well-oriented sections free from tears, folds, and compression. This has left many gaps in our knowledge.

The pathology of skin seems to be limitless. Skin disorders may be intrinsic, extrinsic, and psychosomatic. It is not always possible to be sure when the origin of the disturbance is due to any one, two, or all three of these factors. Skin responds to different disturbances in the same way. Generalized hyperplasia of the epidermis, for example, can be caused by a great variety of stimuli which range from mite bites to exposure to X-rays.

Skin is the barrier as well as the principal organ of communication between the animal and its environment. It reflects the well-being or the disorders of the organism. It is a turbulent tissue, and it grows, differentiates, and renews itself at all times. Skin is versatile; it performs numerous functions and produces several and different end products. One of the most important functions of skin is the normal production, by the surface epidermis, of a dead horny layer of keratin which protects the organism from its environment. Nearly all of the complex biological syntheses which take place in the epidermis are aimed toward this end point. The entire cutaneous system can be considered a huge glandular system. With the exception of the sweat glands the system is essentially a holocrine one. Thus, keratin, like sebum, can be thought of as a secretion of the epidermis and hair follicles.

With the formation of a holocrine secretion, epidermal cells die. Keratin and sebum are accumulations of these dead cells. All of the living, metabolic processes in each epidermal cell are devoted to the manufacture of lipids or fibrous protein. As these syntheses are completed, life is sapped away from each cell. The fully keratinized, dead cells are monuments which testify to the orderliness and grace of the dying process in epidermal cells.

However different the cutaneous appendages may be superficially, each is composed of cells the indifferent forms of which are morphologically and dynamically similar. Indifferent epidermal cells are structurally indistinguishable from the indifferent sebaceous cells or from the cells in the matrix of hair follicles. Under stress of injury, or in abnormal conditions, these cells respond similarly. Epidermal cells are biased to differentiate in a particular prescribed way, yet they behave as if they were equipotential. Indifferent epidermal cells, regardless of the appendage that they are a part of, may differentiate into sebaceous cells or they may form keratin.

There is increasing evidence that epidermal cells differentiate into different appendages and maintain their integrity only as long as they are under the inductive, regulatory influence of the stroma. With this in mind, the particular regulatory mechanism must be sought in the dermis rather than only in the epidermis.

It is customary to consider the cutaneous appendages as independently functioning entities. Yet, there is an interdependence of growth and function between the sebaceous glands and hair follicles, and between the pilosebaceous units and the whole skin. There are striking morphological and chemical differences between skin in which hair follicles are growing and that in which they are resting. In the mouse and rat the whole skin is several times thicker when hair is growing than when it is resting. Furthermore, skin with growing hair contains glycogen and more cytochrome oxidase per gram of tissue than skin with resting hair.

Skin is an ever-changing organ, and many of its alterations are reflected by changes in its morphology. A good knowledge of its histology, and particularly its chemical cytology, should give greater significance to its physiology and biochemistry. Whenever possible the discussions in this book have centered around human skin, but the many gaps in our knowledge about human skin have had to be filled with observations from the skin of other mammals. There are species differences, but the basic biologic principles are probably similar in most mammalian skin. Rather than indulge in extrapolations, however, let us first be sure of our ground by knowing facts.

The list of references at the end of each chapter is really cut down to a minimum, in spite of its apparent length. Interminable exhaustive bibliographies which have not been selected with care are of little use to the reader not already familiar with the literature. The references here should give a useful list of the major works in the field.

It should become evident to the reader that in spite of the many basic phenomena that underlie the biological properties of all cutaneous appendages, it is not safe to generalize. In fact, the more we know about each entity the more distinctive it becomes. Our knowledge about cutaneous structures has expanded so much that to treat each fully would require several volumes. Thus, the chapters on the pilary system and the dermis are short in proportion to their importance. There is nothing on the nail because we have been unsatisfied with the work done so far either by us or by others. Horstmann (1957), however, has an excellent account of it.

The following people have made notable contributions to various sections of this book.

Chapter 2. The Epidermis

PROFESSOR W. S. BULLOUGH, Birkbeck College, University of London, England. Section on mitotic activity.

DR. A. GEDEON MATOLTSY, Boston University, School of Medicine, Boston, Massachusetts. Section on keratohyalin and keratinization.

DR. GEORGE SZABÓ, Massachusetts General Hospital, Boston Massachusetts. Section on melanin.

DR. GEORGE ODLAND, Washington University School of Medicine, Seattle, Washington, has furnished most of the superlative electron micrographs of the epidermis.

Chapter 3. The Dermis

DR. GIUSEPPE MORETTI, University of Genova, Italy, has written the greater part of the section on cutaneous blood vessels.

Chapter 5. The Sebaceous Glands

DR. JOHN S. STRAUSS, Boston University School of Medicine, Boston, Massachusetts, has advised the author on sebaceous glands.

Chapters 6 and 7. The Eccrine Sweat Glands and The Apocrine Sweat Glands

DR. TSUYOSHI AOKI, Tohoku University School of Medicine, Sendai, Japan, has contributed reviews of our knowledge of the pharmacological properties of eccrine and apocrine sweat glands.

REFERENCES

Adachi, K. and W. Montagna. 1961. Histology and cytochemistry of human skin. XXII. Sites of leucine aminopeptidase (LAP). *J. Invest. Dermatol.* (In press.)

Fruton, J. S. 1946. On the proteolytic enzymes of animal tissues. V. Peptidases of skin, lung, and serum. *J. Biol. Chem.* **166**: 721-738.

Gordon, M. (ed.) 1953. "Pigment Cell Growth." Academic Press, New York.

Hamilton, J. B. (ed.) 1951. The Growth, Replacement, and Types of Hair. *Ann. N.Y. Acad. Sci.* **53**: 461-752.

Horstmann, E. 1957. Die Haut. *In* "Handbuch der mikroskopischen Anatomie des Menschen" (W. von Möllendorff, ed.), Vol. III/3, pp. 1-276. Springer, Berlin.

Hurley, H. J. and W. B. Shelley. 1960. "The Human Apocrine Sweat Gland in Health and Disease." C. C Thomas, Springfield, Illinois.

Kuno, Y. 1956. "Human Perspiration." C. C Thomas, Springfield, Illinois.

Loewenthal, L. A. 1954. The effects of vitamin A deficiency on skin and hair growth in mice. Ph.D. Thesis. Brown University, Providence, Rhode Island.

Montagna, W. 1954. Penetration and local effect of vitamin A on the skin of the guinea pig. *Proc. Soc. Exptl. Biol. Med.* **86**: 668-672.

Montagna, W. (ed.) 1960. "Advances in Biology of Skin," Vol. I: Cutaneous Innervation. Pergamon Press, New York.

Montagna, W. and R. A. Ellis (eds.) 1958. "The Biology of Hair Growth." Academic Press, New York.

Montagna, W. and R. A. Ellis (eds.) 1961. "Advances in Biology of Skin," Cutaneous Blood Vessels and Circulation. Pergamon Press, New York.

Montagna, W. and R. A. Ellis (eds.) 1962. "Advances in Biology of Skin," Vol. III. The Eccrine Sweat Glands. Pergamon Press, New York.

Pillsbury, D. M., W. B. Shelley and A. M. Kligman. 1956. "Dermatology." Saunders, Philadelphia, Pennsylvania.

Rademacher, A. H. and W. Montagna.   1956.   Response of the skin of mice to
    methyl ether of vitamin A and vitamin A palmitate. *J. Invest. Dermatol.* **26**:
    69-75.
Riley, J. F.   1959.   "The Mast Cells." E. & S. Livingstone Ltd., Edinburgh and
    London, England.
Rook, A. (ed.)   1960.   "Progress in the Biological Sciences in Relation to Derma-
    tology." Cambridge Univ. Press, London and New York.
Rothman, S.   1954.   "Physiology and Biochemistry of the Skin." The University of
    Chicago Press, Chicago, Illinois.
Rothman, S. (ed.)   1959.   "The Human Integument." American Association for the
    Advancement of Science, Washington, D.C.
Sherrington, C.   1950.   "Man on His Nature." Doubleday, Garden City, New York.
Szent-Györgyi, A.   1951.   *Trans. 1st Josiah Macy Conf. on Connective Tissues,*
    pp. 35-36.
Winkelmann, R. K.   1960.   "Nerve Endings in Normal and Pathologic Skin." C. C
    Thomas, Springfield, Illinois.
Wolstenholme, G. E. W. and M. O'Connor (eds.)   1959.   "Pain and Itch Nervous
    Mechanisms," Ciba Foundation Study Group No. 1. Little, Brown, Boston,
    Massachusetts.

CHAPTER 1

The General Anatomy of Skin

Skin, or *integumentum commune,* envelops the entire surface of the body, and its epithelium is continuous with that of the external orifices of the digestive, respiratory, and urinogenital systems. Skin is smooth in some regions of the body but rough and furrowed in others. It is glabrous in some areas, downy in others, and hairy in still others (Figs. 1–5). It is thick, horny, and taut in some areas, but thin, translucent, and pliable in others. Over bony regions it is firm; over soft parts it may glide easily and may be flaccid. The thickness and character of the superficial horny layer and the amount and nature of the secretion of the cutaneous glands in any one region make skin rough or smooth, dry or moist. Tensile strength and resiliency vary in the different regions of the body, in different individuals, and in the same individual with aging. Differences in the amount of pigments, in vascularity, and in the thickness of the dead outer layer determine the color of skin, which differs greatly from individual to individual. To understand normal skin, one must be familiar with these and other differences and understand the factors which bring about such differences, yet also be aware of the basic similarities in all skin regardless of apparent differences.

Skin is a veneered or stratified tissue. At the surface is the epithelium called *epidermis,* and under this is a connective tissue layer called *corium* or *dermis.* Underneath the dermis is the fatty layer, or *panniculus adiposus.* Below the fatty layer is a discontinuous, flat sheet of skeletal muscle called *panniculus carnosus,* which separates the rest of the body tissues from the integument. The panniculus carnosus, well developed in most mammals, is vestigial in man, and the *platysma* of the neck is all that remains of it. Bundles of smooth muscle fibers, *arrectores pilorum* muscles attached to hair follicles, are widely distributed in the dermis. Oriented smooth muscle fibers are found in the dermis of the scrotum and the penis, where they form a relatively continuous layer called the *tunica dartos.* Smooth muscle fibers are also numerous in the nipple and aureola of the breast and in the perineal and circumanal regions. A bed of loose areolar tissue, or *tela subcutanea,* binds the skin to the superficial skeletal muscles and to other tissues. Integumentary appendages such as hairs, quills, horns, claws, nails, hoofs, and cutaneous glands, grow directly from the epidermis and are integral parts of skin.

1

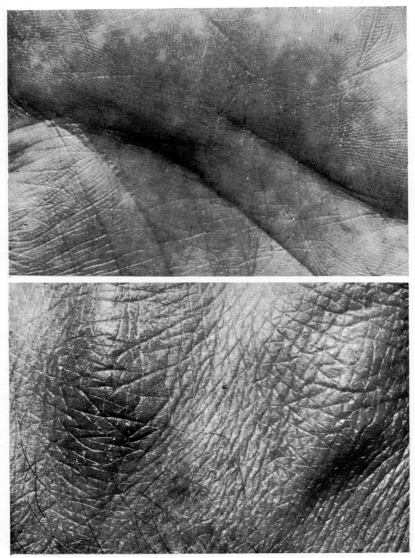

Fig. 1. In the upper figure the palmar surface of the hand shows sulci, ridges, and flexure lines. The lower figure shows the anconal surface of the middle and the third metacarpal joints. The many fine lines outline delicate geometric patterns. The hairs are very small and only a few of the coarse ones can be seen in the lower part of the figure. (Courtesy of Dr. R. R. Suskind.)

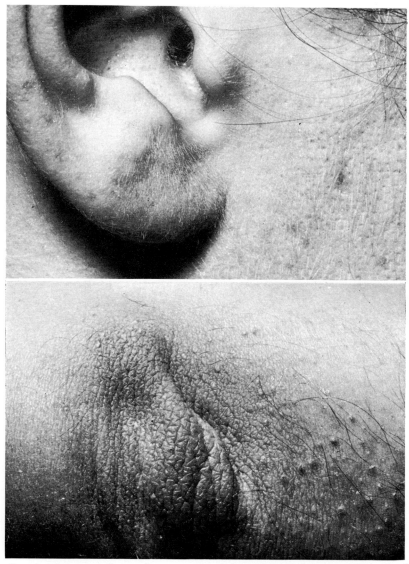

Fig. 2. The upper figure shows a part of the pinna of the ear and cheek of a woman. The entire surface, with the exception of the concha, is covered with very fine vellus hairs. In the concha are seen very large sebaceous orifices. The lower figure shows the wrinkled skin over the elbow. When the forearm is extended, the skin is loosely gathered over the olecranon. Fine, concentric flexure lines radiate out and become progressively smaller. A few coarse and fine hairs grow around the area. (Courtesy of Dr. R. R. Suskind.)

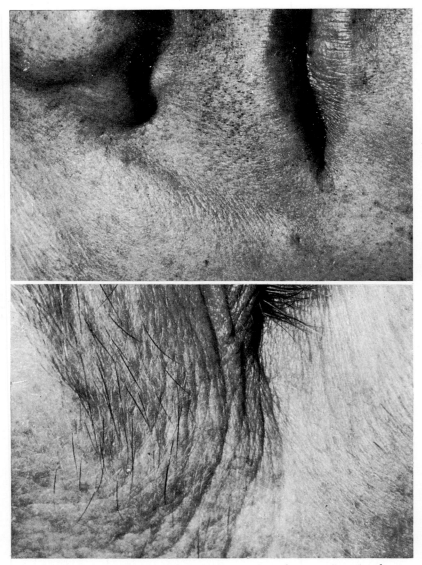

FIG. 3. The lower figure shows the skin lateral to the eye. Contrast the coarse hairs of the brows and cilia with the vellus hairs over the rest of the skin. "Crow's feet," acquired flexure lines, are very clear. The rest of the skin is furrowed by very fine intersecting lines which map out triangles and rhomboids. The upper figure illustrates the glabrous skin of the lips and the hirsute, shaved male skin. (Courtesy of Dr. R. R. Suskind.)

Skin is thicker on the dorsal and extensor surfaces than on the ventral and flexor surfaces. It is thicker in men than in women, but the tela subcutanea is usually thicker in women.

The capacity of the skin to move and be stretched depends on its own thickness, the number of its folds, its intrinsic elasticity, firmness of fixation by the tela subcutanea, and on the age of the individual (Figs. 3 and 5). The skin of the abdomen has the greatest capacity

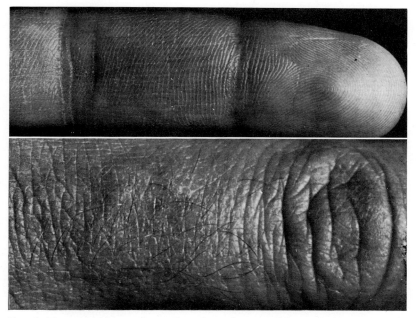

FIG. 4. The upper figure shows the sulci, ridges, and flexure lines on the palmar side of the index finger. The lower figure shows the skin of the dorsal surface of the same finger. The skin is flaccid and gathered into folds over the extended joint. (Courtesy of Dr. R. R. Suskind.)

for distension. When distended beyond its limits, skin becomes damaged. During pregnancy, for example, tears called *striae gravidarum* appear as red streaks on the surface of the skin. After parturition the tears remain as permanent white lines called *lineae albicantes*. Similar lines may be found in other parts of the body after the loss of excessive fat or swelling.

The skin of infants is relatively free of creases. The direct pull of muscles on the integument, such as on the face, the scrotum, and the circumanal region, causes permanent wrinkles to be formed. In old

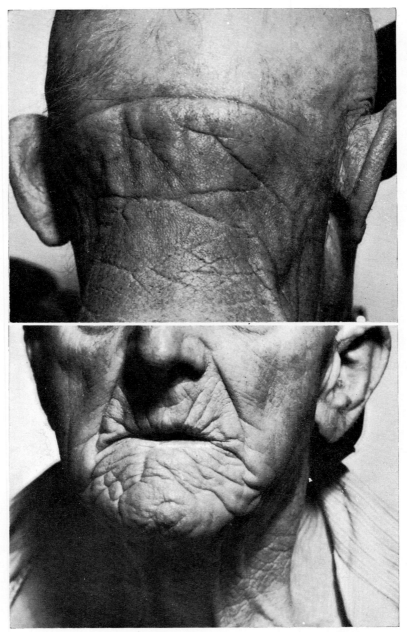

FIG. 5. The upper figure shows the deep grooves on the neck and back of the head, brought about by senile fatty degeneration of the skin. Below are the exaggerated, radiating folds of the edentulous mouth of a man 80 years old. (Courtesy of Dr. Francesco Ronchese.)

6

age, with the loss of elasticity and the decrease in the fat content of the tela subcutanea, the skin sags and becomes furrowed by wrinkles (Fig. 5). In addition to the wrinkles and furrows which are acquired with age and with use, skin possesses congenital flexure lines (Figs. 1 and 4). These are fixed creases, or "skin-joints," which indicate planes of firmer anchoring of the integument and the arrangement of the collagenous fibers in the dermis. The more loosely anchored skin on either side of these lines is folded passively toward them during movement.

FIG. 6. Actual print of the distal region of a right palm. The loop configuration in the middle of the upper portion (third interdigital area) is a true pattern; all other areas present are patternless configurations known as open fields. (Courtesy of Dr. H. Cummins.)

Flexure lines, ridges, furrows, and folds are formed in definite patterns in the embryo. The first ridges are formed in 13-week-old embryos on the palmar and plantar sides of the tips of the digits (Hale, 1952). These so-called ridges of Blaschko later extend over the entire palmar and plantar surfaces. The width of the furrows increases at the same rate as the growth of the hands and feet (Hale, 1949). The patterns established remain unchanged during the lifetime of each individual and can be altered only by damaging the underlying dermis.

The palmar and plantar surfaces are grooved by continuous alternating ridges and sulci (Figs. 1, 4, and 6). The details of these ridges and sulci and their configurations are collectively known as dermatoglyphics (Cummins, 1942, 1946). Each region has striking regional and individual structural variations. The configuration patterns of the ridges and sulci can be grouped according to the characters they have in common, but all areas have ridge details which are not matched elsewhere in the same individual or in any individual. This peculiar signa-

FIG. 7. Fingerprint with an arch pattern. (Courtesy of Eleanor Fife Montagna.)

ture and the permanence of dermatoglyphics make them the best known characters for personal identification. In dactyloscopy only the finger tips are normally used for identification, but other areas are just as individually distinctive. The ridge details are classed into pattern and patternless configurations (Figs. 6–10). The patterns consist of arches, loops, and whorls, particularly well developed on the tips of the digits. The patternless configurations are composed of straight or gently curved ridges. The function or significance of dermatoglyphics is perhaps to provide a better friction surface and to heighten tactile sensitivity. They

FIG. 8. Fingerprint with a loop pattern. This is actually a slight composite pattern. (Courtesy of Eleanor Fife Montagna.)

are definitely established during the third and fourth fetal months. The genetic control of dematoglyphics seems to be subject to a multiple factor control. In identical twins, or twins developed from a single fertilized egg, the dermatoglyphics are similar, but they are never identical

(Fig. 11). The right and left hand exhibit distinct differences in dermatoglyphics, some of which seem to be associated with manual dominance and handedness. Handedness, then, must be determined in the third and fourth fetal months. In women the dermatoglyphics have fewer whorls

Fig. 9. The author's left thumb print, outlining a whorl. (Courtesy of Eleanor Fife Montagna.)

and more arches on the fingers than in the men. Mentally deficient, epileptic, and insane persons often show marked deviations from normal trends in the patterns of dermatoglyphics. Presumably, the factors responsible for or predisposing to the conditions mentioned above must have been at work in or before the fourth fetal month to alter the dermatoglyphics being laid down at that time. Perhaps dermatoglyphics are affected by the same agencies which impair the nervous system (Cummins, 1946).

FIG. 10. A relatively typical composite pattern in which can be recognized a mixture of a partial loop and a partial arch. (Courtesy of Eleanor Fife Montagna.)

Fingerprints are impressions of the dermatoglyphics (Figs. 6–11). They contain about 99% water and 1% organic and inorganic compounds (Odén and von Hofsten, 1954). When the water evaporates, the remaining fingerprint can be visualized by the use of the ninhydrin

Fig. 11. The left thumb prints of identical twins showing *similar*, but not identical whorls. (Courtesy of Eleanor Fife Montagna.)

reaction (Odén and von Hofsten, 1954). In this way, even prints on old papers can be demonstrated with striking clarity. This presents interesting prospects in establishing the authenticity of old manuscripts and documents. Fingerprints can also be made visible with reagents that have been used in the visualization of protein spots in paper electrophoresis.

The skin over the body is furrowed by a specific pattern of grooves called the *cleavage lines of Langer*. These lines are roughly similar, but not identical in all individuals, and they are so oriented as to indicate the direction of elastic tension of skin. Cleavage lines, sulci and ridges in the palms and soles, inherent flexure lines, and the countless fine lines over the entire surface of the skin are all congenitally formed. Many flexure lines are acquired after birth through use. Occupational marks, for instance, are imprints acquired through excessive use. Aging also influences the acquisition of new flexure lines and the exaggeration of lines already present. Yet, in spite of the many devastating senile changes we know very little about what forms grooves and furrows in skin. Whether congenital or acquired, sulci, folds, or flexures have apparently similar anatomical features. They are brought about and influenced by the thickness of the epidermis, by a special disposition of the collagenous and elastic fibers in the dermis, by the underlying fat, by muscle pull, and by other factors.

REFERENCES

Cummins, H. 1942. The skin and mammary glands. *In* "Morris' Human Anatomy," 10th ed. Blakiston, Philadelphia.

Cummins, H. 1946. Dermatoglyphics: significant patternings of the body surface. *Yale J. Biol. Med.* **18**: 551-565.

Hale, A. R. 1949. Breadth of epidermal ridges in the human fetus and its relation to the growth of the hand and foot. *Anat. Record* **105**: 763-776.

Hale, A. R. 1952. Morphogenesis of volar skin in the human fetus. *Am. J. Anat.* **91**: 147-181.

Odén, S., and B. von Hofsten. 1954. Detection of fingerprints by the ninhydrin reaction. *Nature* **173**: 449-450.

CHAPTER 2

The Epidermis

Introduction

The epidermis is a stratified squamous epithelium that covers the entire outer surface of the body. *Squamous* describes only the cells in the upper strata which are flat and scale-like. Depending upon their position in the epidermis, the living cells may be cuboidal, columnar, fusiform, or polyhedral. Scattered between the lower cells of the basal layers of the epidermis are the dendritic melanocytes with branching processes, the cytoplasm of which manufactures melanin granules.

The properties of the epidermis show remarkable topographic differences. In the palms and soles the thick outer dead layer is compact, but in the epidermis of the general body surface, the thinner dead outer layer is flaky. On the dorsal surface of the terminal phalanges of the digits is the dense, translucent nail lamina, which is probably homologous to the dead outer layer of the epidermis. On the scalp, the face, the axilla, the scrotum, etc., the epidermis is thick; on the abdomen, the anticubital and the popliteal fossae, the medial side of the thigh, etc., it is thin. The epidermis is usually slightly translucent; over the cornea it is transparent. Since calluses and ectopic flexure lines are readily acquired, it might seem that regional differences are also brought about in response to usage, but this is not so. The epidermis of the soles and palms is thicker than that of the rest of the body, even in the embryo. The more prominent flexure lines are recognizable in 12-week-old human embryos (Medawar, 1953). Furthermore, when the epithelium of the foot pads is transplanted to regions where it is not subjected to its normal stresses of use, it retains its own characteristic features without acquiring those of the surrounding epidermis. Palmar flexure lines do not change when, as a result of injury, the skin is so displaced that the pattern of creasing and folding is altered. Fragments of guinea pig corneal epithelium grow very well when transplanted to the richly vascularized skin of the chest, but the epithelium does not lose its characteristic transparency. Conversely, body skin transplanted into the cornea retains its original properties. These tissues, then, seem to be genetically biased to differentiate in a certain way, and suggest that the epidermis differentiates within rigid limits. Medawar (1953) concludes that "the difference between a cell in the sole-of-foot and general body skin epithelium is of the same kind as that which distinguishes a thyroid

14

cell from a neurone, or an osteoblast from a melanocyte; it is of developmental origin, and it is perpetuated in somatic cellular heredity." Surely these differences in the epidermis seem to be "perpetuated in somatic cellular heredity," but it would be wrong to think of epidermal cells only in terms of rigidity, since they also show a remarkable willingness to modulate. The cells of the outer root sheath of hair follicles and those of the ducts of sweat glands, for example, readily grow and differentiate

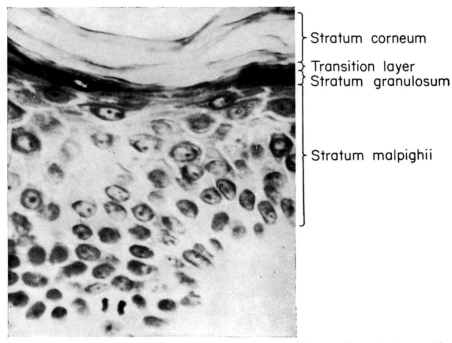

Stratum corneum

Transition layer
Stratum granulosum

Stratum malpighii

FIG. 1. Epidermis from the axilla, stained with the Papanicolau technique, with all of the layers indicated.

into surface epidermis during wound healing. The different types of epidermis are biased to differentiate in a particular way, rather than being unalterably determined tissues; during stress the bias is eliminated or overcome, unmasking the pluripotentiality shared by all cells derived from the epidermis. The cornea, or the epidermis of the palms and soles may have a bias which is more deeply rooted than that of the epidermis elsewhere.

The epidermis is composed of a living *stratum Malpighii*, which rests upon the dermis, and a dead, horny, superficial *stratum corneum* (Figs.

1 and 2). Malpighi, who first described it, called the living part of the epidermis, *rete mucosum*, a name still used by some anatomists, notably the French. For the sake of uniformity, stratum Malpighii is arbitrarily designated as the term of choice, since it pays homage to the man who first studied skin closely and is the most widely used. The stratum Malpighii is subdivided into several layers: the one-cell deep *basal layer,*

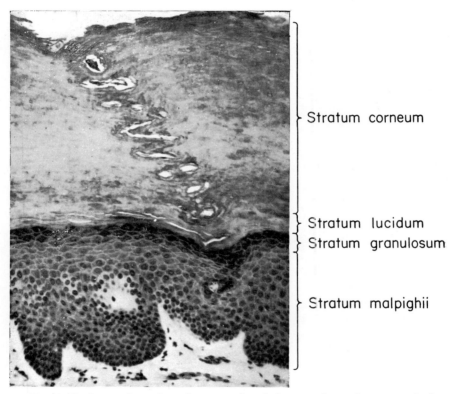

Stratum corneum

Stratum lucidum
Stratum granulosum

Stratum malpighii

FIG. 2. Epidermis from the palm, stained with hematoxylin and eosin, with the principal layers indicated. Observe the path of the duct of a sweat gland.

stratum basale, or *stratum germinativum* proper, in contact with the dermis, and a layer of variable thickness above it, the *stratum spinosum, prickle cell layer,* or *spinous layer.* As the cells of the spinous layer ascend to the surface they become progressively larger and accumulate granules that are readily stainable with most basic dyes, and the cells together establish a *granular layer* or *stratum granulosum.* Where the epidermis is very thick, a hyalin layer, seldom colored with histological stains, was named *stratum lucidum* by Oehl (Fig. 3). A pronounced stratum lucidum is not usually seen in the thinner epidermis of the general body surface, but a thin hyalin layer one or two cells deep just above the granular layer is found in all human epidermis (Fig. 1). The outer dead layer of the epidermis, *stratum corneum,* is composed of flattened cells, which when dissociated resemble scales. The cells of the thick stratum corneum of the "pressure areas," unlike those in the stratum corneum elsewhere in the body, retain some cellular integrity, are

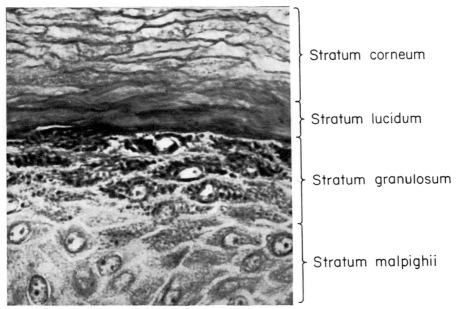

Stratum corneum

Stratum lucidum

Stratum granulosum

Stratum malpighii

FIG. 3. The epidermis of the sole, stained with hematoxylin and phloxin, showing the stratum granulosum and the stratum lucidum.

firmly cemented together, and do not exfoliate readily (Fig. 3). The thickness of the epidermis is variable, but it is characteristic of the different parts of the body. Although the epidermis is relatively similar in most mammals, the details may be enormously different in different species. In the mouse and the hamster the epidermis is very thin, consisting of a stratum Malpighii two or three cells thick; the spinous and granular layers are not distinct, and the stratum corneum varies in thickness from 5 to 10 layers of cells. In the thicker epidermis of the rat and guinea pig, the stratum Malpighii has well-defined basal, spinous, and granular layers. The epidermis of the volar surface of the pes, manus, and digits of all mammals shows all of the layers with conspicuous clarity. Among the higher primates, the epidermis of the chimpanzee probably resembles that of man most closely.

In human epidermis, the cells in the basal layer are usually cuboidal or columnar. Some cytoplasmic process from the cells located in the second layer, the "Flügelzellen" (Schaffer, 1933), may be squeezed between the basal cells and reach the basement membrane. The polyhedral cells of the stratum spinosum become increasingly flattened horizontally as they ascend to the stratum granulosum.

Development

Except for the early German investigators, only Achten (1959) and Pinkus (1958) have studied the development of human skin.

The epidermis of mammals consists of two distinct types of cells of different origins. The epidermal cells proper arise from the general surface ectoderm, and those of the pigmentary system come from the neural crest. These two systems are intimately associated, but if the pigment-producing cells are destroyed experimentally, or as a result of disorders, or if they are prevented from reaching the epidermis, the epidermal cells proper remain perfectly normal (Rawles, 1953).

In the generalizations that follow, the reader is reminded that there is great dyschrony in development of the epidermis in the different parts of the body. The epidermis of the back and chest, for example, remains relatively undifferentiated until the fourth fetal month while that of the eyebrows, lips, and nose has undergone great specialization even at 3 months.

The human embryo until 3 months is covered with a uniformly two-layered epidermis, each layer being one cell thick. The outer layer, the *periderm,* constitutes a protective covering, and the lower *germinative layer* is proliferative. The periderm corresponds to the corneal layer of the more advanced epidermis (Cedercreutz, 1907; Unna, 1889). The polymorphic cells of the periderm have a vacuolated cytoplasm and an oval nucleus. In older embryos the periderm is stratified, particularly on the forehead, eyebrows, and around the opening of the mouth and nostrils. The germinative layer of early embryos is composed of low cuboidal cells with large, clearly stainable nuclei, and a smooth basal surface, which allows an easy separation from the dermis. Later, the basal cells become columnar, with large, darkly staining nuclei, and in subsequent development the epidermis becomes pluristratified. The lower surface of the cells in contact with the dermis becomes serrated, as cytoplasmic processes grow into the upper layer of the dermis.

At about the fourth fetal month, a *stratum intermedium*, proliferated from the basal layer, develops between the basal layer and the periderm. This third layer is always more precocious around the mouth and nose. Toward the end of fetal life the intermediate layer, now called *stratum spinosum*, or *prickle cell layer*, is several cells thick. Together with the basal layer it forms ridges and convexities on the underside of the epidermis which fit into the concavities and over the ridges of the upper surface of the dermis. All epidermal cells make contact with adjacent ones by way of cytoplasmic projection called *intercellular bridges*. At the point of contact the cytoplasmic bridges form swellings called the *nodes of Bizzozero,* or *desmosomes.*

Although the periderm appears to undergo cornification during the second fetal month, its cells are actually viable, highly vacuolated (containing large amounts of glycogen and fat), and often contain superficial blebs that terminate in spherules on the surface. By the fourth and fifth months, the epidermis is pluristratified, and although it is cornified it contains very small amounts of —SH or —S—S— groups and cannot be keratinized; these cells remain laden with glycogen. Even in the palms and soles keratinization does not occur until later in the sixth and seventh months (Ernst, 1896). As long as the cells of the periderm retain stainable nuclei, the underlying cells of the stratum spinosum show no keratohyalin granules. At the end of the fifth month keratohyalin granules appear where the epidermis is thickest, and particularly around the orifices of the hair follicles, but the general epidermis has no stratum granulosum. Keratinization progresses only when the stratum granulosum is formed. During the later epochs of differentiation glycogen gradually fades away from the epidermis, leaving only traces in the stratum spinosum. There is a *pari passu* increase in the amounts of —SH and —S—S— groups in the epidermis as glycogen disappears.

Dermoepidermal Junction

In histological sections the dermoepidermal junction of human skin appears as an irregularly wavy line. Epidermal cones and ridges of different sizes, erroneously called *rete pegs,* but better called *ridges,* project into the dermis, enclosing between them vascularized dermal papillae. The underside of the epidermis separated from the dermis shows that the epidermal cones and ridges seen in sections are series of branching ridges and mounds of different sizes which enclose between them valleys and craters (Hoepke, 1927). Horstmann (1952, 1957) has minutely reviewed the architecture of the underside of the skin from all the principal regions of the human body, and those interested in the greater details of these patterns should consult his work. After whole skin is macerated in acetic acid, or "split" by treatment with trypsin, or with heat (Medawar, 1941, 1953), the epidermis can be cleanly separated from the underlying dermis and mounted underside up. Such

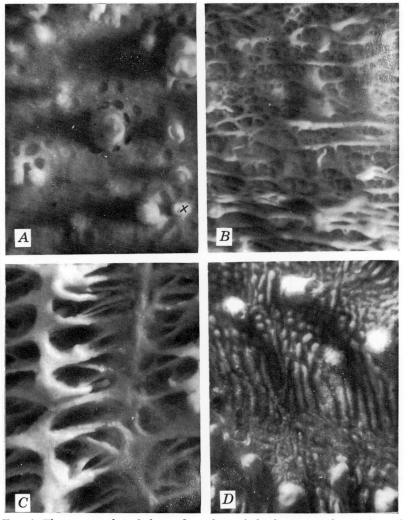

Fig. 4. The topography of the undersurface of the human epidermis from different regions of the body. (A) The forehead, with the ducts of the sweat glands concentrically arranged around hair follicles; the epidermal papillae, one marked with X, are clearly seen. (B) The *rima ani*; (C) the large toe; (D) the eyelid. From Horstmann (1952). (Reproduced by permission of the author and S. Karger.)

preparations show that in addition to complex systems of different-sized ridges, the underside of the epidermis is blistered by protuberances and pitted by craters (Figs. 4 and 5).

The characteristic regional differences in the architecture of the epidermal ridges and papillae are related to the arrangement of hairs and sudoriparous glands. The terminal portions of the sudoriparous glands

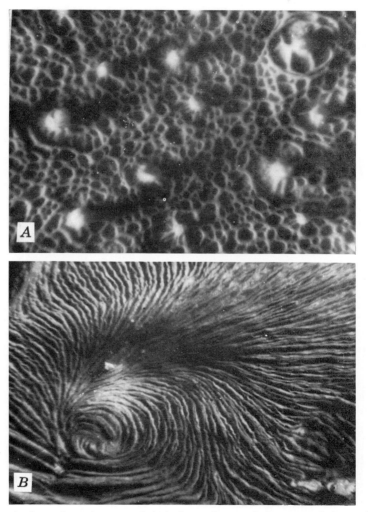

Fig. 5. The undersculpturing of (A) the epidermis of the ear, and the epidermis of a 21-cm embryo (B). From Hortsmann (1952). (Reproduced by permission of author and S. Karger.)

and ducts are usually arranged around the orifices of hair follicles in a clock-dial pattern. Epidermal ridges tend to radiate toward the ducts of sweat glands and hair follicles in rosette patterns. The ridges may also be arranged concentrically around these structures, defining cock-ade motifs. Rosettes occur most often around hair follicles and cockades around sweat glands. The hairs in those regions of the skin that are sub-ject to shearing forces are so small that the regions have erroneously been referred to as glabrous; the volar surfaces of the pes and manus are altogether glabrous and are provided with well-developed and elaborate ridges and papillae. The surfaces of contact between the epidermis and dermis, being interlocked, bear a negative imprint of each other.

It is common practice to consider human skin a uniform organ with the same properties throughout, and textbooks mostly give a standard description of the epidermis, dermis, and skin appendages. Yet, the character of the integument varies from region to region, and even the well-known variations are seldom mentioned. The distribution of skin appendages, for example, is not the same all over the body. Hair follicles vary in numbers, in size, and in their rate of growth. Compare, for ex-ample, the coarse hairs of the beard, eyebrow, pubic and axillary regions with the very fine down hairs on the forehead. There are great regional differences in the thickness of the epidermis and in the character of the dermoepidermal junctions. Let us consider here briefly only some of the regional variations of the dermoepidermal junction as described by Dr. George Szabó.

The head, the cheek and the upper lip are unique in having almost no epidermal ridges between the numerous hair follicles (Fig. 6A). Ridges, however, are well formed in the forehead, the scalp, chin, and ear skin, and they are arranged in characteristic diamond-shaped patterns in the eyelid. In these regions the ridges often join the wall of the pilary canals and appear to "anchor" the follicle to the epidermis. In contrast, the ridges surround, but do not join the ducts of the sweat glands. On the neck the epidermis has single parallel ridges.

On the trunk, the characteristic architecture of the underside of the epidermis of the chest and the back consists of cobweb-like ridges. On the abdomen, peculiar rows of short parallel ridges lie across the creases on the surface of the skin. In fat individuals and in the female breast the cobweb pattern is broken up into islands of parallel bridges sepa-rated by flat epidermis (Fig. 6C).

On the extremities, the diamond-shaped designs of the flexure lines on the surface of the thigh (Fig. 6B) correspond to the flat epidermal

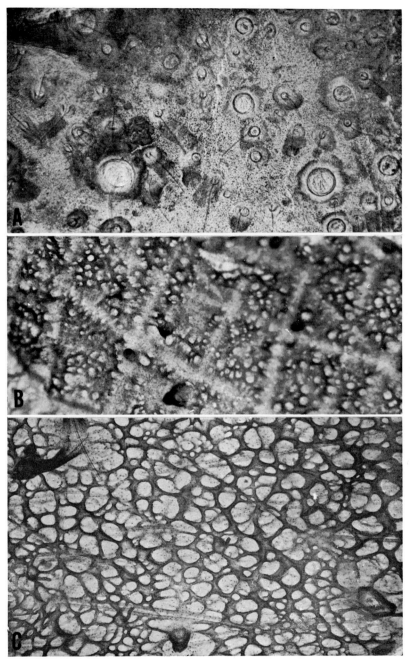

Fig. 6. The undersurface of the epidermis in (A) the cheek, (B) the thigh, (C) the breast, split by digestion with trypsin. (Courtesy of Dr. G. Szabó.)

valleys between the ridges; finger-like dermal papillae also leave circular imprints on the basal layer between these regions. The architecture of the basal layer in the forearm and the leg is characterized by wide flat areas; on the thigh and arm, however, there are no patternless areas.

On the hand and foot, cobweb patterns of epidermal ridges are basically the same on both the dorsal and ventral surfaces. They are much deeper in the plantar and solar surfaces.

Fig. 7. The underside of the epidermis of the tip of a finger, split by digestion with trypsin. (Courtesy of Dr. G. Szabó.)

On the fingers, the dermoepidermal junction is sculptured by intricate systems of parallel ridges and valleys in the form of loops and whorls. All of the ridges bear the ducts of sweat glands; the ridges run parallel (Fig. 7).

On the external genitalia, the epidermal ridges of the scrotum are parallel, but those on the penis and clitoris are arranged in horseshoe patterns. These configurations provide great elasticity.

The epidermal ridges of the oral mucosa are long and finger-like; they are shorter on the nasal mucosa. The ridges on the underside of the vermillion surface of the lips and on that of the perianal region are characteristically tall and anastomosing.

The number of hair follicles and ducts of sweat glands also shows striking regional differences. There are about 10 times as many hair follicles in the integument of the face as elsewhere; variations in numbers of sweat glands are less pronounced. For example, there are about

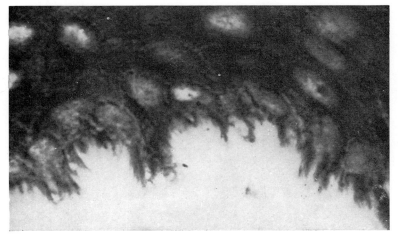

FIG. 8. The epidermis of the palm, treated with the technique of Barnett and Seligman (1952) for the demonstration of disulfide groups, showing the delicate cytoplasmic processes of the basal cells.

three times as many glands in the forehead as in the thigh, and about three or four glands to each hair follicle on the trunk and on the extremities. On the head, however, the ratio is 0.3.

During old age the undersculpturings tend to flatten out, and there is some reduction in the number of the appendages on the skin. The skin of most laboratory mammals, such as the mouse, rat, and rabbit, has no epidermal ridges, and the dermoepidermal junction is less intimate. However, in the skin of these animals the hair follicles are very close to each other and may take the place of the ridges and papillae found in the skin of man.

The cells of the basal layer send into the dermis a number of delicate protoplasmic processes which provide a still closer union between the dermis and the epidermis (Schäfer, 1912). These cytoplasmic denticles are so small that they are infrequently seen in ordinary preparations. They can, however, be demonstrated in unstained frozen sections viewed under the phase-contrast microscope or in thin, well-fixed and well-stained preparations (Fig. 8). Basal cells are so intimately associated with the dermis that Martinotti (1914a, b) believed that a condensation of the delicate collagenous fibrils insinuated between the cells of the

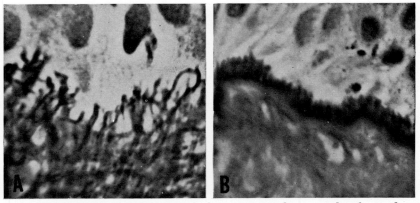

FIG. 9. (A) The argyrophil network, basement membrane, under the epidermis of the scalp. (B) The basement membrane is strongly PAS positive.

basal layer forms the *basement membrane*. Dick (1947) speculated that reticular fibers could run up to the epidermal cells and anchor them either by entering the cell membrane or by filling the spaces between the basal processes. The relationship between the elastic fibers of the dermis and the cells of the basal layer is also very intimate, and these

FIG. 10. Electron micrograph of the basal processes of two adjacent basal epidermal cells, from the flexor surface of the forearm, separated in the upper center of the figure by a melanocyte process seen in cross section. The "basal" membrane is indicated by the arrow. The cytoplasm of the basal cells is pervaded by fine filaments (tonofilaments), except where they are displaced by mitochondria and small vesicles. Ill-defined dense plaques are disposed along the basal contour of the plasma membrane. These are interpreted as sites of attachment of aggregates of tonofilaments that correspond to tonofibrils. In the lowermost portions of the figure are seen ill-defined densities of the connective tissue of the dermis. The contour of the epidermal cell membrane is apposed to a moderately dense layer, the submicroscopic basement membrane (arrows), which is separated from the epidermal cell by an apparently structureless low-density zone about 300 Å thick. There is no structured continuity between the tonofilments of the epidermal cell and the collagen fibril of the dermis. Fixed in buffered OsO_4 and embedded in epoxy resin and unstained. Magnification: $\times$ 25,000. (Courtesy of Dr. G. F. Odland.)

fibers could anchor down the epidermis. Trypsin, which readily attacks elastic fibers, cleanly and rapidly separates the epidermis from the dermis (Medawar, 1953).

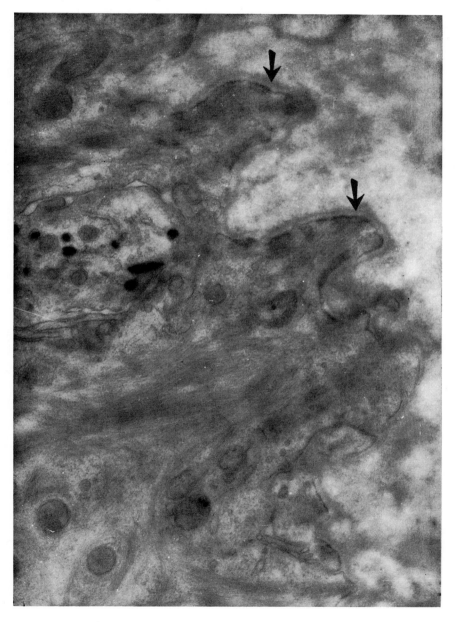

There is little agreement on the nature and composition of the membrane that separates the epidermis from the dermis (Born, 1921; Busacca, 1922; Hoepke, 1927; Laguesse, 1919a, b; Martinotti, 1924). Herxheimer (1916) believed that a translucent membrane is intimately associated with the protoplasmic processes on the underside of the basal cells. Frieboes (1920, 1921, 1922) visualized the basement membrane as a complex argyrophil reticulum, the meshes of which are occupied by the cytoplasmic processes of the basal epidermal cells (Fig. 9). The basement membrane visible under the light microscope does consist of a continuous meshwork of argyrophil fibrils around, and compressed between, the basal epithelial processes (Odland, 1950).

The basement membrane of the epidermis of amphibians is very thick and its spectacular architecture has engaged the attention of electron microscopists (Weiss and Ferris, 1954a, b; Porter, 1954; Palade, 1953, 1955). Under the electron microscope this basement membrane is a three-layered structure composed of an inner dense layer of granules just under the cell membrane and a structureless middle layer that blends into a thick, fibrillar, veneered third layer. The fibrils of the third layer, with a diameter of 130–150 Å, are striated at intervals of 350–400 Å. The fibrils are arranged in layers all parallel to the surface of the epidermis and successive ones oriented at right angles to each other. There is no basement membrane in mammalian skin that corresponds to the complicated structure in amphibian skin.

In mammals, a submicroscopic, 350 Å thick membrane follows the basal contours of the epidermal cells, and is separated from them by a space of 300 Å. No filaments, either epidermal or dermal, cross this membrane (Fig. 10). To distinguish this structure from the thicker, more complex "basement membrane" of other epithelial structures, Selby (1955) called it the "basal membrane." The connective tissue near the dermoepidermal junction shows no great change, and no band of amorphous and reticular substance is associated with it as in the true basement membrane such as that which surrounds the renal tubules. The continuity and the intactness of the dermal membrane rules out the possibility that there is a continuity of basal cell cytoplasm with connective tissue. Vesicles just within the plasma membrane in the basal portion of the epidermal cells are probably avenues of metabolic exchange between the capillaries in the dermis and the cells of the epidermis (Odland, 1958).

Though genetically determined, the dermoepidermal junction is morphologically adapted to the various shearing forces to which the skin is exposed. In the palms and soles, the basal cytoplasmic processes of the epidermal cells are long and the development of the argyrophil reticulum between the processes is extensive. Moreover, the epidermal ridges and cones attain a great depth and complexity in these areas. In contrast, the epidermal ridges in the medial side of the thighs or the abdomen are shallower and the union of the epidermis with the dermal reticulum is less distinct.

Intercellular Bridges and Tonofibrils

The membrane of adjacent epidermal cells makes contact at numerous small areas that are separated by intercellular spaces. Such morphologic arrangement forms on the surface of the cells characteristic cytoplasmic processes called intercellular bridges. Since in fixed, dissociated epidermal cells these processes stick out like spines, the cells have been called prickle or spinous cells. Living dissociated epidermal cells, however, show none of these processes and the plasma membrane is smooth. The earlier belief that epidermal cells have cytoplasmic continuity with each other (Chambers and Renyi, 1925) is no longer tenable, as will be seen later. Intercellular bridges are best defined in the stratum spinosum, they gradually become less distinct in the stratum granulosum, and virtually disappear in the stratum corneum. Roughly midway between two cells, each cytoplasmic bridge possesses a spindle-shaped swelling, the node of Bizzozero (1871) or desmosome (Fig. 11). Intercellular bridges and desmosomes are most clearly delineated in the thick epidermis of the friction areas. Scattered through the cytoplasm of epidermal cells are delicate striations, the "tonofibrillen" of Heidenhain, first described in detail by Ranvier (1879). In fresh or formalin-fixed frozen sections, tonofibrils are anisotropic (Litvac, 1939; Schmidt, 1937); in paraffin sections they are stainable with a variety of methods, among them Heidenhain's hematoxylin or Mallory's phosphotungstic acid-hematoxylin. Tonofibrils have been branded as artifacts more often than other fine structures, since the clarity of their definition depends largely upon the type of fixing agent used. But, as Medawar (1953) says, "it would be frivolous to dismiss tonofibrils as artifacts. All histological appearances are artifacts of one sort or another, i.e., represent the consequences of optical, mechanical, and chemical transformations of the living system. An artifact is only mischievous if one fails to inquire into the credentials of the transformation process, or assumes that no such process has taken place. It is likely that intracellular tonofibrils (like neurofibrils and myofibrils) are artifacts in the sense that they represent artificial coarsenings, to the level of microscopical visibility, of an underlying fine structure of oriented fibrous protein molecules." Tonofibrils are most distinct in the cells of the malpighian layer; they are less clear in the stratum granulosum and seem to disappear in the stratum corneum (Patzelt, 1926; Rosenstadt, 1910; Shapiro, 1924; Weidenreich, 1900; Jarret *et al.*, 1959). There is confusion in the older literature concerning the nature and origin of tonofibrils, and much of this confusion has stemmed from the presence of the thick *spiral filaments of Herxheimer* in the cells of the basal layer (Herx-

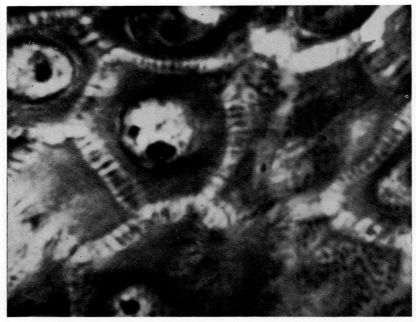

FIG. 11. Epidermis from the human axilla, stained with Regaud's hematoxylin, showing intercellular bridges, nodes of Bizzozero, and faint striations that indicate tonofibrils.

heimer, 1889). Some authors considered the spiral filaments to be intercellular fibrils (Argaud, 1914; Branca, 1899); others believe that they are the mitochondria of the basal cells and that the tonofibrils might develop from them (Favre, 1950; Favre and Regaud, 1910a, b; Regaud and Favre, 1912). Since the basal cells contain Herxheimer filaments as well as mitochondria, Firket (1911) stated that the spiral filaments are tonofibrils just formed from mitochondria. Martinotti (1914a, b) thought that tonofibrils arise from a coalescence of cytoplasmic granules and that the fibrils later multiply by splitting longitudinally.

Most of the earlier attempts to study the fine structure of the epi-

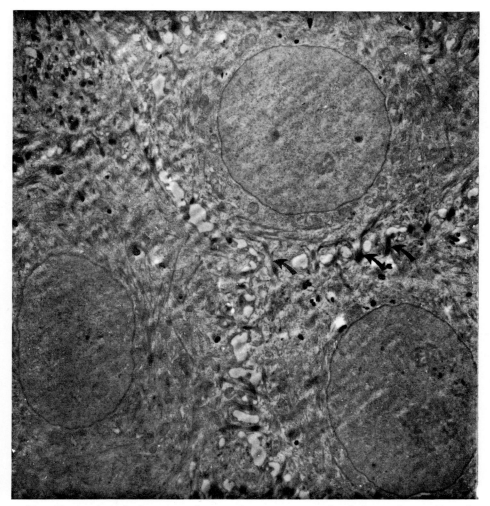

FIG. 12. A relatively low magnification electron micrograph of the epidermis from the flexor surface of the forearm, showing nuclei and portions of the cytoplasm of three cells in the stratum spinosum. Despite the low contrast inherent in unstained epon-embedded tissues, the salient morphologic features of epidermal cells can be seen: a perinuclear halo of cytoplasm, devoid of filaments, contains membranes of the endoplasmic reticulum studded with ribonucleoprotein (RNP) particles, smooth-surfaced membranes and vesicles (associated with the Golgi complex), rosettes of RNP particles and melanin particles. Near the periphery of the cell, aggregates of tonofilaments "peel" out through a thin filament-free cortical region and attach at the inner face of the cell membrane near the desmosomes (arrows). Fixed in buffered OsO_4 and embedded in epoxy resin and unstained. Magnification: × 6500. (Courtesy of Dr. G. F. Odland.)

dermis with the electron microscope yielded meager results (Adolph *et al.*, 1951; Gessler *et al.*, 1948; Gray *et al.*, 1952; Laden *et al.*, 1953; Pease, 1951). These reports contained assertions and denials of the

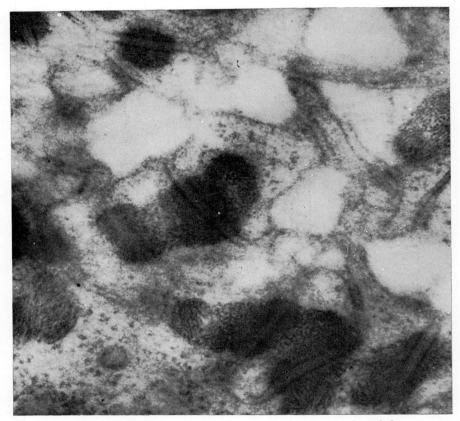

FIG. 13. High magnification electron micrograph of human epidermal desmosomes from the flexor surface of the forearm. This is an area where three or more adjacent cells come together. Tonofilaments adjacent to the internal face of the attachment plaque in the desmosomes are cut in cross section. Observe the lamellar densities of the desmosome complexes. Fixed in buffered OsO_4, embedded in epoxy resin, and stained with uranyl acetate. Magnification: × 86,000. (Courtesy of Dr. G. F. Odland.)

syncytial nature of the epidermal cells and of the presence or absence of tonofibrils. None of the earlier studies, however, added significantly to our knowledge of the structure of epidermal cells until Porter (1954), and Weiss and Ferris (1954a) first produced superlative electron micro-

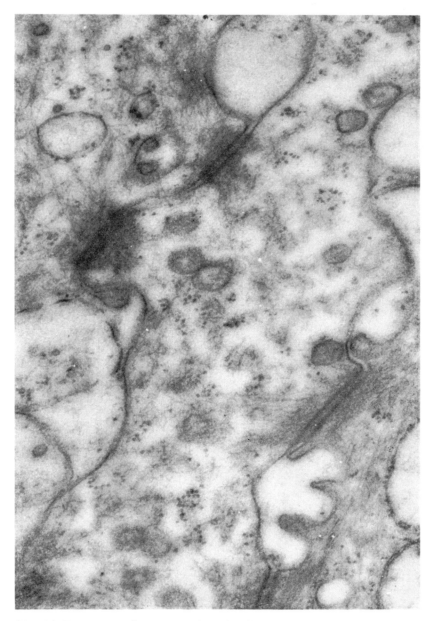

FIG. 14. Desmosomes between epidermal cells from the thumb pad of a frog. Tonofilaments radiate from the attachment plaques. Magnification: × 57,600. (Courtesy of Dr. P. Parakkal.)

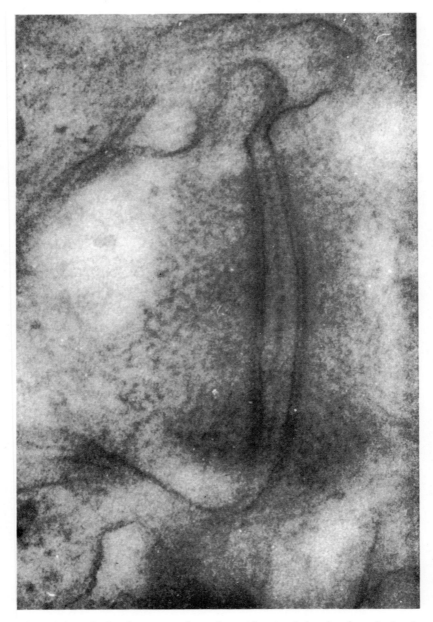

FIG. 15. Detail of a desmosome from the epidermis of the thumb pad of a frog, showing great similarity to the desmosomes in mammalian epidermis. Magnification: × 182,000. (Courtesy of Dr. P. Parakkal.)

graphs of epidermal cells. These authors showed that intercellular bridges are small regions of contact between adjacent cells, characterized by (a) a thickening of the plasma membrane of both cells, (b) tufts of fibrous material directed toward them from the interior of the cells, and (c) the presence of striae across the fibrous tufts. In the cytoplasm are rich skeins of fine filaments approximately 60 Å thick

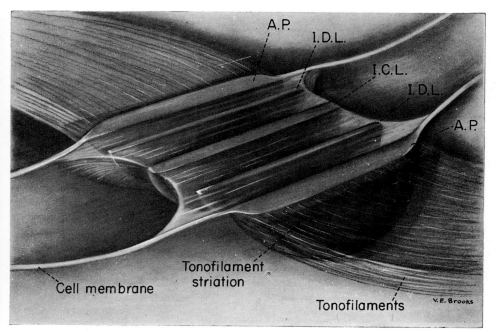

FIG. 16. Dr. George Odland's schematic representation of his conception of the human epidermal attachment zone (intercellular bridge). This drawing corresponds to a "node of Bizzozero" cut on a plant parallel to the long axis of the substituent tonofibrils. The initials indicate: (A.P.) the attachment plaques, (I.D.L.) the intermediate dense layers, and (I.C.L.) the intercellular contact layer. From Odland (1958). (Reproduced by permission of the author and the *Journal of Biophysical and Biochemical Cytology*.)

(Figs. 12–16). The tonofibrils seen in histological preparations could represent a matting together of the filaments and other cytoplasmic inclusions.

Several excellent electron microscopical studies have been published on the epidermis of man and the rat (Selby, 1955, 1956; Odland, 1958, 1960; Hibbs and Clark, 1959; Horstmann and Knoop, 1958). The structure of the desmosomes has been studied with such care that only a brief general statement can be given here. The thickening of the plasma membranes at the point of contact in the desmosome constitutes two attachment plaques, one from each epidermal cell, precisely 750 Å apart.

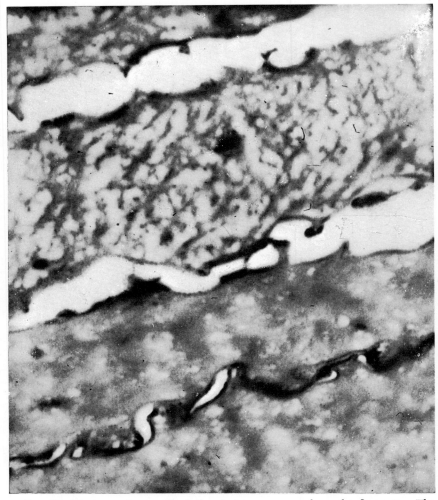

Fɪɢ. 17. Electron micrograph of the stratum corneum from the finger tip. The upper two cells are about to scale off and the desmosomes are split. The lower cells are still lightly attached. (Courtesy of Dr. G. A. Matoltsy.)

The point of contact between two cells is midway between two opposed plaques; several intervening layers of different densities are symmetrically arranged on either side of the intercellular contact layer,

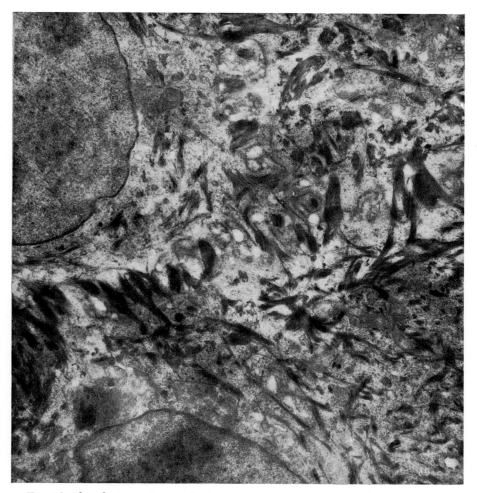

Fɪɢ. 18. This electron micrograph of a specimen from the flexor surface of the forearm has been stained with uranyl acetate to enhance the contrast of the tonofilaments and desmosomes. This treatment renders the mitochondria less conspicuous by the relatively great density of the tonofilaments. Three epidermal cells of the stratum spinosum, two above and one below, are shown. The most conspicuous adjacent cell margins traverse the figure from a point below the middle on the left side to a point just above the middle on the right side. The tonofibrils "peel" out of the cortical array to their points of insertion at the internal faces of the attachment plaques of the desmosomes. Fixed in buffered OsO_4, embedded in epoxy resin, and stained with 2% aqueous uranyl acetate for 2 hours. Magnification: × 16,000. (Courtesy of Dr. G. F. Odland.)

between the two plaques. Fibrils (tonofibrils) go from the center of the cell toward the plaques where they are attached by way of their constituent filaments, the tonofilaments (Figs. 14–16). Desmosomes are few and small between adjacent cells of the basal layer; they are most numerous and best developed in the spinous layer, tend to become smaller in the granular layer, and are inconspicuous in the stratum corneum. Actually, although not clearly defined, attachment plaques are found even between the cells of the stratum corneum (Fig. 17). Hibbs and Clark (1959), finding fewer and smaller desmosomes in the cells of the basal layer and in those deep in the rete ridges, believe that these cells are not firmly bound and, thus, are better adapted to divide and glide over each other during mitosis. In this connection, they believe that cells which are about to divide have a "ground glass" cytoplasm. The cells of the spinous layer, which are solidly anchored to each other, do not divide; the occasional cells that do divide there have a "ground glass" cytoplasm like those in the basal layer.

The cytoplasm of epidermal cells is full of skeins of fine filaments approximately 60 Å thick, bundles of which correspond to the tonofibrils. Filaments are distributed loosely in the cytoplasm of the basal cells of thin epidermis, but are more numerous and organized into fibrils in thick epidermis. When thick bundles of filaments are directed toward the dermoepidermal junction, they form Herxheimer fibers (see pp. 39, 40). Fibrils are directed toward the cell membranes, and fray out into their constituent filaments which terminate at the inner face of the attachment plaques of the desmosomes (Fig. 18). The number of tonofilaments in the cells of the basal layer seems to be the same as that in the succeeding higher layers; since the tonofibrils contain α-proteins, the formation of keratin begins in the basal layer. In the stratum granulosum some of the fibrils appear less electron dense and lack a filamentous structure. This probably indicates a macromolecular rearrangement and tonofibrils may be considered to be prekeratin. In the stratum lucidum the ultrastructure of fibrils is altered but the hyalin fibrils terminate at the desmosomes as do those in the cells of lower layers. The tonofibrils of the stratum corneum are not clearly seen under the electron microscope because the cell matrix in which they are embedded is as electron dense as the fibrils themselves are.

Mitochondria

The terminology for mitochondria is unnecessarily clumsy. Mitochondria in living cells are continuously changing shape (Frederic and Chévremont, 1952; Lewis and Lewis, 1915), and the various names that designate the different shapes serve little purpose. Mitochondria, as used here, designate: (a) intracytoplasmic elements demonstrable in living cells with a dark-field or phase-contrast microscope as motile filaments, rods, or granules with a definite polarity; (b) those elements that are stained selectively supravitally with Janus green; (c) those pleomorphic cytoplasmic entities in appropriately fixed tissue which can be stained with Regaud's and Heidenhain's hematoxylin or with Altmann's technique, or (d) those entities that, under the electron microscope, show the precise internal structure described herein.

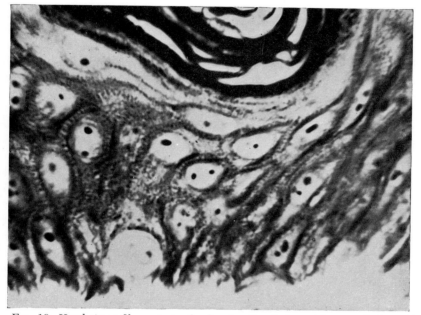

Fig. 19. Herxheimer filaments in the basal cells of the epidermis of the axilla, stained with Heidenhain's iron hematoxylin.

Mitochondria are difficult to demonstrate in epidermal cells. Even in good preparations, confusion in interpretation has arisen from the presence in the same epidermal cells of pleomorphic mitochondria, tonofibrils, spiral filaments of Herxheimer, and pigment granules.

In the cells of the basal layer, thick, corkscrew-shaped spiral filaments of Herxheimer (Fig. 19), first considered intracellular lymphatic spaces, were later thought to be shrunken parts of the cell membrane resulting from fixation artifact (Herxheimer, 1889; Herxheimer and Müller, 1896). Since these filaments are coexistent with typical mitochondria, most authors now conclude that they consist of epidermal fibrils (Firket, 1911; Kollmann and Papin, 1914; Kromayer, 1892; Rabl, 1897; Selby, 1955; Odland, 1958). Spiral filaments are demonstrated best in the cells of the basal layer and less easily in the lower cells of the spinous layer when tissues are fixed in Regaud's fluid and postchromed for a long time (Favre, 1920a, b; 1924, 1946, 1950; Favre and Regaud, 1910a, b; Regaud and Favre, 1912). In such preparations, the filaments and the nodes of Bizzozero may stain like mitochondria. Although a postchromation of skin for one month is sufficient to demonstrate the filaments in the stratum basale, longer postchroming is necessary to reveal them in the upper strata. The spiral filaments are larger and more numerous and show less polymorphism in palmar and in plantar epidermis than in the general body skin. In both types of epidermis they are aligned parallel to the long axis of the cells. In the basal layer, the spiral filaments are largely within the cytoplasmic processes that extend into the dermis. Lesser spiral filaments are found throughout the malpighian layer; in the granular layer they are said to be progressively fragmented. Both histological methods and electron microscopy leave no doubt that Herxheimer filaments are bundles of filaments similar to tonofibrils.

When skin is stained with Altmann's acid fuchsin-methyl green, the spiral filaments of the epidermis are stained only moderately, but typical mitochondria stain clearly (Fig. 20). Many mitochondria, mostly in the form of short filaments, are gathered around the nucleus of the epidermal cells. Smaller and usually granular mitochondria radiate laterally in the cytoplasm. The nodes of Bizzozero are also stained with this technique, but this is not a proof that mitochondria are there, and studies with the electron microscope have dispelled any such thoughts. Mitochondria gradually disappear from the cells in the upper layers of the malpighian layer, but they can be seen even in the granular layer (Parat, 1928).

Mitochondria are very sensitive indices of cellular change and damage. In psoriasis and in inflammatory conditions, for example, the nuclei in the cells of the lower layers of the epidermis are displaced distally, and the polymorphic mitochondria move to the subnuclear cytoplasm. In epidermal neoplasms, mitochondria become strikingly pleomorphic; Favre (1950) illustrates basal-cell carcinoma with the mitochondria like those of normal spinous cells and squamous-cell carcinoma with mitochondria like those in normal basal cells.

Electron micrographs of epidermal cells show long, narrow mitochondria similar to those found in the cells of other organs (Palade,

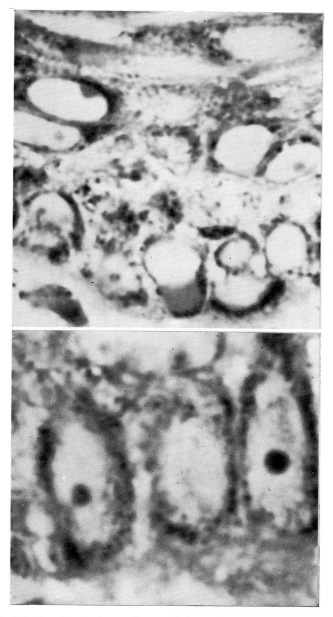

FIG. 20. Mitochondria in the epidermis of the axilla, stained with Altmann's acid fuchsin-methyl green. Above, seen in low magnification; below, basal cells under greater magnification.

1952). The internal structure of each mitochondrion is denser than that in other organs, but one can recognize the series of ridges (cristae mitochondriales) that protrude from the inner surface toward the interior of the mitochondrion (Fig. 21). Each mitochondrion is surrounded by numerous small protein granules that probably represent the earliest precursors of keratin filaments. Mitochondria are the seat

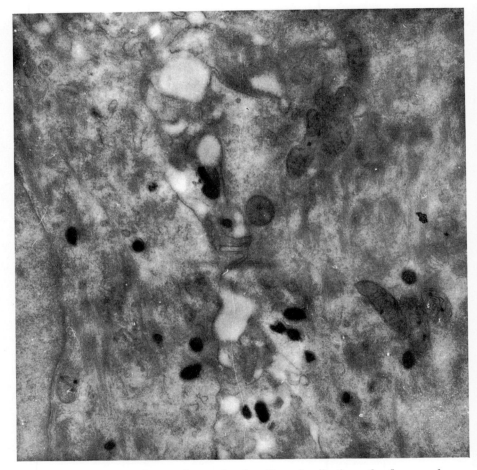

Fig. 21. Portions of two adjacent basal epidermal cells, from the flexor surface of the forearm, showing mitochondria, tonofilaments, vesicles, and melanin particles, some of which are bounded by a membrane. Between the adjacent cells can be seen an intercellular space pervaded by microvilli. A desmosome is seen in the center of the illustrations. Fixed in buffered OsO$_4$ and embedded in epoxy resin; unstained. Magnification: × 22,000. (Courtesy of Dr. G. F. Odland.)

of all important biological syntheses, and the process of keratinization must be mediated by them.

In well-fixed, well-prepared ultra-thin sections, the electron microscope shows many submicroscopic spherical granules in the cytoplasm of the flattened cells immediately beneath those of the granular layer (Odland, 1960). These granules are most numerous in cells that do not contain keratohyalin granules. The lowermost cells of the granular layer that contain small keratohyalin granules have fewer submicroscopic granules, and the granular cells that contain large keratohyalin bodies have very few submicroscopic granules. The small spherical granules have neither the density nor the structural organization of melanin granules, and some of them have a distinctive internal structure that resembles the cristae of mitochondria. They are probably attenuated or fragmented mitochondria.

The Golgi Apparatus

When fresh epidermis is stained supravitally with neutral red, the cells of the basal layer have a compact supranuclear mass of neutral red-stained vacuoles (the *vacuome* of Parat), that often descends along the sides of the nucleus (Parat, 1928). In the cells immediately above the basal layer, the system of neutral red-stained vacuoles is as dense as in the basal cells; in cells nearer the granular layer, the vacuoles are dispersed among the keratohyalin granules and often encircle the granules; the larger vacuoles are located basally and along the sides of the nucleus, while the smaller ones are found apically. The "vacuome" disappears in the more keratinized cells.

In recent years, the cytologist has had several changes of heart about the Golgi apparatus. Avidly studied immediately after its discovery by Golgi in 1898, it later became branded as an artifact and a figment of the cytologist's imagination until Dalton (1951) unerringly demonstrated it with the electron microscope. Now reinstated as a proper organelle, the Golgi apparatus is even studied by the physiologist who dabbles in electron microscopy. Although it was extensively studied in nearly all other tissues, only a few authors have looked for it in the epidermis (Cajal, 1914; Cowdry and Scott, 1928; Da Fano, 1921; Deineka, 1912; Ludford, 1924, 1925; Parat, 1928; Tello, 1913, 1923). Cowdry and Scott (1928) stained it supravitally with neutral red in the epidermis. With osmic acid the Golgi apparatus of the cells of the basal layer appears as a juxtanuclear network or a group of rodlets in the distal end of the cell, the mitochondria being heaped up at the proximal end (Ludford, 1925). This precise polarity is lost in the upper cells of the spinous layer, where the Golgi apparatus is dispersed irregularly, as are also the mitochondria. In cells laden with keratohyalin granules the Golgi elements are no longer demonstrable with osmium tetroxide. After silver impregnaticn, the cells of the stratum germinativum have a system of compact rodlets and tubules, typical of the Golgi apparatus. These structures comprise the "dictyosome" and have the same orientation as the "vacuome." In the stratum granulosum, scattered Golgi elements appear as "appendages" of the keratohyalin granules (Parat, 1928).

Although it is not possible to determine from his work whether or not keratohyalin granules arise from the Golgi element, Parat (1928) has made an important contribution to the understanding of the nature of this organelle. He was the first cytologist to look for a Golgi net in living cells, and he found instead a series of vacuoles. The subsequent work on the Golgi element in other cells has substantiated Parat's observations and added to them (Baker, 1944, 1949; Cain, 1947, 1949; Hirsch, 1939; Palade and Claude, 1949a, b; Thomas, 1948; Worley, 1944, 1946). The electron microscopist has now completely vindicated his views. A Golgi net seems to develop during fixation at the site of a system of spherules, all, or part, of them being lipoidal in nature. Epidermal cells contain lipid spherules which lie close to the nuclear membrane and which are usually clustered at the distal pole of the nucleus (Montagna, 1950). The cells of the stratum granulosum contain only barely visible lipid granules. Phospholipid granules, demonstrable with the acid hematein test, are identical with perinuclear sudanophil bodies (Baker, 1946; Cain, 1949). In preparations impregnated with silver or with osmium tetroxide, rodlets or granules occupy the same general areas in the cells occupied by these lipid granules. The perinuclear lipid granules in the epidermal cells, then, are comparable to the "vacuome" of Parat, and must, but not without caution, be considered either as the Golgi complex or as a part of it. Since the Golgi complexes are clearly definable in epidermal cells with a variety of histological and histochemical methods, it is remarkable that the electron microscope has not elucidated its structure (Selby, 1955). This failure may be due to poor fixation as a result of slow penetration of the fixative through the tissue.

Glycogen and Other Carbohydrates

In contrast with the stratified squamous epithelium of mucous membranes, which are rich in glycogen, normal mammalian epidermis contains relatively small amounts of glycogen demonstrable with histochemical methods. In none of the skin surfaces studied is glycogen abundant; it is found sporadically in restricted sites (Fig. 22) and is often present in the epidermis of the scrotum and scalp. Its presence in the epidermis is usually associated with the structural features to be described below. When present in the epidermis, glycogen is found in the cells of the upper stratum spinosum; with rare exceptions, the cells of the lower layers are free of it (Fig. 22) (Montagna *et al.*, 1951,

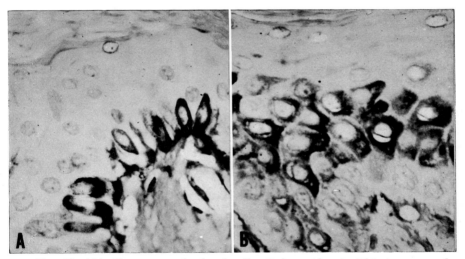

FIG. 22. (A) Glycogen in the basal cells of the epidermis. This is not usual and probably denotes some disturbance. (B) Glycogen in the stratum spinosum. This may also be the result of some irritation.

1952). The epidermal cells around the pilosebaceous orifices and around the orifices of the sweat glands usually contain some glycogen. Skin crevices, or pilosebaceous orifices, that enclose blocked cornified material are surrounded by elongated epidermal cells that are always rich in glycogen. Thus, the epidermis contains demonstrable glycogen particularly where the normal rate of keratinization seems to have been slowed down or impaired. Since glycogen is not found in epidermis with normal keratinization and mitotic activity, its presence may indicate sites of abnormal situations. When epidermal cells are rich in it, glycogen is in the form of small granules aligned in rows that resemble fibrils sweeping through the cells.

In the two- or three-layered epidermis of the human fetus, younger than 4 months, basal as well as peridermal layers are laden with glycogen (Lombardo, 1907, 1934; Sasakawa, 1921; Achten, 1959); the cells of the periderm are particularly replete with it. When in the fourth month the basal cells begin to form the anlagen of the cutaneous appendages, glycogen largely disappears from these cells, particularly at the sites of rapid cell division, but it remains abundant in the upper layers. A dramatic reduction in the content of glycogen in the epidermis is seen when keratinization begins to take place. Although this begins in the fourth month, it does not make real progress until the sixth month. Even at 6 months, however, appreciable amounts of glycogen are found in the upper layers of the spinous layer. Some glycogen remains there until term and in the newborn. These observations emphasize again the inverse relation between the presence of glycogen and the process of keratinization. V. Patzelt (1954), who also studied glycogen in relation to keratinization, concluded that keratohyalin, "eleidin," and trichohyalin are "fibrogenic substances chemically related to carbohydrates." Patzelt also assumes that the carbohydrates are used in the production of energy, and in this way are not stored in normal, keratinizing epidermis.

Claude Bernard (1859, 1878), who first devised a method for the demonstration of glycogen in tissues, found it in the fetal epidermis of the pig, lamb, cat, and calf, but not in that of the adult skin. In the developing hoof of the pig he saw glycogen disappear from the epidermal laminae concomitant with the "organization" of the tissue, and particularly with the process of keratinization. He concluded that "C'est dans ces cas où il semble évident que la matière glycogène entre dans l'organisation des tissus."

The adult epidermis of laboratory animals, which contains no demonstrable glycogen, stores it in abundance after injury. Glycogen always disappears during recovery of the injury (Argyris, 1952; Bradfield, 1951; Firket, 1951). Human skin autografts similarly store glycogen in the epidermis when first transplanted; when they are fully restored to normal function, glycogen disappears (Scothorne and Scothorne, 1953). Normal human epidermis, which has been mildly injured by stripping the stratum corneum with Scotch tape, undergoes certain predictable changes that involve the storage of glycogen (Lobitz and Holyoke, 1954). Eight hours after the infliction of the injury, there is complete cessation of mitotic activity in the swollen basal cells of the epidermis, and most of these cells become heavily laden with glycogen. Sixteen hours after the injury, the number of basal cells containing glycogen decreases to approximately 70%, and at 24 hours only 50% are involved. As glycogen decreases in the basal cells, it gradually accumulates in the middle region of the stratum spinosum. After 48 hours, when the basal cells are free of it, the cells in the upper spinous layer contain an appreciable amount of glycogen, and some may remain there for as long as 5 days. It is important to relate here the changes that take place in the epidermis with the accumulation of glycogen. The basal cells become at once hypertrophied and mitotically inert. Later, as the size of the basal cells subsides, mitotic activity reappears and increases at the same rate that glycogen disappears. The stratum corneum, having been stripped off, the surface epidermal cells form a protective, apparently parakeratotic layer. The epidermis requires about 5 days to cast off this layer and to re-establish a normal corneal layer under it. Whether this is of primary or secondary significance, storage of glycogen in the basal cells is inversely related to mitotic activity and that in the stratum spinosum is related to a retardation of keratinization. Glycogen is stored in nearly all epidermal lesions that are accompanied with parakeratotic changes, as in psoriasis or senile keratosis.

Morphologic aberrations in the epidermal cells are usually accompanied by an accumulation of glycogen. When the cells become hypertrophied and vacuolated, and the cytoplasmic basophil substances become diluted, glycogen, as a rule, appears. It is not certain what the reason is for this accumulation of glycogen. During injury, the rate and quality of keratogenesis is altered; the keratin layer produced during or immediately after injury is parakeratotic, which implies an altered keratogenesis. Perhaps this is a problem of supply and demand: if the injured cells took up glycogen as rapidly as the normal cells do, but utilized it more slowly, it could become dammed or stored. As soon as normal keratogenesis and/or mitotic activity is resumed, the stores of glycogen disappear from the epidermis. There are, undoubtedly, other reasons for such an accumulation (Bradfield, 1951).

The epidermis also contains PAS-positive, nonglycogen substances that are not hydrolyzed by saliva or diastase. These substances, therefore, must also be capable of reacting with periodic acid to produce aldehydes and are presumably polysaccharides. Such reactive substances may be found in the nodes of Bizzozero and in the intercellular spaces. Occasionally, reactive particles may be found also in the stratum granulosum (Leblond, 1950, 1951; Wislocki et al., 1951).

When sections of skin are stained with weak solutions of toluidine blue buffered to pH 4.0 to 6.0, the basophil color of the cytoplasm of the epidermal cells has a lavender tinge. The intensity of this meta-chromatic staining varies with the different fixatives used. For example, in skin fixed in Bouin's fluid it is absent; after fixation in Zenker-formol it shows as a trace; in saline formaldehyde buffered to neutrality it is stronger still, and in tissues fixed in alcohol, acetone, and particularly in trichloroacetic acid in 80% alcohol, the epidermis stains distinctly metachromatically. Trichloroacetic acid in 80% alcohol is the preferred fixative for the demonstration of alcohol and water-insoluble, protein-bound sulfhydryl groups (Barrnett and Seligman, 1952). In sections of human sole and palm fixed in trichloroacetic acid, the entire stratum Malpighii has a strong metachromatic color; the keratohyalin granules are distinctly red, and the entire stratum corneum stains pink. Achten (1959), who reports no metachromasia in the epidermis, failed to use the proper fixative. The epidermis, then, like other cutaneous structures to be discussed later, contains substances that stain metachromatically. These substances are largely lost when fixatives other than alcoholic trichloroacetic acid are used. The freezing-drying method recommended by Sylvén (1950) should be the best method for the preservation of these substances; unfortunately, skin is not easy to freeze-dry.

Most substances that stain metachromatically represent acid poly-saccharides. The skin of man and that of other mammals investigated contain appreciable amounts of mucopolysaccharides. Some of these substances are present in the epidermis where, judging by their distribu-tion, they bear some relation to the process of keratinization (Hale, 1946; Holmgren, 1940; Lison, 1935; Meyer, 1947; Meyer and Chaffee, 1941; Meyer and Rapport, 1951; Pearce and Watson, 1949; Sylvén, 1941; Wislocki et al., 1947).

Lipids

Epidermal cells, when well prepared, have several perinuclear sudan-ophil lipid granules. Lipid granules are often found in the intercellular spaces, but these cannot be taken too literally; such lipids are usually found in poorly fixed tissues or in tissues kept in the fixative a long time. The number of intercellular lipid droplets is often seen to increase as the intercellular lipids decrease. The nodes of Bizzozero show minute amounts of lipid when colored with Sudan black or with the acid hematein test for phospholipids. Injury of various sorts to the epidermal cells may cause a disorientation and diffusion of the perinuclear lipid bodies and the appearance of lipid particles in the intercellular spaces, a situation which is not found in the normal skin. In prolonged injury that results in a hypertrophy of the epidermal cells, the cells may attain so much lipid that they come to resemble sebaceous cells.

The lipids in the stratum corneum, first described by Ranvier (1898), must come from three sources: (a) from a lipophanerosis in the epidermal cells, (b) from the secretion of sebaceous glands, and (c) from the secretion of sweat. It is said that the stratum spinosum of the human epidermis is relatively rich in free cholesterol but not in cholesterol esters. The stratum corneum, on the other hand, contains approximately equal amounts of free and ester cholesterol. Whereas the cholesterol secreted by sebaceous and sweat glands is easily oxidized, the intracellular cholesterol of the epidermis is not (Unna and Golodetz, 1909). Kvorning (1949) analyzed lipids secreted on the face of normal subjects and found only small traces of cholesterol. The stratum corneum in skin areas which contain no sebaceous glands is also sudanophil, and the lipids must be derived from lipophanerosis and from sweat, if sweat glands are present. In experimental animals in which the sebaceous glands have been plugged or destroyed for a long time, the stratum corneum remains sudanophilic (Montagna and Chase, 1950), as in the stratum corneum of the porpoise, which has no cutaneous appendages. These lipids must come from the unmasking of bound lipids in the epidermal cells. When frozen sections of skin of man, or of other mammals, are treated with Nile blue sulfate, the stratum corneum is colored pink, indicating perhaps the presence of neutral lipids (Montagna and Hamilton, 1949; Montagna et al., 1948). The stratum corneum is Schultz-positive, indicating the presence of cholesterol or its esters; it can be colored with Baker's acid hematein test for phospholipids, and it is birefringent. After extraction with organic solvents the birefringence is partially lost, the residual birefringence being a property of keratin.

For a fuller account on the chemical properties of lipids on the surface of the skin, the reader is referred to Rothman (1954), Wheatley (1952), and Nicolaides and Wells (1957).

Ascorbic Acid

In the burr of the horse, the hoof of the pig, and the epidermis of the guinea pig, the stratum germinativum has been shown to contain a considerable amount of ascorbic acid. Only traces of this substance were found in the cornified portion of these structures (Giroud et al., 1935a, b). These structures are also sites of high concentration of —SH groups, and it is interesting to find both of these substances in comparable amounts.

Basophilia

The cells in the malpighian layer are intensely basophilic when stained with basic dyes. The cytoplasm of the cells in the stratum granulosum is less basophilic, but the keratohyalin granules are usually strongly stained. The stratum lucidum and the stratum corneum stain very weakly or not at all. Treatment of sections of skin before staining with a solution of ribonuclease abolishes some of the cytoplasmic basophil staining (that of the nucleolus is completely abolished), but the intact nuclei and the keratohyalin granules stain clearly. Presumably, then, the basophilia which is eliminated by this enzyme is due to ribonucleic acid. After treating sections of skin with ribonuclease and then staining them with basic dyes such as toluidine blue or azure A, there is always a variable amount of residual basophil-staining material in the epidermal cells. The intensity of staining of this residual substance varies according to the concentration of the dye and to the pH of the solution. With the use of very dilute solutions of dyes buffered from pH 2.7 to 8.0, a great deal can be learned about the nature of the basophil substances (Montagna et al., 1951). All basophil material in the cytoplasm which is stained with the dyes buffered up to pH 5.0 is abolished by ribonuclease. In the keratohyalin granules, the intensity of staining is reduced, but there remains an appreciable amount of stained material (Leuchtenberger and Lund, 1951). When tissues are stained in solutions buffered from pH 5.0 to 8.0, using the identical staining conditions as with dyes buffered below pH 5.0, there is a progressive increase in the stainability of the epidermis. At pH 8.0 the cells take up so much dye that digestion with ribonuclease does not appreciably diminish the staining. When these dilute dyes are buffered below pH 5.0, they reveal only nucleic acid in the cytoplasm of the epidermal cells, but when they are buffered above pH 5.0, they reveal other proteins.

Oxidation of sections of skin with periodic acid before staining with toluidine blue greatly enhances the basophilia normally present in epidermis (Dempsey et al., 1950). This induced basophilia does not correspond to the basophilia presumably due to ribonucleic acid. When nucleoproteins and/or acid mucopolysaccharides are destroyed by treating sections with hydrochloric acid and the sections are then oxidized with periodic acid and stained with toluidine blue, the epidermis shows no diminution of dye uptake when compared with sections oxidized with periodic acid but without acid hydrolysis. Sections treated only with hydrochloric acid and stained without oxidation show a complete loss of cytoplasmic basophilia, although keratin remains basophilic. It appears

from this that acid groups other than nucleic acids or mucopolysaccharides exist in the epidermis, and the newly formed basophilia might be
related to the sulfur content of proteins. Oxidation of disulfide and of
sulfhydryl groups might conceivably lead to the formation of sulfonic
acids responsible for the induced basophilia (Dempsey *et al.*, 1950).

The malpighian layer, then, contains three biologically active substances: sulfhydryl groups, ascorbic acid, and ribonucleic acid. Ascorbic
acid might mediate the transformation of —SH groups to —S—S—
groups. Nucleic acid indubitably plays a role in protein synthesis, a role
probably shared with the —SH groups.

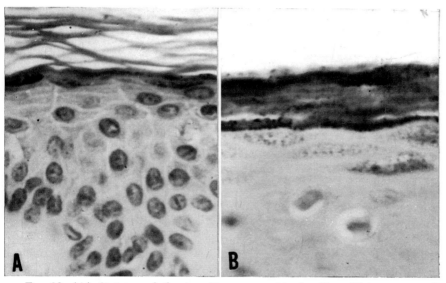

Fig. 23. (A) Staining of the transition zone with the Gram-Weigert stain of
the general body epidermis, and (B) in the epidermis of the palm.

When *normal* epidermis is stained with the Gram-Weigert technique
(Flesch *et al.*, 1960), a narrow "transition zone" between the malpighian
and horny layers becomes colored (Fig. 23). In the palms and soles,
however, the staining of the "transition zone" is more extensive, and
scattered Gram-positivity is also found in the more superficial cells of
the granular layer and especially around the ducts of the sweat glands;
the surface layer, however, remains unstained. Under certain pathologic
conditions, such as psoriasis, the Gram-positivity increases, as does also
the concentration of —SH groups. The Gram staining of these structures,
however, is not due to the —SH groups (Flesch *et al.*, 1960), but perhaps to a complex, highly resistant acid mucopolysaccharide in them.

Enzyme Systems

As new histochemical methods are devised and perfected, the list of enzymes demonstrated in the epidermis grows steadily. It is impossible, therefore, to give here either a complete list or a detailed description of them.

Reference is often made to the presence of cytochrome oxidase in the epidermis (Rogers, 1953; Steigleder, 1957), but no one has really studied its distribution. Histochemists have avoided investigating this enzyme because the older method of Gräaf, which used the Nadi reagent, gives poor resolutions and is often unreliable. The newer techniques of Burstone (1959, 1960), however, give neater and more precise histochemical results (Fig. 24A). The strongest reaction of cytochrome oxidase in the epidermis is found in the basal cells and in the spinous cells immediately above them. Reactive particles decrease in numbers in the upper part of the spinous layer, and they disappear in the granular layer. The sequence of the disappearance of the enzyme follows closely that of the disappearance of the mitochondria in the epidermal cells. The epidermis is a very active tissue, its two main functions being the synthesis of fibrous proteins (keratin) and mitotic activity. Mitosis is influenced and guided by many factors and is a cyclical phenomenon. At least in the mouse, mitotic activity in the epidermis is influenced by the particular state of activity of the hair follicle in the area (Chase et al., 1953; Bullough and Laurence, 1958). Parallel with this, quantitative methods show that the amounts of cytochrome oxidase in the epidermis of the mouse fluctuate with the various stages of the hair growth cycles. The highest peaks of enzyme activity correspond with the periods of highest mitotic activity (Carruthers et al., 1959).

The distribution of histochemically detectable succinic dehydrogenase activity is similar in the epidermis of all mammals (Serri, 1955a, b; Formisano and Montagna, 1954; Braun-Falco and Rathjens, 1955; Montagna and Formisano, 1955; Steigleder, 1957, 1958). A number of modifications of the original technique of Seligman and Rutenburg (1951) have been used to demonstrate the enzyme, but none is more satisfying than that of Farber and Louviere (1956). This method is easy to perform, the preparations are fairly permanent, and the localization is excellent. The cytoplasm of the basal cells is replete with discrete granules indicative of enzyme activity (Fig. 24B). Reactive granules become progressively sparser in the spinous layer and very few are found in the cells of the granular layer; none are found above this layer. Succinic dehydrogenase, like cytochrome oxidase, is found only in the living cells and specifically in the mitochondria. In quasi-quantitative histochemical studies, Serri (1955a) has shown that the skin of young individuals contains appreciably greater quantities of succinic dehydrogenase than that of older ones. The relative amounts of succinic

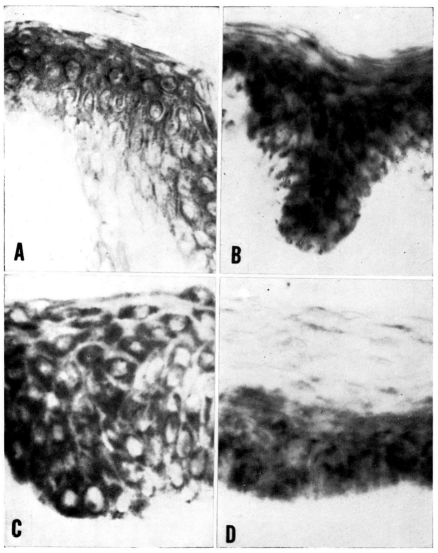

FIG. 24. Enzymes in the epidermis of the axilla: (A) cytochrome oxidase; (B) succinic dehydrogenase; (C) monoamine oxidase; (D) amylophosphorylase.

dehydrogenase activity in the epidermis, like that of cytochrome oxidase, fluctuates with the different stages of the hair growth cycle. In the mouse, when hair follicles are quiescent, the epidermis in the area has little enzyme activity (Argyris, 1956); during the early stages of hair growth, when the epidermis becomes temporarily thicker, succinic dehydrogenase activity is at a very high level. When the follicles are fully differentiated and growing rapidly (Anagen VI of Chase *et al.*, 1953), the epidermis again shows a reduced succinic dehydrogenase activity.

The distribution of carbonic anhydrase has been investigated only in the skin of man (Braun-Falco and Rathjens, 1955), with the technique of Kurata (1953). This method is of dubious specificity (Fand *et al.*, 1959), but the results obtained in the skin are interesting and will probably come into better perspective when these studies have been repeated and expanded. Granules, which apparently indicate enzyme activity, are concentrated mostly in the cells of the basal layer of the epidermis. In thicker epidermis, the lower cells of the spinous layer may also show a few reactive granules. However, Braun-Falco and Rathjens (1955) failed to inhibit the reaction in the granules with Diamox, which is a potent inhibitor of carbonic anhydrase.

The presence and distribution of monoamine oxidase in the skin was first investigated only by Hellmann (1955) and Shelley *et al.* (1955). These authors found very little enzyme activity in the epidermis. Using the technique of Glenner *et al.* (1957), we now find that there is a fairly intense distribution of this enzyme in all of the living cells of the epidermis, the strongest concentration being in the basal cells and in the lower cells of the malpighian layer. The reaction fades gradually upward and disappears in the granular layer (Fig. 24C). Since monoamine oxidase is localized mostly in the mitochondria (Hawkins, 1952), its distribution is like that of both cytochrome oxidase and succinic dehydrogenase. Whereas cytochrome oxidase and succinic dehydrogenase are inhibited by potassium cyanide, monoamine oxidase is not affected by it, and the two groups of enzymes can be separated histochemically by adding this substance to the incubation mixture. Monoamine oxidase is present in the epidermis of all the mammals we have studied. Enzyme concentration is always greater in the thicker epidermis and is particularly strong in the epidermis of the mucous surfaces.

The synthesis of branched polysaccharides, such as glycogen, requires two separate enzymes: phosphorylase (amylophosphorylase) and amylo-1,4—1,6-transglucosidase (branching enzymes, Q-enzyme). Both of these enzymes can be shown histochemically with the technique of Takeuchi and Kuriaki (1955). Several authors have surveyed the distribution of these enzymes in human skin (Braun-Falco, 1956a; Takeuchi, 1958; Ellis and Montagna, 1958). These two enzymes are usually found in the same sites in the skin of man. In the epidermis, variable amounts of amylo-1,4—1,6-transglucosidase and phosphorylase can be detected in the lower cells of the spinous layer, and less intensely in the cells of the basal layer (Fig. 24D). When the skin is irritated, or wounded, the amount of both enzymes in the epidermis increases. There are greater amounts of both enzymes in the epidermis of the fetus and of children than there are in the normal epidermis of the adult. In the epidermis of the very young, enzyme activity may extend to the stratum granulosum (Takeuchi, 1958). There are enormous species differences in the distribution of these enzymes in the epidermis. Traces may be found in various mammals, but only some of them have an epidermis rich in amylophosphorylase. In contrast, the epidermis of all primates always contains appreciable amounts of both enzymes (Montagna and Ellis, 1959).

Dermopeptidase, a proteolytic enzyme with extreme sensitivity to slight acidity, has been found in the skin of rabbits and of man (Fruton, 1946). Since peptidases with similar properties are also found in other tissues and in serum, these peptidases may have a common origin. They are probably liberated into tissue fluids by the disintegrating leucocytes (Fruton, 1946). Burstone (1956) and Burstone and Folk (1956), who devised a histochemical technique for demonstrating aminopeptidase, found practically no reaction in the epidermis in the skin of man and the rat. However, the method of Nachlas et al. (1957, 1960), shows a moderate reaction throughout the malpighian layer. When the epidermis is thicker the reaction is stronger in the basal malpighian layers and in the granular layer (Adachi and Montagna, 1961). The epidermis of the palms and soles has a strong reaction in the basal layer, a weak one in the spinous layer, and an intense reaction in the granular layer that extends to the lower cells of the stratum lucidum. In cases of dermatitis with bullous formations, intense aminopeptidase activity develops in the epidermis with a very strong reaction in the intracellular spaces (Braun-Falco, 1957; Braun-Falco and Salfeld, 1957). When large intra-epidermal bullae are formed, the epidermal cells at the base of the blisters are rich in aminopeptidase, but those above the blisters are practically negative. In acne, all of the epidermis around the lesion is strongly reactive for aminopeptidase (Braun-Falco, 1957). The lymphocytes in the infiltrated perivascular regions are always strongly reactive.

Regardless of whether one uses the azo-dye techniques or the cobalt sulfide technique (see Gomori, 1952), alkaline phosphatase is rarely demonstrated in the normal, intact epidermis. None of the various substrates used have given a positive reaction, not even glucose-6-phosphate (Braun-Falco, 1956b). The stratum granulosum of the epidermis of the friction areas often shows a positive reaction, but this reaction is present even when the substrates have been eliminated from the incubation mixture, or when the enzyme has been inactivated in various ways; the reaction, therefore, is not due to an enzyme (Braun-Falco, 1956b). In the transition between cutaneous and mucous surfaces, the epidermis may show a moderate alkaline phosphatase reaction. None of the many different mammals we have studied shows alkaline phosphatase in the intact epidermis. Any disorder which specifically affects the epidermis, however, causes an immediate appearance of variable amounts of alkaline phosphatase in it.

Although the epidermis has no alkaline phosphatase, it abounds in acid phosphatase, whether in the skin of man (Moretti and Mescon, 1956), or in that of other mammals. A number of factors, however, easily inactivate the enzyme, and only when one applies histochemical techniques to frozen sections does one obtain reliable results. Although the cells of the basal layer have practically no reaction, the cells of the spinous layer show a gradual increase in reactivity as one proceeds upward. The entire granular layer and the cells immediately above have a very intense reaction; even the stratum corneum may be strongly reactive.

Using a modification of Gomori's (1948) technique, Meyer and Weinmann (1955, 1957) demonstrated phosphamidase activity in a number of keratinizing epithelia in the rat. The enzyme is precisely localized in the stratum granulosum of the epidermis. Where the cells replete with keratohyalin granules form a compact, narrow band, a strong phosphamidase reaction is confined to the keratohyalin granules. Where the stratum granulosum is spread over a wide area, and its cells contain only a few small granules, enzyme activity is diffuse in the cytoplasm of the cells of the granular layer and in the cells of the spinous layer beneath them. There is also a variably intense phosphamidase reaction in the dermoepidermal junction. The distribution of phosphamidase in tissues suggests that it may be a part of a mechanism that makes possible the utilization of high rate energy. Phosphamidase in the cells of the granular layer of the epidermis could participate in the processes of the withdrawal of water from the cells, the removal of nuclear and cytoplasmic constituents from them, and in the formation of disulfide bonds.

Mammalian epidermis contains β-glucuronidase (Braun-Falco, 1956c; Montagna, 1957; Seligman *et al.*, 1954). The enzyme can be demonstrated in frozen sections (Seligman *et al.*, 1954) fixed in neutral formaldehyde, or in a mixture of formaldehyde and chloral hydrate (Fishman and Baker, 1956). The technique has the disadvantages of requiring long incubation periods, and the preparations change color after a few days. All of the viable epidermal cells, from the basal layer to the stratum granulosum, have a moderate concentration of β-glucuronidase in their cytoplasm. The cells of the stratum granulosum and those immediately above them are so strongly reactive that they delineate a band that corresponds to the keratogenous zone (Braun-Falco, 1956c; Montagna, 1957). The stratum corneum above this band is unreactive.

Skin contains large amounts of esterases (Ottolenghi-Lodigiani, 1957); these probably constitute an esterase spectrum consisting of more or less specialized enzymes that act on certain esters of carboxylic acids (Chessick, 1953). Nonspecific esterases and lipases are relatively hardy enzymes; they resist fixation in formaldehyde and are amenable to histochemical tests. The distribution and concentration of the esterases in skin have been reported by several authors (Braun-Falco, 1956d; Chessick, 1953; Findlay, 1955; Montagna, 1955; Montagna and Formisano, 1955; Montagna and Ellis, 1958; Steigleder, 1958; Steigleder and Schultis, 1957a, b; Ottolenghi-Lodigiani, 1957). Not all authors, however, agree about their exact localization, but the discrepancies in their findings are probably caused by the fixative used, the length of fixation, the sensitivity of the methods used, and by the care with which the tests are carried out.

The rigors of fixation in alcohol or acetone, and the subsequent embedding in paraffin are enormously detrimental to esterases. For example, whereas no Tween esterase activity (Gomori, 1952) is demonstrable in paraffin sections of human skin (Montagna *et al.*, 1948), there is abundant enzyme activity in frozen sections of skin fixed in formalin (Montagna and Ellis, 1958). Alcohol or acetone greatly reduces enzyme activity; formalin causes less inactivation and prevents diffusion (Seligman *et al.*, 1950; Malaty and Bourne, 1955). Different substrates may give different results; the azo-dye coupling techniques, when rigidly standardized, give clear and repeatable results. Although the activity demonstrated with the various substrates and techniques may not be indicative of different enzymes, we follow the principle of Gomori (1952) and identify each of these with the name of the substrate which it splits. *Tween esterases* which split Tween 60, are activated by sodium taurocholate and are probably similar to pancreatic lipase (Gomori, 1952; Steigleder and Schultis, 1957a, b). *Alpha,* or *nonspecific esterases* split α-naphthyl acetate. *Indoxyl acetate* esterases convert indoxyl acetate to indigo blue (Barrnett, 1952). *AS esterases* split naphthol AS (Gomori, 1952). *Specific cholinesterase* splits acetylthiocholine iodide and is inhibited by eserine; *nonspecific cholinesterases* or *pseudocholinesterases* split either acetyl or butyrylthiocholine iodide and are not completely inhibited by eserine.

In the general body epidermis the entire malpighian layer shows strong Tween esterase activity, but the stratum granulosum and the stratum corneum do not; the epidermis of the palms and soles has less activity (Fig. 25B). The malpighian layer of the general body epidermis has moderate amounts of α-esterases; a concentration of the enzymes in a band of cells between the stratum granulosum and the stratum corneum (Montagna, 1955; Findlay, 1955; Braun-Falco, 1956d) corresponds to the stratum lucidum, or more precisely, to the keratogenous zone (Fig. 25A) (Eisen *et al.,* 1953). The stratum corneum shows variable amounts of α-esterase activity. Even the free surface of the intact skin contains appreciable amounts of α-esterase activity; Steigleder and Elschner (1959a, b), using a modification of the histochemical technique directly to the living skin, have demonstrated variable amounts of enzyme activity. They have also shown that an even stronger enzyme activity is obtained with this method in the layer above the stratum granulosum after the stratum corneum has been stripped off with Scotch tape. This is in agreement with the results obtained in tissue sections. The epidermis of the palms and soles has a weakly reactive malpighian layer and no reaction in the stratum granulosum and the stratum lucidum, thus lacking the esterase-rich band found in the general epidermis; the thick stratum corneum has no reaction. The entire malpighian layer has indoxyl acetate esterase which is rarely found in the keratogenous layer. The stratum corneum contains wavy, reactive rodlets. In the palms and soles, the malpighian layer and the stratum granulosum also contain evenly distributed, reactive indoxyl acetate esterase.

All of the nerves in the skin of the human embryo, including the large, deeper trunks, have a strong concentration of specific cholinesterase. This is particularly pronounced in the volar surface of the digits where reactive branches from the deeper trunks go to the surface of the digits, branch several times, and terminate at the base of the epidermal ridges. In adult skin, only the small, presumably unmyelinated terminal nerves, have variable amounts of cholinesterase; the large, recognizably myelinated nerves rarely show a reaction.

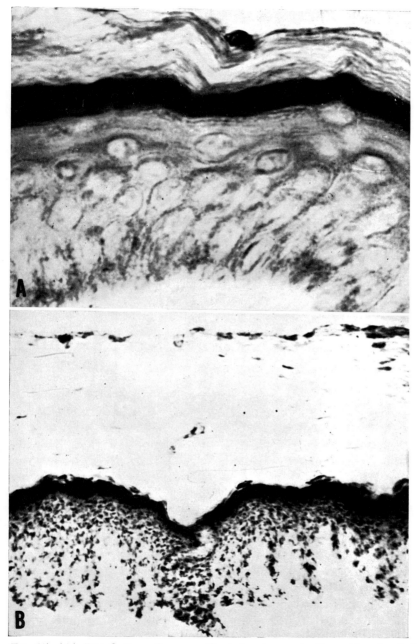

FIG. 25. (A) Distribution of nonspecific (α) esterases in the epidermis of the axilla. (B) Distribution of Tween esterases in the epidermis of the sole.

Sulfhydryl and Disulfide Groups

The early studies of the presence of sulfhydryl groups employed sodium nitroprusside. When treated with this reagent the epidermis shows a moderate reddish coloration in the malpighian layer, a strong reaction in the stratum granulosum and the stratum lucidum, and no reaction in the stratum corneum. This reaction was believed to be due to glutathione and a thermostabile sulfhydryl constituent (Kaye, 1924; Walker, 1925). Using sodium nitroprusside, Giroud and Bulliard (1934, 1935) concluded that two sulfhydryl substances are involved in *soft* and *hard* keratinization: one soluble substance, probably glutathione, in soft keratinization, and another sulfhydryl-containing insoluble substance, in much larger quantities, associated with hard keratinization. The nitroprusside test produces a weak color reaction which diffuses rapidly and is not a satisfactory histochemical technique. The Prussian blue reaction, whereby —SH groups reduce ferric ferricyanide to produce a strong blue color, is somewhat more satisfactory. This method produces a delicate color in the malpighian layer and an intense color in the keratohyalin granules in the granular layer. The stratum corneum remains unstained (Chévremont and Frederic, 1943).

The application to human skin of 1-(4-chloromercuriphenylazo)-naphthol-2, a reagent apparently specific for sulfhydryl groups, stains the cytoplasm of the cells of the malpighian layer. It stains the spinous layer weakly and the stratum corneum minimally (Bennett and Yphantis, 1948; Mescon and Flesch, 1952). The reaction in the stratum corneum, however slight, is interesting, since direct chemical methods have shown that cornified substances contain some free sulfhydryl groups (Gustavson, 1949; Rudall, 1946).

The method of Barrnett and Seligman (1952) specifically demonstrates alcohol-and-water-insoluble thiol groups and gives sharp color reactions. In the epidermis of laboratory animals and of man, the malpighian layer shows a homogeneous distribution of —SH groups from the basal layer to the cells of the stratum granulosum. This is true for the epidermis from all regions of the body. The cytoplasm of the cells of the stratum granulosum has a moderate amount of —SH groups, but the keratohyalin granules show no reaction. The stratum corneum is mildly reactive (Barrnett, 1953; Eisen *et al.*, 1953; Montagna *et al.*, 1954; Matoltsy, 1958). In human skin, and less clearly in that of the guinea pig, a narrow band of partially keratinized cells which separates the stratum granulosum from the stratum corneum is very strongly reactive (Fig. 26). This band corresponds to the "keratogenous zone" found in hard keratinization. This point is significant since the mucous membranes of the oral and buccal cavities, the esophagus, and the vagina, and the cutaneous lesions which show parakeratosis, give intense

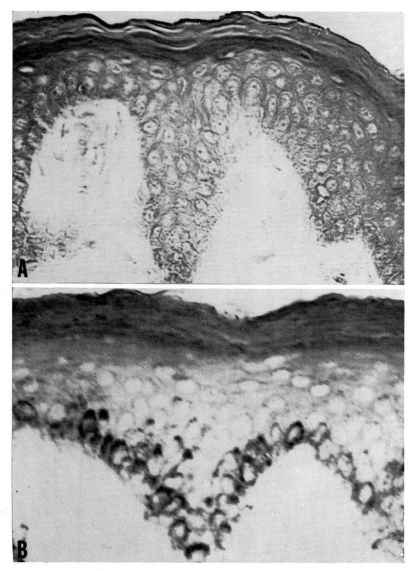

FIG. 26. The epidermis of the scalp showing (A) the localization of —SH groups, and (B) the localization of —S—S groups.

reactions in the corneal layer. The distribution of —SH groups in human palms and soles is essentially similar to that in the skin elsewhere, but the epidermis has a more definitely stratified appearance. The malpighian layer has the strongest concentration; the stratum granulosum remains nearly unstained except for the cell membranes; the stratum lucidum has a moderate concentration and the stratum corneum has a weak concentration. The basal cytoplasmic processes of the stratum germinativum have an appreciable concentration of —SH groups, as do also the intercellular bridges and nodes of Bizzozero. When preparations for —SH groups are viewed under the phase-contrast microscope, the tonofibrils can be seen very clearly, and it appears that most of the —SH groups within the cells are localized on the tonofibrils.

The technique of Barrnett (1953) shows simultaneously —SH and —S—S— groups in tissue. When these preparations are compared with sections of epidermis in which only —SH groups are demonstrated, the principal differences are that the stratum corneum of the preparations also showing —S—S— groups is darkly stained and all of the epidermal elements are stained more intensely (Fig. 26). In the palms and soles the details are more sharply brought out. The basal cytoplasmic processes of the basal layer show a strong reaction as do also the intercellular bridges, nodes of Bizzozero, and tonofibrils. These details are brought in sharp contrast when these preparations are studied under the phase-contrast microscope. Van Scott and Flesch (1954) report that the disulfide content of the malpighian layer of the sole is in the same range as in the horny layer. The keratohyalin granules in the stratum granulosum show no —S—S— groups. These granules, then, long considered to be intermediary steps in the formation of keratin, contain neither —SH nor —S—S— groups (see next section on keratinization).

Two possible roles might be attributed to the sulfhydryl groups in the epidermis: (1) that they participate in forming the disulfide bonds of keratin in the stratum corneum; (2) that they may be concerned with cell division. A transformation of —SH to —S—S— groups, not yet fully demonstrated, remains a logical assumption.

Keratinization

The best early descriptions of the process of keratinization in epidermis are those of Langerhans (1873) and Ranvier (1879). In the epidermis of man, Ranvier recognized a "keratogenic" layer which Unna later called the stratum granulosum. Ranvier called the granules of the stratum corneum *eleidine en graine* and the content of the cells of the stratum lucidum *eleidine en flaques.* Waldeyer (1882) called the granules in the stratum granulosum, "keratohyalin" granules. In the stratum granulosum, keratohyalin granules are usually aggregated at the poles of the nucleus. The granules may be stained with most basic dyes as well as with acid dyes such as Congo red, acid fuchsin, and others.

It is not known which cell component or components are responsible for the elaboration of keratin. On the assumption that the keratohyalin granules are the forerunners of "keratin," Favre (1950) presents a detailed account of the metamorphosis of mitochondria in the different layers of the epidermis and concludes that since mitochondria are responsible for the elaboration of keratohyalin granules, the process of keratinization must actually begin, although imperceptibly, in the basal layer of the stratum germinativum. Parat (1928), on the other hand, implicated the Golgi apparatus. Kollmann and Papin (1914) believed that keratohyalin granules represent transformed nucleolar extrusions. Ludford (1924) stated that although the Golgi apparatus and the nucleolus are partially involved, the process of keratinization is essentially a function of the ground cytoplasm of the cell. Martinotti (1914a, b, 1915, 1921) concluded that keratohyalin is formed from: (a) epidermal fibrils by a process of "fibrillorhexis"; (2) the ground cytoplasm, probably the basophilic granules in the cells of the stratum Malpighii; (c) the nucleus by "karyolysis," and (d) the cell membrane. Other authors are of the opinion that keratinization begins with the tonofibrils and then proceeds to the interfibrillar cellular substance and to the cell membrane (Branca, 1907; Firket, 1911; King, 1949).

When sections are microincinerated (Fig. 27), keratohyalin granules are the most heavily mineralized cytoplasmic components of the cells of the stratum granulosum, and it is believed that they contain calcium (Opdyke, 1952). The granules are Feulgen-negative and, therefore, do not contain deoxyribonucleoprotein. They are surrounded by a film, or capsule, of ribonucleoprotein, the basophilic staining of which is partially abolished by treatment with ribonuclease. The granules stain somewhat metachromatically with toluidine blue after proper fixation, indicating the probable presence of acid mucopolysaccharides. They stain well with elastin stains such as Verhoeff's stain and Krajian's stain and are Gram-positive. These staining properties are not altered by digestion with ribonuclease, hyaluronidase, or trypsin. Not all keratohyalin granules have similar tinctorial characteristics. For instance, those found at the orifices of pilosebaceous canals and sweat ducts stain strongly with basic fuchsin, whereas those of the rest of the epidermis stain weakly. The keratohyalin granules in mucous membranes have much greater dye affinity at low pH than those in the cutaneous membranes (Opdyke, 1952). In mucous membranes the granules are not stainable with toluidine blue after treatment with ribonuclease and they are not metachromatic. Those in cutaneous surfaces are resistant to the enzyme and are metachromatic. Keratohyalin granules seem to be more numerous in sites of slow keratinization than in those of rapid keratinization, and they are usually absent from sites of parakeratosis.

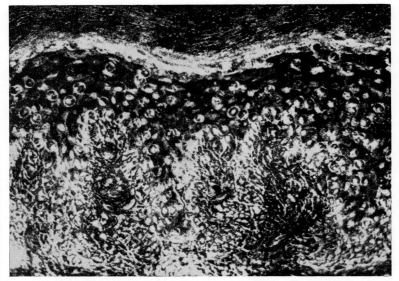

FIG. 27. Microincinerated epidermis of the palm, with abundant ash residue in the stratum granulosum. (Courtesy of Dr. D. L. Opdyke.)

The most thorough study of the keratohyalin granules and their relation to keratinization is that of Matoltsy and Matoltsy (1961). The account that follows is based entirely on their work.

When fragments of skin are treated with buffers ranging from pH 2.8 to 4.4, the keratohyalin granules shrink, but in buffers varying from pH 6.0 to 8.6, they become swollen. Since minimum swelling occurs around pH 3.9, this might indicate that the isoelectric point of the protein component of the keratohyalin granule is around this pH value. Keratohyalin granules dissolve in acid solution of pH 1.9 and in alkaline solution of pH 10.1 or higher. Solubilization of the horny component, however, occurs only in alkaline solutions of pH 11.7 and pH 12.0.

When skin is treated with 1 or 2 M urea all constituents of the epidermis become swollen. Urea in 3 *M* concentration causes intense swelling of the keratohyalin granules, and, with the exception of the horny cells, all other cells of the epidermis become disrupted. After treatment with 4, 5, or 6 *M* urea, the region between the horny layer and the dermal surface becomes filled with the remnants of dissolved cell constituents, including fragments of keratohyalin granules; the

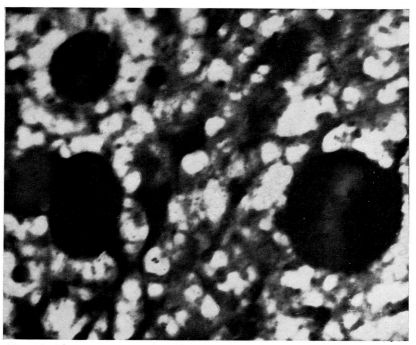

FIG. 28. Electron micrograph of keratohyalin granules in the epidermis of the rat after treatment with urea. (Courtesy of Dr. A. G. Matoltsy.)

horny layer becomes swollen but does not dissociate after treatment with 1, 2, or 3 *M* urea. The electron microscope also shows that keratohyalin granules are resistant to treatment with urea; the remnants of the cytoplasmic fibrils often form artifacts that resemble a highly vacuolated reticular network, but the cell membranes of the granular cells are well preserved (Fig. 28). The keratinizing cells above the granular cells and the cornified cells appeared as in the control preparations. When epidermis is placed in solutions of 4, 5, or 6 *M* urea, only some fragments of cell constituents remain below the stratum corneum.

A solution of 0.1% trypsin, which digests both stratum basale and stratum spinosum of the epidermis, only swells the stratum granulosum and the stratum corneum, and the keratohyalin granules can still be stained clearly with hematoxylin. When skin fragments are treated with a 1.0% solution of trypsin, the epidermis separates from the dermis in a few minutes. If treatment is prolonged to one hour, the stratum basale, stratum spinosum, and parts of the stratum granulosum are digested. The nuclei and portions of the cytoplasm of the remaining granular cells stain poorly, but the keratohyalin granules retain their stainability with hematoxylin. Electron microscopic investigations of samples of skin treated with 1.0% solution of trypsin also show that the keratohyalin granules resist the action of trypsin. The cell membranes of the granular cells and those of the horny layer remain intact.

Histochemical studies show that keratohyalin granules contain neither —SH nor —S—S— groups. The keratogenous zone of the epidermis abounds in —SH groups and the entire stratum corneum shows a weak reaction. A positive test for —S—S— is found in the stratum corneum.

The horny component of cornified cells is well stabilized by —S—S— bonds and some free —SH groups also occur. It is also a characteristic property of the horny component that it is insoluble in buffers in the range from pH 1.9 to pH 10.9. Furthermore, it resists the action of urea up to 6 M concentration as well as that of trypsin in 0.1 to 1.0% solutions. It dissolves only in solutions having a pH of 11.7 or 12.0, an alkalinity high enough to rupture the —S—S— bonds.

Although keratohyalin granules reveal properties similar to those of the horny component, such as a resistance to tryptic digestion, they are most significantly different in lacking strong cohesive forces, such as the —S—S— bonds. While keratohyalin granules are stable in buffers in the range of pH 2.9 to 8.6 and resist urea in 1 to 3 M concentrations, they pass into solution in urea of 4 to 6 M concentrations, in acid solution of pH 1.9, or in alkaline solutions of pH 10.1 to 12.0. Accordingly, it appears that mainly hydrogen bonds and salt linkages are involved in their stabilization.

The cytoplasmic fibrils in the epidermal cells are rich in —SH groups but seem to contain no —S—S— bonds. Since these fibrils are readily dissociated in weak solutions of urea or trypsin, they probably represent a weakly stabilized precursor of the horny component.

Under the electron microscope, isolated keratohyalin granules appear to be in aggregates of large and small granules, indicating that they become attached to each other during the process of isolation. The peripheral region of the granules consists of a material that is much less electron dense than the thick central portion. The periphery, and occasionally also other parts of the granules, show a very fine granular substructure. Filaments cannot be seen within the main body of the granules or attached to them.

Thus, keratohyalin granules consist of a fine granular, highly osmiophilic material. Filaments (Horstmann and Knoop, 1958) probably occur only in the peripheral region and constitute a small fraction of the keratohyalin granules or none at all. Keratohyalin granules are resistant to tryptic digestion and to urea in concentrations less than a 4 M solution; while they are stable in buffers that range from pH 2.9 to 8.6, they pass into solution in acid solution of pH 1.9 or in alkaline solution of pH 10.1.

The electron microscope clearly indicates that keratohyalin granules are specific products of epidermal cells, which become a part of the final horny component of cornified cells. The granules develop in the cytoplasm of epidermal cells as submicroscopic corpuscles at the time the cells enter their course of differentiation. The granules grow to various sizes independent of one another and cease to grow when the cells are mature. The mechanism involved in the formation or in the growth of keratohyalin granules is not known. Since Brody (1959) noted that their fine granular component also occurs freely dispersed in the cytoplasm, perhaps the fine granules are synthesized at scattered points in the cytoplasm and the first keratohyalin granules are formed by an accumulation of the fine granular material which later grows by accretion.

The most voluminous constituents of transforming epidermal cells are the cytoplasmic fibrils (Fig. 29) and the keratohyalin granules, considered equally involved in the formation of the final horny component. Keratohyalin granules do not undergo a fibrillar transformation, as reported by Mercer (1958), but seem to become dissociated and mixed with the fibrous content of keratinizing cells; their ultimate fate seems to be a dispersion into the interfibrillar spaces. Brody (1959) assumed such a fate for keratohyalin granules based on the observation that the staining properties of the interfibrillary material in cornified cells is identical with that of the particles of keratohyalin granules. A structural arrangement of this type also leads to the conclusion that the fibrillar component of cornified cells, formed from the cytoplasmic fibrils, represents a sulfur-rich material, whereas the interfibrillar substance, containing material of keratohyalin granules, is trypsin resistant and poor in sulfur. In this regard it is well to recall that Birbeck and Mercer (1957a, b) also find two components in the cells of the cortex of the hair, but they assume that the fibrillary component is poor in sulfur whereas the interfibrillar material is rich in it.

Loss of fluids is an essential process of the final stages of keratinization. Since dehydration of transforming cells starts at a distance from the skin surface and at a level where normally hydrated cells also occur, dehydration does not seem to be due to a simple desiccation and evapo-

Fig. 29. High magnification electron micrograph of keratin fibrils in the lower layers of the stratum corneum. (Courtesy of Dr. A. G. Matoltsy.)

ration of water. Loss of fluids at this level is probably caused by syneresis, or some similar process through which the proteins release their bound water molecules. At higher levels, desiccation and evaporation of water may be at work, leading to complete consolidation of the cell content.

Jarrett et al. (1956, 1959) studied keratin and keratinization in a different way. They treat both fresh and alcohol-fixed tissues with various fluorescent dyes, and then observe the tissues under ultraviolet light. Certain substances have an affinity for certain dyes, and additional specificity to the uptake of the fluorochrome is inferred by treating the tissues with various enzymes before they are stained. The authors conclude that the principal keratinogenic changes in the epidermis occur in the granular layer, where the formation of disulfide linkages and other linkages involves exothermic reactions in the presence of trace metals. Pre-existing polypeptide chains in the granular layer would break down and then be resynthesized into keratin. The authors believe that a high energy system is located in the granular layer, but there is no proof of this.

Keratin formation has also been studied with the use of S^{35}-labeled cystine, cysteine, and methionine (Bern *et al.*, 1955; Bern, 1954; Harkness and Bern, 1957; Belanger, 1956; Ryder, 1959). Shortly after they are injected into experimental animals, the labeled amino acids can be recovered throughout the malpighian layer, but the greatest concentration of them is in the keratogenous zone where normally the highest concentration of protein-bound —SH groups is also found. This concentration suggests that the S^{35}-labeled substances are in transit in malpighian cells and that many of those dammed in the keratogenous zone may be protein-bound cysteine. If tissues that contain labeled cystine are extracted with thioglycolate, there is no diminution of S^{35}, suggesting that the cystine is not bound to side groups by —S—S— linkages, but that it may be linked by peptide linkages as cystine into the chains of the keratin molecules (Bern *et al.*, 1955). Although the fibrous component of keratin begins to be formed in the keratogenous zone, just beneath the stratum corneum (Harkness and Bern, 1957), the precursors must be formed all through the malpighian layer.

The epidermis has probably equal total amounts of protein and lipids (Wicks and Suntzeff, 1942). The horny layer of the epidermis also contains choline, bonded to keratin, that can be liberated only after treatment with hot sulfuric acid under high pressure (Ottenstein *et al.*, 1952). Since during the process of keratinization the phospholipids in the lower layers of the epidermis seem to disappear, and some of the cholesterol is esterified (Kooyman, 1932), the phospholipids are probably bonded to the keratin fibrils by the choline group, and, therefore, cannot be extracted easily. The cholesterol and fatty acids, some of them perhaps esterified, are presumably situated around the keratin fibrils, their hydroxylic and carboxylic groups making up an outer electron-dense layer (Swanbeck, 1959). This part of the lipid layer can be removed with lipid solvents. It has been suggested that the lipids covering the fibrils could come from the breakdown of the membranes of the mitochondria and the Golgi elements (Swanbeck, 1959). Tono-filaments, with a diameter of 90 to 100 Å, then, which are synthesized in the cells of the malpighian layer, aggregate in the keratin layer in bundles of 5 to 10, with a thickness of about 259 Å. At approximately the granular layer and above, there is a decomposition of the cell content, the lipids are liberated, and the proteins break down into peptides and amino acids, forming the water-soluble fraction of the horny layer (Szakall, 1955). The lipids gather around each tonofilament before these aggregate into the fibrils of the horny layer, and each fibril is surrounded by a lipid layer 80 Å thick, making up a total diameter of about 400 Å. On the basis of studies of the wide-angle and low-angle diffraction patterns, Swanbeck (1959) believes that the hypothetic model for the molecular organization of the fibril unit of keratin may be that of fibrils consisting of protein cylinders surrounded by a lipid layer, with the lipid chains arranged radially on the protein cylinder.

There is no histochemical test that demonstrates keratin specifically. The Millon reagent and the xanthoproteic test have been used, since these tests demonstrate proteins which contain tyrosine in their mole-cule; actually a color reaction is given by nearly all proteins and phenolic compounds (Serra, 1946).

Unna and Golodetz (1909) identified two types of keratin in epi-dermis: keratin A, which is insoluble in nitric acid and in a mixture of sulfuric acid and hydrogen peroxide; and keratin B, which is soluble in these reagents. The keratin molecule is believed to consist of closely packed polypeptide chains which are held together by the disulfide bond of cystine, the resistance to solvents and enzymes being associated with the close packing of the chains. The major portion of hair, horn, hoof, feather, nail, and the stratum corneum of the skin is made up of albuminoid proteins. The keratin of hair, nails, and other cutaneous appendages contains from 3 to 5% sulfur, while that of skin contains one to 3%, nearly all of which is in cystine (Hawk *et al.*, 1947). Keratin is insoluble in dilute alkalies, in water, and in organic solvents, and on acid hydrolysis yields such quantities of histidine, lysine, and arginine that the molecular ratios of these amino acids are, respectively, approximately 1:4:12 (Block and Vickery, 1931). Actually, these amino acids are closer to a molecular ratio of 1:5:15 (Wilkerson, 1934). The isoelectric points for keratin, hair, and nails are 3.70, 3.67, and 3.78. Since the isoelectric points are practically the same, and since the basic amino acids are present in approximately the same molecular ratios, possibly the amino acids responsible for the acid groups are also present in a definite molecular ratio in these three chemically, physically, and embryologically related structures (Wilkerson, 1934, 1935). These figures show the remarkable unity which exists among the keratins from different cutaneous appendages.

Most mammalian keratins, in the normal state, give approximately the same X-ray diffraction diagrams, with a periodicity of 5.15 Å, which is characteristic of the α form (Astbury, 1933). When keratin is stretched, changing from α-keratin to β, there is an extension of the polypeptide chains of about 100% (Astbury and Woods, 1930). The α- and β-keratins seem to be stereoisomers, that is, two different structures which have similar molecular configurations. The lip of the ox (Derksen and Heringa, 1936), the human nail (Derksen et al., 1938), the burr of the horse, and the hoof of the calf (Giroud et al., 1934), all show the X-ray diffraction of α pattern of keratin. The polypeptide skeleton possessing the periodicity of 5.15 Å seems to be pre-existent in the stratum germinativum even before the keratinization becomes evident, and the tonofibrils are probably the elements involved in keratinization. In the stratum corneum from thick sections of hoofs of embryonic calves, the birefringence produced by α-keratin (or keratin B of Unna) is destroyed by chilled 2% potassium hydroxide (Champetier and Litvac, 1939). With the same treatment the keratinized cell membranes (keratin A of Unna) remain intact and are isotropic. Pepsin and trypsin digest the tonofibrils in the stratum germinativum, but these enzymes do not digest α-keratin in the keratinized region. This is explained by the fact that the keratinized cell membranes (keratin A of Unna), which are resistant to proteolytic enzymes, protect the enclosed α-keratin. X-Ray diffraction patterns of untreated epidermis show that patterns for α- keratin are obtained wherever the tonofibrils are present, either in the nonkeratinized malpighian layer or in the keratinized upper layers. From these observations it has been concluded that the tonofibrils are responsible for the characteristic X-ray diffraction pattern of α-keratin. Under pressure or after exposure to heat, keratin is transformed to β-keratin. X-Ray diffraction diagrams of relatively pure (extracted with KOH) membrane keratin (keratin A of Unna) are unlike those of either α- or β-keratin, and they must represent something quite different. Treatment of the malpighian layer of epidermis with urea yields an extract from which a protein, "epidermin," may be precipitated with ammonium sulfate. X-Ray diffraction patterns of epidermis are similar to those of α-keratin (Rudall, 1946, 1947, 1953). The cells of the spinous layer, then, seem to contain the basic proteins of keratin. These proteins could be oriented within the cells in such a way as to favor, upon fixation, their precipitation into microscopically visible, birefringent fibrils (Medawar, 1953).

Under the polarizing microscope, human epidermis shows very discrete birefringence (Fig. 30). The cells of the entire stratum Malpighii, from the basal layer to the stratum corneum, contain birefringent fibrils. These are packed within each cell and they are oriented perpendicular to the surface of the skin. At the stratum granulosum, and continuing through the stratum corneum, the birefringent fibrils are suddenly oriented parallel to the surface.

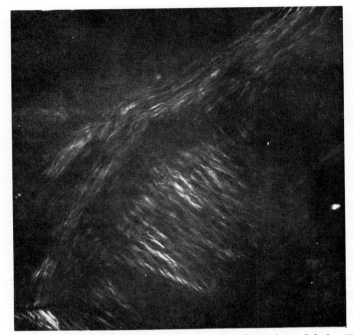

FIG. 30. Human epidermis of the scalp viewed under polarized light. The birefringent fibrils from the basal layer to the granular layer are oriented perpendicular to the surface of the skin; above this point they are oriented parallel to the surface.

Two fundamental types of keratins, "soft" and "hard," are usually recognized (Giroud *et al.*, 1934; Giroud and Leblond, 1951). Soft keratin is found in the epidermis, the internal root sheath of hair follicles, and the medulla of the hair; hard keratin is found in nails, the cortex, and cuticle of hair. In both types of keratinization the metabolic activity of the stratum germinativum culminates in the formation of tonofibrils. Since an X-ray diffraction pattern with a periodicity of 5.15 Å has been found wherever tonofibrils are present, it is likely that this protein is the principal component of tonofibrils and thus the precursor of keratin. Soft keratin is characterized by (a) its relative suppleness and pliability, (b) a low to moderate sulfur content and a fairly high lipid content, (c) its ready stainability with routine histological stains, and (d) a spontaneous and continuous desquamation. Hard keratin differs from soft keratin by (a) its toughness and firmness, (b) the presence of an —SH-rich "keratogenous zone," which is a gradual transition between the malpighian and keratinized layers, (c) a high sulfur and low lipid content, (d) its failure to stain with some histologic dyes, and (e) its permanency. These generalizations do not fully survive critical appraisal. An —SH-rich "keratogenous zone," as has been shown earlier under —SH and —S—S— groups, is not limited to hard keratinization.

The Melanocyte System of the Mammalian Integument

To avoid confusion in nomenclature, only the following names will be used to designate cells that form, or contain pigment (Fitzpatrick and Lerner, 1953): (a) *melanoblasts* are cells of neural crest origin that develop into melanin-forming cells; (b) *melanocytes* are differentiated melanin-forming cells that discharge melanin granules by way of their dendrites, and (c) *melanophores* are pigment effector cells of lower vertebrates. Mammalian melanocytes are not coloring cells in the same sense as the melanophores of lower vertebrates; they are color-forming and color-distributing cells. Sometimes melanocytes are less pigmented than their neighboring, nonmelanin-forming receptor cells.

Weidenreich (1900), who envisioned the pigmentary system of vertebrates to consist of four "envelopes," *perineural, perivascular, pericelomic, and peridermal,* suggested that all pigment-forming cells may be embryologically related to the nervous sytem. These pigment "envelopes" of Weidenreich are readily demonstrable in lower vertebrates where they are the site of spectacular color changes (Du Shane, 1943, 1944). In mammals, and especially in man, it was assumed that pigment is formed in cells located in the basal cells of the epidermis.

Using an ingenious new histochemical technique, the "dopa" reaction, Bloch (1917) first demonstrated in human skin dendritic, melanin-producing cells sandwiched between the cells of the basal layer of the epidermis. He assumed, however, that the dendritic cells are ad hoc variants of the basal cells of the epidermis and that they arise under such stimuli as actinic rays. In spite of this erroneous conclusion, Bloch demonstrated for the first time (a) the role of an enzyme in the formation of melanin, and (b) the presence of *melanocytes* in Caucasian epidermis. The second point ended the controversy about the racial superiority of white skin over colored skin, since the former was allegedly free of melanocytes (Becker, 1934; Beerman *et al.*, 1955; Adachi, 1903; Zimmerman and Becker, 1959).

Raper (1926, 1928, 1932) first demonstrated that *tyrosinase*, a copper-bound, widely distributed enzyme in plant and animal tissues, is the melanin-forming ferment. Histochemical studies by Laidlaw (1932; Laidlaw and Murray, 1933), Becker (1927, 1930, 1933, 1942, 1949, 1954), Radaeli (1953), and Boyd (1949a, b, 1950) have shown melanocytes at the dermoepidermal interface of the integument in every region of the human body, including the oral mucosa. The melanocytes in hair follicles (cf. Chase *et al.*, 1951), where first described by Riehl (1884), who suggested that melanin granules from the melanocytes are transferred onto the cells of the hair matrix. Such a transfer, observed particularly clearly in amphibian melanophores (Ehrmann, 1885; Stearner, 1946), was later called "cytocrine action" by Masson (1948, see below). The melanocytes in the hair follicle and those in the epidermis have the same origin; those of the hair follicles are "carried down" from the epidermis together with the developing hair bulb (Danneel and Weissenfels, 1953; Danneel and Cleffmann, 1954). The melanocytes of the epidermis and hair are interchangeable (cf. Billingham and Medawar, 1953; Pepper, 1954), although those of the hair follicles show a characteristic pattern of activity that follows the growth cycle of the hair follicles (Fitzpatrick *et al.*, 1958). Keeping in mind that differences exist in the life cycle of melanocytes according to their particular habitat (Fitzpatrick and Kukita, 1959), what is said here about melanocytes can be inferred for both those in the epidermis and those in hair follicles.

The melanocytes in hair follicles are sensitive cells for the study of the relationship between genetic determination of melanogenesis and environmental effects. Following the earlier experiments of Reed *et al.* (Reed and Sanders, 1937; Reed, 1938; Reed and Henderson, 1940), Silvers and Russell (1955) "offered" genotypically different melanocytes to hair follicles and studied the interreaction of the genetic locus (in this case *agouti locus*), the general tract differences in hair follicles and their local tract differences. From his results, Silvers (1957b, 1958a, b, c) proposed the theory that the type of pigment formed in hair follicles (eumelanin or pheomelanin) depends upon environmental influences.

Albinism affects hair follicles as well as the general body integument. The epidermis of human albinos contains melanocytes (cf. Becker, Jr. *et al.*, 1952), as do also their white hairs (Silvers, 1956a). The follicles of white hairs in spotted fur, however, have no melanocytes (Silvers, 1956a).

There seems to be an inverse relationship in some cases between the density of hair follicles and the presence of melanogenic melanocyte systems in the epidermis. Rabbit, rat, and mouse may bear a pigmented, dense furry coat, yet the melanocytes in their general body epidermis are amelanotic (see Table I). Guinea pigs, monkeys, apes, and man may possess a melanogenic melanocyte system in both locations. Seals, dogs, monkeys, and cats have both a thick coat of hair and a rich pigmentary melanocyte system in the epidermis.

Hair melanocytes, which can be activated by irradiation (Quevedo and Isherwood, 1958), are so susceptible to it that there is a ratio between the dosage of irradiation and the number of melanocytes destroyed in the follicle (Chase, 1949, 1951). While irradiation may cause a darkening of the epidermis, it may, at the same time, cause graying and a loss of hair (Quevedo and Grahn, 1958).

Overemphasis on neoplastic changes in the melanocyte system has been followed by a neglect of basic research in mammalian melanogenesis. The controversy of "epidermal" versus "dermal" origin of neoplastic melanocytes, for example, has obscured the real issues: (a) of whether or not the normal pigment-forming cells of man are homologous with those of lower vertebrates, and (b) of the biochemical basis of melanin formation. Since melanocytes share morphological characteristics with Schwann cells, Masson (1926, 1948, 1951) voiced the view that they may be of "neural" origin. Allen (1949) and Allen and Spitz (1954) rejected this. Masson also likened melanocytes to unicellular glands transferring their product to other cells which do not produce melanin themselves, and called the process "cytocrine action."

Several questions about the genesis of mammalian melanogenesis still need clarification:

1. Are Bloch's dopa-positive cells adventitious or regular constituents of the epidermis?

2. Are dendritic melanocytes homologous to the pigment-forming cells of lower vertebrates?

3. What enzyme systems are involved in melanogenesis?

The pigment-forming cells of the skin arise from the neural crest (Du Shane, 1943; Silvers, 1958a); those in the retinal pigment epithelium of the eye, however, arise from the optic cup (Oppenheimer, 1949). When the skin of rat embryos is explanted before the cells of the neural crest have invaded it, the skin remains free of the pigmentation characteristic of the strain (Rawles, 1940, 1947). The ascension of melanoblasts to the basal layer of the skin of human embryos has been observed *in vitro* (Chlopin, 1932) and *in vivo* (Becker and Zimmerman, 1955; Zimmerman and Becker, 1959).

The various homologous types of pigment-forming cells found in lower vertebrates (melanocytes, melanophores, xanthophores, guanophores, iridophores, leucophores, etc.) gradually decrease in numbers during phylogenetic ascension, and mammals have only one type, the melanocyte. Together with a reduction in variants of color-producing cells, the distribution of these cells has also become more restricted.

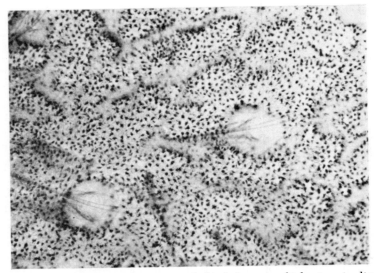

FIG. 31. Epidermal sheet from a region behind the ear, split by trypsin digestion, and treated with the dopa technique, showing the even distribution of the melanocytes population. (Courtesy of Dr. G. Szabó.)

In mammals, only the peridermal system is fully developed; the perineural is said to be restricted to the eye and to the pia mater (Snessarew, 1929; Becker, Jr. *et al.*, 1952). The perivascular and perineural tissue of many primates with deeply pigmented skins has a rich population of melanocytes.

When intact epidermal sheets are separated from the dermis with the trypsin skin-splitting technique (Medawar, 1941), and treated with the "dopa" reaction (Billingham, 1948, 1949; Becker, 1942), the melanocytes in the dermoepidermal interface can be studied in three dimensions (Fig. 31). Dopa-positive epidermal melanocytes are present in every region of the skin of man. In mice and rats, dopa-positive melanocytes are present in the epidermis of the tail, nose, and ear, but not in that of the general body epidermis (Holmes, 1953; Reynolds, 1954; Nichols and Reams, 1960). The dopa-negative, nonmelanotic melanocytes in the general body epidermis can be activated with a number of irritants (Cleffmann-Brenner, 1959) and with advancing age.

The disparity in the ability of the melanocytes of different mammals to form pigment is illustrated in Table I.

TABLE I
AFFINITY OF MELANOCYTES TO DOPA IN GENERAL BODY EPIDERMIS

Species	Reactivity	Author
Opposum	Negative	Szabó, unpublished
Guinea pig	Positive	Billingham, 1948
Mouse	Negative	Holmes, 1953 Reynolds, 1954
Rabbit	Negative	Billingham, 1948 Holmes, 1953
Rat[a]	Negative	Holmes, 1953
Seal	Positive	Szabó, 1959
Dog	Positive	Szabó, unpublished
Cat	Positive	Szabó, unpublished
Pig	Positive	Szabó, unpublished
Rhesus monkey	Positive	Szabó, unpublished
Gibbon	Positive	Szabó, unpublished
Man	Positive	Bloch, 1917

[a] Except in tail, ear, nose, palm, and sole, where the epidermal melanocyte system is dopa positive.

All of the mammals listed above may have functioning melanocytes in the hair follicles (Danneel and Cleffmann, 1954), and some of them have melanocytes in the dermis. In man, melanocytes are found consistently in the dermis only during fetal life (Zimmerman and Becker, 1959), and in some nevi. Many other primates, however, have rich populations of them. The fate of the melanocytes in the dermis of man is unknown; perhaps they migrate into the epidermis, or they lose their affinity to dopa.

The combination of the skin-splitting and dopa methods, give excellent preparations for quantitative studies of the population of melanocytes (Fig. 31). The skin of the guinea pig (Billingham and Medawar, 1953), the normal and pathological skin of man (Szabó, 1954, 1959), and the melanocytes in different races of man (Staricco and Pinkus, 1957) have been studied in this way (see Table II).

TABLE II

REGIONAL FREQUENCY DISTRIBUTION OF MELANOCYTES IN THE GUINEA PIG[a]

Region	Mean number of melanocytes per mm² of skin surface ± S.E.
Ear	893 ± 85
Trunk	403 ± 26

[a] Billingham and Medawar (1953).

Billingham and Medawar (1953) in the guinea pig, and Szabó (1959) in man, found no significant differences in the density of melanocyte population between the symmetrically opposite sides of the same animal or subject (see Table III).

TABLE III

RELATIVE PROPORTION OF THE NUMBER OF MELANOCYTES BETWEEN THE RIGHT AND THE LEFT SIDE OF THE SAME INDIVIDUAL ± S.E.

Number of Cases		Author and area
13 Cases	1.04 ± 0.076	Szabó, 1959; human skin
8 Cases	0.973 ± 0.044	Billingham and Medawar, 1953; guinea pig ear
8 Cases	1.006 ± 0.049	Billingham and Medawar, 1953; guinea pig trunk

The color of the skin, then, depends less upon the density of the melanocytes than on the amount of color that they produce. The differences in skin coloration between the races of men are not due to differences in the density of melanocytes, but to their functional variations in the production of melanin (Staricco and Pinkus, 1957). There are great individual and regional variations in the melanocyte systems in man and in the guinea pig (Szabó, 1954, 1959; Billingham and Medawar, 1953). The thickness of the epidermis and the architecture of the undersculpturing are different in various regions, and perhaps there is a density gradient in the original population of melanoblast that invades the skin. Postnatal stretching of the skin, which plays a major role in establishing the regional differences in the distribution of skin appendages, has little effect upon the distribution of melanocytes (Szabó, 1959). Solar radiation, long believed to be a major factor in increasing the density of melanocytes (Bloch, 1917; Becker, Jr. et al., 1952), seems to have no effect; such areas as the mucous membranes of the oral and nasal cavities, and the scrotum, which are protected from solar rays, are densely populated with melanocytes.

The variations in regional density, however, are within certain limits

(Szabó, 1959). One in every ten cells in the basal layer of the epidermis is a melanocyte (Table IV); in some regions there may be one in every four.

The dendrites of melanocytes may be in contact with more than one malpighian cell, which is circumstantial anatomical evidence that the melanocytes are the only cells capable of forming and distributing melanin in the basal layer of the epidermis (Figs. 32 and 33).

TABLE IV

RELATIVE PROPORTION OF MELANOCYTES TO MALPIGHIAN CELLS

Region	Number of specimens	Ratio: $\dfrac{\text{Malpighian cells}}{\text{melanocytes}} \pm$ S.E. mean
Cheek	9	4.53 ± 0.29
Arm	7	10.41 ± 3.02
Thigh	11	10.21 ± 2.57

That internal factors regulate the density of melanocytes is shown by the repopulation by melanocytes of newly formed human epidermis in scars (Szabó, 1959; Breathnach, 1960). The population of melanocytes in scar epidermis may be somewhat lower than that in the surrounding normal skin, but it approaches a normal range. Knowing what the distribution of melanocytes in normal epidermis is, it is possible to appraise the changes that occur in abnormal skin, such as vitiligo (Jarrett and Szabó, 1956; Hu, 1959), freckling (Breathnach, 1957), albinism (Becker, Jr. et al., 1952; Reynolds, 1954; Silvers, 1956a), or the changes reflected by the influence of sex hormones (Bischitz and Snell, 1959a, b; Snell and Bischitz, 1959, 1960).

The number of melanocytes in a given area is related to their shape and to the length of their dendrites (Szabó, 1954; Staricco and Pinkus, 1957). When there are more than 1000 per square millimeter, melanocytes are small and have short dendrites; in areas where the number is smaller than 1000 per square millimeter, the melanocytes are larger, have an angular shape and longer dendrites. In scars, the melanocytes are usually spindle-shaped (Szabó, 1959) as are also those in leptomeninges (Snessarew, 1929; Becker, Jr. et al., 1952). Under the electron microscope, the cytoplasm of melanocytes is somewhat clearer than that of the epidermal cells; they have no desmosomes and the cell membrane, in contrast with that of the malpighian cells, is smooth (Dalton and Felix, 1953; Barnicot et al., 1955; Birbeck, et. al., 1956; Birbeck and Mercer, 1957a, b; Clark et al., 1958; Barnicot and Birbeck, 1958; Birbeck and Barnicot, 1959; Wellings and Siegel, 1960). The dendrites of melanocytes seem to penetrate the epidermal cells, but they may be engulfed by them, thus transferring melanin granules to recipient cells (Birbeck *et al.*, 1956).

There are contrasting views about the relationship of mitochondria to melanin granules. DuBuy *et al.* (1949) believe that they have a common origin, but Baker *et al.* (1960) and Birbeck and Barnicot (1959)

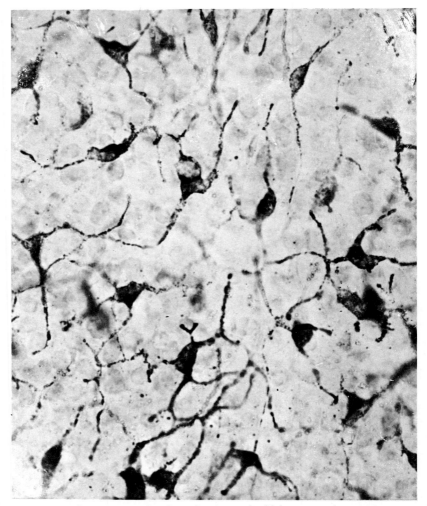

Fig. 32. Melanocytes in the skin of a 3-month-old human embryo. (Courtesy of Dr. A. Zimmerman.)

assert that melanin granules, *melanosomes,* are cell organelles *sui generis* (see below).

Normal and abnormal human melanocytes grow readily *in vitro* (Grand *et al.,* 1935; Hu *et al.,* 1957; Hu, 1959; Weissenfels, 1956; Hsu and Lou, 1959), but they do not migrate from the transplant (Grand

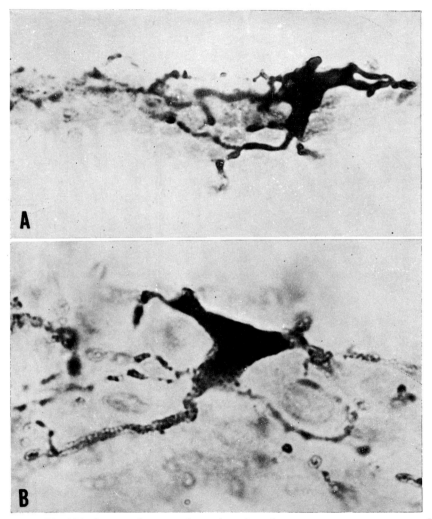

FIG. 33. (A) Giant melanocyte from the edge of a vitiligenous plaque, treated with the dopa technique. (B) Another melanocyte from a vitiligenous lesion, treated with the dopa technique. In both figures observe the extent of the dendritic processes. Actually, only a few of the dendrites are visible. (Courtesy of Dr. G. Szabó.)

et al., 1935). In cultured melanocytes melanin granules come out of their dendrites (Fig. 34); the ends of the dendrites often break off by *clasmosis.* In the melanocytes of the fowl, grown *in vitro,* melanin appears to be formed in special areas distinct from other cytoplasmic entities (Weissenfels, 1956). *In vitro,* when the melanin-forming area of melanocytes is full of granules, melanogenesis slows down. In contrast, the cell body of melanocytes growing *in vivo* is relatively free of

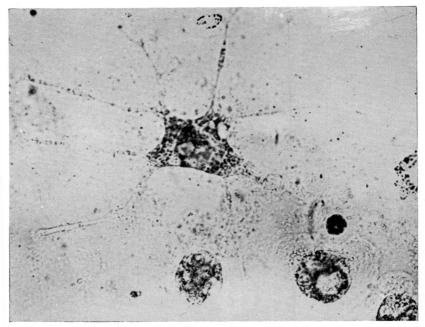

Fig. 34. Living melanocyte of the guinea pig, cultured *in vitro.* The delicate dendritic processes are barely visible. (Couretsy of Dr. G. Szabó.)

melanin, and the granules are concentrated mostly in the dendrites. Extrusion of nuclear material has been shown in cultured Cloudman melanoma (Hsu and Lou, 1959), and in the pigmented cells of the choroid epithelium of the chick and rabbit embryos (Szily, 1911). No one has shown that the nucleus of normal melanocytes contributes directly to melanogenesis.

Melanin is formed from the amino acid tyrosine (Bloch, 1917, 1929; Raper, 1926, 1928, 1932; Mason, 1959). Emphasis on the one-key, one-lock enzyme-substrate system, however, has kept alive a long controversy concerning the enzyme involved. Tyrosine is ineffective in demonstrating tyrosinase in human melanocytes, whereas with dopa, the oxidized derivative of tyrosine, the melanocytes become dark. This issue is further confused by the nonspecific reaction of leucocytes with dopa. In spite of this, dopa is a specific histochemical substrate for melanin-forming melanocytes. Since the formation of melanin in mushrooms begins with tyrosine, and not with dihydroxyphenylalanine, it has been assumed that two enzymes, tyrosinase and dopa oxidase, may be responsible for the formation of melanin in mammalian melanocytes (Fitzpatrick et al., 1950; Hogeboom and Adams, 1942).

The name "tyrosinase" for the melanin-forming enzyme in mammalian melanocytes is justifiable on biochemical evidence (Fitzpatrick et al., 1950; Hogeboom and Adams, 1942). "Malignant" neoplasms of melanocytes can be separated from "benign" ones with the use of the histochemical technique of Fitzpatrick (1952). When tyrosine is used as a substrate in vitro instead of dopa, malignant human melanomas become laden with pigment, but no pigment is formed in normal skin and in benign nevi. Radioactive tyrosine is also useful (Fitzpatrick and Kukita, 1956, 1959). Melanocytes in skin exposed to thorium irradiation also form pigment when incubated in tyrosine. The melanocytes in normal epidermis that have been exposed to sun rays, and those in the genital regions have a positive tyrosine reaction in trypsin-separated epidermal sheets (Szabó, 1957). In all of these examples the number of tyrosine-positive cells is the same, or very similar to that in control sections treated with the dopa reaction. Melanocytes in regions that are usually covered with clothing have a variable or negative reaction. The variation in the reaction of melanocytes to tyrosine may reflect natural differences in their tyrosinase activity, as in the case of "freckles" (Breathnach, 1959), or it may be due to external stimuli, as in the face. In the melanocytes of rodents (Foster, 1951, 1952, 1956, 1959; Foster and Cook, 1953, 1954; Foster et al., 1956), it appears that tyrosine is the natural substrate of melanin, tyrosine becoming converted slowly into dopa under the action of tyrosinase. Tyrosine has been shown to be the substrate of genetically controlled pigment formation in chick embryos (Brunet, 1960). Tyrosine labeled with C^{14} in the side chain, when injected into 5-day-old embryos is uniformly taken up by the feather follicles of Black Minorcas but it is not incorporated into the follicles of White Leghorns. (For further aspects of the recent advances in this field, see Brunet, 1960.)

In the skin of the chick, the formation of melanin in vitro is enhanced when tyrosine is added to the medium (Saunders et al., 1955). Since the incorporation of phenylalanine decreases the rate of pigmentation, there may be a competitive inhibition between the two substrates.

The biochemical events in melanogenesis can be summarized as follows:

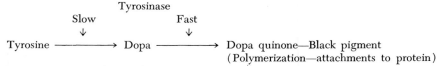

With the pheomelanin of red human hair, tryptophan or its metabolite, and not tyrosine may be the substrate (Fitzpatrick *et al.*, 1958). Melanogenesis proceeds in two stages: the formation of melanin granules and the melanization of the granules. Since fractions of low-speed centrifugates stain with Janus green B, or similar vital stains, DuBuy *et al.* (1949) believe that melanin granules are specialized mitochondria. The electron microscope, however, indicates that mitochondria and melanin granules are distinct entities (Barnicot and Birbeck, 1958; Dalton and Felix, 1953). In high-speed fractionations of mouse melanomas and of retinal pigment of chick embryos, the mitochondrial fraction is distinct from that of the melanin granule fraction (Baker *et al.*, 1960; Seiji *et al.*, 1960). Mitochondria fractions have high succinoxidase and glutamate oxidase activity, whereas the melanin granule fractions have low or no succinoxidase activity, but a high tyrosinase activity. As melanin is formed in melanomas, or in the retina of chick eyes (after the seventeenth day of incubation), tyrosinase activity declines, suggesting that tyrosinase is "used up" or "coated" with melanin during melanogenesis and must be formed anew together with the new melanin granule or "melanosome" (Seiji *et al.*, 1960). In spite of various assertions (Szily, 1911; Hsu and Lou, 1959), it is not known whether or not the nucleus plays a role in the formation of melanin granules.

Mammalian melanogenesis is hormonally controlled (Lerner *et al.*, 1954; Lerner, 1959; Lerner and Lee, 1955; Lerner and Case, 1959). The darkening of human integument in adrenal cortical deficiency can be explained by an increased action of the mammalian homolog of intermedin (melanocyte-stimulating hormone) of lower vertebrates. Intermedin does not stimulate melanogenesis, but aids in the dispersal of melanin granules already formed (Chavin, 1959). Lerner (1959) has localized an agent from the pineal gland, "melatonin," which induces the aggregation of melanin granules in the cytoplasm of the melanophores of amphibians. The endocrine basis of seasonal changes of the coat color of certain mammals still remains a paradox.

The size and the shape of mammalian melanocytes are under genetic control. "Centrifugal" melanocytes have short dendrites and centripetal" ones have long dendrites (Markert and Silvers, 1956). Environmental conditions, such as location in the hair follicles, and the cyclic growth activity of the follicles may also be a major factor in the expression of the color phenotype of the animal. In the fowl, branching of the melanocytes can also be evoked by chemical stimuli (Reams *et al.*, 1959).

An intriguing pigmentary phenomenon is the "pigment spread," or the enlargement of dark areas at the expense of lesser colored ones during postnatal life. Billingham and Medawar (1948a, b, 1950) maintained that in the skin of the guinea pig, melanocytes may not only pass granules to malpighian cells but may "infect" each other by exchanging granules. Silvers (1956b, 1958c) and Breathnach (1959), however, explain pigment spread by a migration of cells. Billingham and Silvers (1960) now regard the phenomenon of pigment spread as a manifestation of cytoplasmic inheritance mediated by particles in the melanocyte.

In a sense, the epidermis is a holocrine gland; during the process of keratinization the basal cells are continuously moving up and being exfoliated, and it is logical to assume that melanocytes, as integral parts of the epidermis (Medawar, 1953), may share their fate. Since melanocytes undergo mitosis (Billingham and Medawar, 1948b) branched cells in the higher levels of the epidermis, described by Langerhans (1868), could be melanocytes that were once melanogenic (Billingham and Medawar, 1953). Silvers (1957a), who finds cells identical with "high level cells" even when melanocytes are absent from the basal layer, questions this assumption. This problem has not yet been resolved.

In conclusion, melanocytes in the skin arise from the neuroectoderm, or neural crest, being ontogenetically related to glia cells and to Schwann cells. Under certain conditions melanocytes are argentophilic or aurophilic, characteristic features that they share with elements of the nervous system. During the differentiation of the various elements of the neural crest, melanoblasts are endowed with the specific capacity to elaborate melanin granules. In addition to the functions of self-maintenance and reproduction, melanocytes must form the matrix of melanin granules and finally disperse the melanized granule. Very little is known about the mechanism by which melanosomes are formed, other than they may be cell particles *sui generis*. Melanization begins with the tyrosine-tyrosinase system, dopa (and tyrosine under certain conditions), a specific indicator of the presence of the tyrosinase system in melanocytes. The mechanism by which melanin granules are dispersed and finally discharged from melanocytes is also unknown.

Genetic control exercises its influence on all phases of melanogenesis:

the size and shape of the melanin granules, and the rate of melanogenesis is species- or strain-specific. The nongenetic control of the first phase is practically unexplored territory; several factors, however, influence the tyrosinase-tyrosine system of the second phase. Ultraviolet radiation and the unknown initiators in the growth period of the hair cycle enhance the transformation of tyrosine into melanin; cortical steroids or cessation of hair growth seem to slow it down or may completely stop it. The third phase is enhanced by the action of "melanocyte-stimulating hormone" (MSH) and is checked by melatonin. Naturally, there may be some overlap in the spheres of action of these various controlling elements. The melanocyte system is subject to age changes, as the entire epidermis itself is. Such changes are dramatic in the case of hair melanocytes, where graying indicates "aging." Whereas it is known that nonmelanin-forming melanocytes are present in albino skin (Silvers, 1956a), the exact fate of melanocytes which were once melanotic in graying hair follicles of man is not yet known. As there are normal hair follicles without a melanocytic complement (Silvers, 1956a; Rawles, 1953), normal hair growth can continue after the melanocytes are lost. The progressive "silvering" in the coat of Champagne d'Argent rabbits, for example, involves a gradual loss of melanocytes (Quevedo and Chase, 1957).

In human epidermis, there is a statistically significant reduction of melanocyte density with increasing age (Szabó, 1959). Together with this change the intensity of dopa reaction becomes variable from cell to cell, some cells remaining strongly positive and dendritic, others becoming almost dopa negative and having short dendrites. Thus, not all malpighian cells may be in contact with melanocytes.

The amplitude of the life cycle of the melanocytes in hair follicles may be higher than that of its epidermal counterpart; consequently, they may "age" at a faster rate (Fitzpatrick, 1959). However, since the exact nature of the changes in the follicular environment during graying is not known, and "young" melanocytes have not yet been "offered" experimentally to graying hair, we do not know why the melanocytes in the hair follicles cease to form melanin, while those in the epidermis remain active.

Melanocytes in mammalian epidermis are ubiquitous; their density of population is characteristic for any given species and for a given region of the body. Their numbers in the epidermis assure that each malpighian cell is in contact with at least the processes of one melanocyte. The quality and quantity of color of the skin depends on the quality and quantity of melanin formed by melanocytes, and not on the density of these cells. Melanocytes seem to share the fate of mal-pighian cells, being desquamated at the surface of the skin.

Functional, melanin-producing melanocytes can be demonstrated by their specific affinity to dopa; nonmelanotic, "white" melanocytes, as well as melanotic ones, can be stained metacromatically with methylene blue. The degree of production of melanin granules and the location of the granules inside the melanocytes and inside the malpighian cells can be demonstrated with gold or silver impregnation techniques.

Melanogenesis is an irreversible process during which an enzy-matically active particle, the melanosome, with a well-defined species specific shape and structure, is transformed into an inert melanoprotein, the melanin granule. Each stage of this process is under the control of genetic and environmental factors, and there is some indication that the nucleus may participate in the processes.

The Nucleus and Mitotic Activity

Epidermal cells have one or two nuclei, the shape being determined by the shape of the cell. The basophil nuclear membrane encloses a granular, or finely reticulated, chromatin and a nucleolus. The nucleolus has a dense basophil membrane, a homogeneous, delicately basophil interior, and one or more peripheral heterochromatic granule. The nuclei are more strongly Feulgen reactive and more basophil in the basal layers of the stratum Malpighii than they are in the upper layers.

The morphology of the interphase nucleus has attracted special attention since the discovery that the nucleus of the female has a distinc-tive sex chromatin whereas that of the male has not (Barr and Bertram, 1949, 1951; Barr et al., 1950). In the majority of the epidermal inter-mitotic nuclei of the human female, the sex chromatin is about one mi-cron in diameter and rests next to the inner surface of the nuclear mem-brane. This body can be identified easily when it lies at the periphery of the nucleus, and, with experience, even when it is otherwise oriented. It stains with basic dyes and is Feulgen reactive. It is larger than the other chromatin particles; it is plano-convex, and is usually against the nuclear membrane (Fig. 35). In contrast, the nucleolus is larger, spherical, usually located at variable distances from the nuclear mem-brane, and its interior is Feulgen negative. A mass of chromatin similar to that of the sex chromatin is rarely found in the nuclei of the epidermis of normal males. The differences between the nuclei of the two sexes are abundantly clear even in small pieces of epidermis. The sex charac-teristic of the nuclei has been demonstrated in nearly all other organs as well.

It is assumed that the female sex chromatin is formed by the hetero-chromatic portions of the two X chromosomes of the female. The XY complex of the male is so small that it cannot be differentiated from the general chromatin.

In an analysis of the nuclei of the epidermis of human hermaphro-dites, the epidermal nuclei in skin biopsy specimens from both sides of the body show either typical female or typical male morphology of the nucleus. It has been assumed in such cases that one side of the body is male and the other female, including the type of sex chromo-some complex.

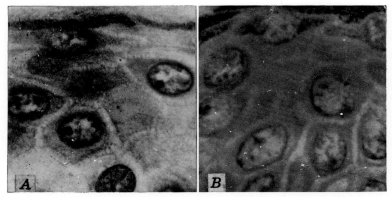

Fig. 35. (A) Male nuclei of human epidermal cells, showing a round nucleolus not attached to the nuclear membrane. (B) Female nuclei showing plano-convex sex chromatin aggregates adherent to the nuclear membrane. (Courtesy of Dr. M. L. Barr.)

It has been assumed that mitotic activity in the epidermis is insuffi-cient to replace cells lost from the exfoliation of the stratum corneum. Some have claimed that a transformation of lymphocytes into epidermal cells makes up for this apparent deficiency in mitosis (Andrew and Andrew, 1949). This assumption is probably based on a misidentification of "clear cells" as lymphocytes. In spite of apparent low mitotic activity, the epidermis is a "reproductively self-sufficient system" (Medawar, 1953) that regenerates entirely from cells resident within it. In rabbits, a thick, normally keratinized epidermis may be regenerated within 15 days from epithelial cells scraped from the ear epithelium and "seeded" over an area on the chest stripped down below the level of the deepest hair follicles (Medawar, 1953).

Cell division in the epidermis occurs chiefly in the basal layer (Flemming, 1884). There is, however, some disagreement about this; since the axes of mitotic figures in the basal layer appear to be parallel to the basement membrane, Thuringer (1924, 1928) believes that these cells do not move up into the stratum spinosum and that the basal layer is a biologic entity separate from the rest of the epidermis. Cowdry and Thompson (1944) conclude that mitotic activity is insignificantly less frequent in the proximal and middle third of the stratum spinosum than in the basal layer.

Single layers of horny cells can be removed from the skin with Scotch tape (Wolf, 1939, 1940, 1944). Cells so removed are replaced relatively quickly, depending upon the number of layers lost (Pinkus, 1951, 1952). In this technique, a strip of transparent Scotch tape 1.25 cm wide and 5 cm long is applied to the flexor surface of the forearm (this area is chosen because hairs there are relatively sparse and small) and then pulled off quickly. Under the microscope it is evident that a single layer of keratinized cells adheres to the sticky surface. The process is repeated over the same area of skin until the surface becomes slightly red and shiny but remains dry. Biopsy punches removed after varying intervals are sectioned serially and stained, and counts of mitotic figures are made with scrupulous care.

Approximately half of the mitotic figures occur in the basal layer and the other half in the layer immediately above it; only a few are seen in the higher levels of the spinous layer. In order to understand this observation, one must appreciate the changes that occur in the epidermis after treatment with Scotch tape. During the first 72 hours of the experiment, the basal cells of the epidermis become hypertrophied, and their number decreases steadily although the number of mitotic figures in them remains constant. In the early hours of the experiment as the cells of the basal layer become hypertrophied, the rete ridges are flattened out, and many of the basal cells are squeezed upward into the spinous layer. A large percentage of the mitotic figures seen in the lowest part of the spinous layer are really basal cells which have been crowded out of place. Complete denudation of the corneal layer is accompanied by some cell damage, by hyperemia and by mild inflammation of the dermis, all of which can induce mitotic activity. However, the loss of only four corneal layers, which also leads to appreciable mitotic activity, is not accompanied by visible changes in the living cells. This indicates that the loss of corneal cells is the direct stimulus for mitosis, although other factors may contribute to it. Most tissues have an intrinsic potential for cell division which is related to the normal loss of cells, but the rate of loss itself may to some extent be dependent upon the rate of production.

Most mitotic cells which appear to be in the spinous layer are actually found in the basal cells around the dermal papillae in other levels, and mitotic activity takes place largely, if not entirely, in the basal layer. This, therefore, is the true stratum germinativum of the epidermis. When human epidermis is grown *in vitro*, only the basal layer survives and grows (Pinkus, 1938).

Storey and Leblond (1951), who studied foot pads of rats after treating the animals with colchicine, calculated that during 24 hours, 5.24% of the epidermal cells undergo mitosis, and that a number of cells equal to 100% would require 458 hours or 19.1 days. This would also be the amount of time required for each cell to travel from the stratum germinativum to the lower level of the stratum corneum. These authors also found that when the floors of the cages in which the rats were kept were heated from 25° to 30° the renewal time of epidermis dropped to 7.3 days.

Hunter *et al.* (1956), by counting the total number of cells in the stratum corneum per area of skin, found excellent correlation between the possible rate of exfoliation and the rate of mitosis in the epidermis of man. They considered that if the time required for a cell to undergo division is one hour, it would require 5 days to renew the entire stratum corneum.

The riddle of the scantiness of mitotic activity in the epidermis began to be solved by Ortiz-Picón (1933), who found a larger number of mitotic figures in mice killed at noon than those killed at night. Carleton (1934) discovered a rhythm of mitosis in the epidermis of the mouse with a maximum frequency from 8 P.M. to midnight and a minimum at about noon. Actually, the period of greatest mitotic frequency in the epidermis of the mouse and rat occurs at noon to 1:00 P.M. and the period of least frequency at 10 P.M., the number of dividing cells in the morning being more than twice that at night (Blumenfeld, 1939; Cooper and Franklin, 1940). Mice and rats are nocturnal, and their quotidian rest and sleep coincide with tissue repair An erratic mitotic cycle in the epidermis of man, unlike that of truly nocturnal animals, is higher in the night hours than in the morning hours (Broders and Dublin, 1939; Cooper, 1939; Cooper and Schiff, 1938).

The physiological status of the epidermis of mice is in some way related to that of the hair follicles (Chase *et al.*, 1953). The hair follicles of mice have a precise period of growth, each follicle requiring about 21 days to complete its cycle. Hair grows in waves, and all of the follicles within the area of the advancing growth wave are approximately in the same stage of growth. When the hair follicles are quiescent the epidermis is usually two layers thick. During the first 4 or 5 days after the initiation of growth of the hair follicles, the mitotic rate in the epidermis increases and the epidermis becomes two to three times thicker. After 6 to 7 days the epidermis attains abruptly the thickness that it had when the follicles were inactive. During the remaining part of the growth period of the follicles, the epidermis is only one or two cells thick.

Mitotic activity and the mechanics of mitosis in the epidermis have been studied best in the mouse (Bullough, 1946, 1948a, b, 1949a, b, c, d, e, 1950a, b, 1953, 1954a, b; Bullough and Ebling, 1952; Bullough and Green, 1949; Bullough and Van Oordt, 1950). In normal adult males and females, the mitotic frequency extends from 10 A.M. to 4 P.M., with a peak at approximately 1 P.M.; this shows that during bodily activity the mitotic rate is low, and during sleep and rest it is high. Excessive muscular exercise or exposure to extreme cold are followed by a nearly complete depression of the mitotic rate. Starvation rations cause a considerable drop in the mitotic rate. These situations induce a drain of the sugar reserves in the body, which might be the critical factor in depressing the mitotic rate. Injections of starch solution subcutaneously cause a marked rise in mitotic rate. Injection of insulin depresses mitotic activity, whereas injections of disodium hydrogen phosphate together with starch increase mitotic activity above that of starch alone. There is a remarkable drop in mitotic rate in animals which are subjected to ischemic shock, and it has been pointed out that although shock raises the blood sugar level, there is a coincident fall in the total oxygen consumption, indicating that less sugar is being oxidized. The number of resting cells entering division at any moment is in direct proportion to the amount of sugar being oxidized. In animals under stress, induced by crowding for 3 weeks, the adrenal medullae increase in size simultaneously with a drop in epidermal mitotic rate. Both adrenaline and cortisone have a powerful antimitotic action *in vivo* and *in vitro,* perhaps either or both of these hormones acting by interfering with carbohydrate metabolism. The powerful antimitotic action of cortisone may be related to an inhibition of hexokinase. Thyroxine decreases, testosterone increases the rate of mitotic activity in the epidermis, and consequently the thickness of the epidermis. When administered together, these hormones induce only a moderate increase in mitotic activity, as if they worked antagonistically (Eartly *et al.,* 1951). Androgenic and estrogenic hormones have a profound effect upon cell division in the epidermis of normal males and females.

The life of male mice can be divided into four periods. During infancy the animals are still growing and their epidermal mitotic rate is generally high. At maturity the mitotic rate is lowered; during middle age mitotic rate increases, and in senility, it becomes reduced. Coincident with these changes, there are changes in spontaneous bodily activity.

The growth of the epidermis of female mice is cyclic and similar to that of the reproductive organs, and the epidermal mitotic rate can be stimulated by injections of estrone (Bullough, 1947). During the estrus cycle, peaks of mitotic activity are obtained in the third day of diestrus and again in early estrus. These peaks coincide with the normal diurnal peaks at approximately 1 P.M. Both glycogen and estrone are mitogenic, but the maximum stimulation obtained with an increase in glycogen concentration is small compared with the stimulation obtained with estrone. In the female albino rat the thickness of the epidermis also fluctuates together with the estrus cycle (Ebling, 1954). Mitotic values are highest in proestrus but are reduced at estrus and the day following it. Although no significant change in the mean mitotic incidence can be increased by treatment with estrogen, the thickness of the epidermis is reduced. It appears, then, that estrogen stimulates keratinization and the subsequent loss of epidermal cells quite independently of any changes in the rate of cell replacement. Furthermore, the effect of estrogen on the loss of cells seems to be independent of mediation by the pituitary, since it can be produced by hypophysectomized rats. Thus, estrogen may affect the thickness of the epidermis and mitotic activity independently, and keratinization and sloughing can exceed the rate of cell replacement.

In male and female mice, the duration of each mitotic division was established at $2\frac{1}{2}$ hours. While glycogen and androgen increase the mitotic rate, neither has an effect upon the duration of each division which remains constant at $2\frac{1}{2}$ hours. Estrogen, on the other hand, not only increases the number of divisions but also reduces the duration of each to less than one hour. When fragments of skin of mice are placed in a phosphate-buffered saline medium and an oxygen gas phase to study the reaction between estrogenic hormones and carbohydrate metabolism (Bullough, 1953), with glucose as substrate, estrone induces a doubling of the mitotic rate; with 1-lactate or pyruvate, however, the double rate is obtained without the addition of estrone, which in such cases provides no further stimulus. The action of estrone seems to be on some rate-limiting reaction between extracellular glucose and intracellular pyruvate and involves hexokinase. Thus, the reaction facilitated by estrone could be glucose to glucose-6-phosphate.

In vitro studies show that glucose is the source of the extra energy required for mitosis (Bullough, 1952a), fructose and pyruvate are also effective carbohydrate substrates for mitosis, but not Krebs cycle intermediates. Mitotic activity is inhibited by a lack of glucose or oxygen, or by any substance that inhibits carbohydrate metabolism or energy transfer. Injections of insulin, ACTH, and cortisone also produce an inhibitory effect (Bullough, 1952b, 1955b). The addition of glucose to tissue in which the mitotic rate has been depressed by the injection of adenosine triphosphate (ATP) or by starvation results in a return to the normal mitotic rate. The normal ability of epidermal cells to undergo mitosis may be limited by the degree of activity of each cell surface to absorb glucose.

The energy required for mitosis must be built up during the antephase, and it is at this stage that inhibition occurs (Bullough, 1952b). This energy build-up is not related to any active nucleic acid synthesis at this time. The stimulus causing the quiescent hair follicle to burst into activity is not nervous, and is not a diffusible substance, but is most probably the lack of an inhibiting substance. Normal epidermal cells could secrete within themselves a substance which inhibits epidermal growth by mitosis; damage of epidermal cells resulting from a wound could result in an increased rate of mitosis since the local abundance of inhibiting substance would be lowered. This mitotic inhibitor would be epidermis specific. Such an inhibiting substance could be in constant production and be lost through the shedding of cornified cells, by diffusion into the dermis, and/or by virtue of its instability. In the neighborhood of a wound, its production would be decreased and it would be drained away into the wound.

Since a culture medium which contains no unknown substance is capable of supporting mitotic activity in fragments of mouse epidermis, it has been possible to study more directly the effects of nutritional and hormonal factors (Bullough, 1955a, b). *In vitro* analyses of this sort eliminate many factors which influence mitosis *in vivo*. For instance, the diurnal cycle of mitotic activity does not persist in fragments maintained *in vitro*, and similar results can be obtained from the epidermis taken from mice at any hour of the day or night. Within a wide range of possibilities, the nutritional state of the animal before the excision of the skin fragment has no effect on the subsequent mitotic activity *in vitro*. Stress and shock, which are potent mitotic depressants, do not affect the rate of epidermal mitosis which develops subsequently *in vitro*. Sex hormones, however, and particularly estrogen, may exert a profound effect on subsequent mitotic activity *in vitro*. Skin fragments from female mice show depressed or elevated rates of cell division according to the phase of the estrus cycle of the animal. Such knowledge has permitted certain standardization of the skin used. For this reason, the castrated mouse should be the ideal animal to use, although the male is fairly adequate. Using these standards, Bullough (1954a, b, 1955a, b) has demonstrated that with glucose as a substrate in the culture media, insulin increases mitotic activity in the epidermis of the mouse *in vitro,* while growth hormone inhibits it. When the hormones are used together they counteract each other. The conclusions that follow, on the possible mechanics of mitosis, were written by W. S. Bullough.

Conclusions: Mechanics of Mitotic Activity

The rate of mitotic activity in adult mammalian tissues is variable. In the epidermis, for instance, mitotic activity has a well-defined diurnal rhythm and a less well-defined estrus rhythm; epidermal mitotic activity is also powerfully depressed by hunger, muscular exercise and stress (Bullough, 1952a, 1955b). Such fluctuations in the mitotic rate are, however, relatively minor variations around a mean mitotic activity that is fixed at some level related to the replacement needs of that tissue. Thus, most epithelia tend to have relatively high mitotic rates whereas most connective tissues seem to be mitotically inactive.

There seem to be at least two sets of factors that determine the mitotic rate of a tissue at any given moment. The first group of factors, nutritional and hormonal, induces the minor fluctuations in activity; the second group, the nature of which is still unknown but which must be an integral part of the state of differentiation, may determine the mean mitotic rate of each tissue.

In order for a cell to divide, it must first duplicate its essential molecular structure; its nutritional requirements at such times must be as diverse as those of the total organism to which it belongs. These essential needs may vary slightly from cell type to cell type and from species to species, and in any particular cell they can be studied best and defined adequately only by means of *in vitro* techniques. Proliferating cells must be maintained in precisely defined media, a technique which has proved to be particularly difficult (see reviews by Fischer, 1946 and Willmer, 1954). For the present purposes, however, this field of research appears to have no particular relevance. Although certain abnormal diets, such as a deficiency of vitamin A (see Rothman, 1954), may strongly influence epidermal mitotic rate, a normal, reasonably well-fed animal does not suffer from shortages of substances for the construction of new cells. It is improbable that any of the normal mitotic fluctuations so far described can be attributed to fluctuating supplies of building materials. A crucial situation may develop in prolonged starvation, during which epidermal mitotic rate is powerfully depressed (Bullough, 1949e; Bullough and Eisa, 1950). However, present indications are that this depressed condition may be primarily due to the fact that the animal is in a state of stress and the actual shortage of food may be of secondary importance.

One particular foodstuff, the carbohydrate used for energy production, must be further examined, since the mitotic rate is closely dependent upon the available energy supply. This subject, fully reviewed by Bullough (1952a) and Swann (1957), can be briefly summarized as follows:

(a) Many more mitotic figures develop in the epidermis of the mouse when maintained *in vitro,* if glucose, fructose, pyruvate, or lactate is added as substrate (Bullough and Johnson, 1951; Bullough, 1952a; Gelfant, 1959, 1960a, b).

(b) Under similar conditions more mitoses usually develop in the presence of higher oxygen tensions (Bullough and Johnson, 1951). In anaerobic conditions mitotic activity usually ceases, although the epidermis can survive anaerobically for at least one week (Medawar, 1947). However, when anaerobic experiments are performed it is essential that the nitrogen gas used be pure; any trace of impurity will injure or kill the cells and so lead to erroneous or equivocal results (cf. Gelfant, 1959, 1960a, b).

(c) While the oxygen tension may be critically important to the mitotic activity of many, if not most adult tissues, some cells can divide under anaerobic conditions. Sea urchin eggs, for example, cannot survive at all in the absence of oxygen, and their cleavage rate is directly proportional to oxygen concentration over a range of 20 to 70% (Amberson, 1928; Clowes and Krahl, 1940). In contrast, the eggs of frogs and toads (Bullough, 1952a, b) and chick fibroblasts *in vitro* (Laser, 1933; Pomerat and Willmer, 1939) can survive and undergo normal mitosis in anaerobic conditions. The epidermal cells of the mouse can survive anaerobically and their mitotic rate is directly proportional to the oxygen tension (Bullough and Johnson, 1951). Evidently, any cell can undergo mitotic activity in anaerobic conditions if it can produce enough energy by anaerobic means. The eggs of frogs and toads may contain an energy store laid down in the ovary; the fact that these eggs can continue to divide in $10^{-3}M$ iodoacetate, which inhibits glycolysis (Bullough, 1952a) gives some support to this theory.

(d) The energy needed by a cell during division must be mobilized and stored before that division can begin (Bullough, 1952a, b, for mammalian epidermis, and Swann, 1957, for cleaving eggs). Once a cell has begun to divide, interference with respiration, such as anaerobic conditions or respiratory inhibitors, is without effect, but will prevent other cells from entering division. The energy store may perhaps be laid down gradually throughout the whole of the interphase, as suggested by Swann (1957), when it may represent only a small fraction of the total energy output of the cell at any given moment. Alternatively, energy sources may be laid down rapidly during a relatively short period in the antephase, immediately before prophase (Bullough, 1952a, b), when it may represent a large fraction of the total energy output of the cell at this time. No definitive experiment to decide between these two views has yet been attempted, and, indeed, the situation may differ in different cells.

(e) Anaerobic conditions prevent the onset of mitosis, as do also the inhibitors of glycolysis, respiration, or phosphorylation. However, although these results fit well with present concepts of the importance of energy storage as a prerequisite for mitosis, the degree of specificity of any inhibitor is always open to doubt (Swann, 1957; Gelfant, 1960a, b). Chick fibroblasts, which are capable of dividing anaerobically will also continue to divide normally in the presence of such respiratory inhibitors as cyanide, azide, and malonate; they cease to divide when glycolysis is inhibited by fluoride or iodoacetate (Pomerat and Willmer, 1939). It, therefore, seems probable that cyanide, azide, and malonate may not inhibit mitosis in the epidermis except through their action on respiration.

The demands of pre-mitotic cells for a suitable carbohydrate substrate and an adequate supply of oxygen can only be demonstrated *in vitro*. The cells of a normal mammal probably never have any real shortage of these raw materials, even those of nonvascularized tissues such as the epidermis.

Attempts have been made to explain the diurnal cycle of epidermal mitotic activity in terms of fluctuating glucose supply (see Bullough, 1952a). Diurnal variations in mitotic activity have been described in various tissues of various mammals, and it is now realized that the mitotic rate is highest during sleep and lowest during active muscular exercise (Bullough, 1948a, b). The theory has been advanced in relation to the epidermis that during sleep extra glucose is available, partly perhaps because of actual deposition of glucose into the epidermis, as the blood sugar level drops, and partly because of the dilation of the capillary network in the superficial dermis. It is not known, however, if the capillary network does open during sleep (Firth, unpublished), and it is doubtful whether, at least in a normal adult mammal, any extra glucose deposition which may occur can exert a sufficiently powerful stimulus to explain the rise in mitotic activity during sleep. It seems now that in a well-fed adult mammal, the epidermis has available in the blood a continuously adequate supply of glucose and oxygen, but that the availability of the supply may be affected by variations in the hormone content in the blood and in the degree of efficiency of certain critical intracellular enzyme systems.

In the event of sudden, abnormally high mitotic activity creating unusual local demands, such as in hair growth (Bullough and Laurence, 1958; Durward and Rudall, 1958), or wound healing (Bullough and Laurence, 1957a, b), there is also a considerable temporary increase in the local blood supply. Mitotic activity in adult tissues depends upon the proper functioning of that mechanism which leads to the duplication of the essential materials of the cells, and that mechanism which leads to the production and storage of energy. The sequence of metabolic reactions through which a cell must pass before it is ready to divide is so complicated that, at some point, there must be reactions which are susceptible to interference. Such interference may be gross, as in starvation and anaerobic conditions, or it may be subtle and specific, as perhaps in the case of the action of some particular hormone.

The effects of hormones on the mitotic activity of adult mammalian tissues seems to range between two extremes. At one extreme are those hormones which are active only in abnormally high concentrations and which probably have little or no significance in the normal animal; at the other extreme are hormones which, even at very low concentrations, function powerfully in stimulating or inhibiting the mitotic activity of specific tissues. As an example of the first it may be recalled that certain estrogens act as inhibitors in high concentrations, probably because of their action as hydrogen carriers (Hochster and Quastel, 1949); at the other extreme is the normal action of estrogens in stimulating the mitotic rate of vaginal and uterine epithelia (Bullough, 1946).

Although the normal function of hormones may be to facilitate or to inhibit particular reactions in specific metabolic pathways, there may be great differences between what they can do in experimental conditions and what they do in a normal animal. Bullough (1955a, b) and Mohn (1958) have surveyed the actions of a variety of hormones on cell division in the epidermis and in hair follicles, and it is not necessary to repeat their conclusions here. It is not obvious from their results which of the reactions are abnormal and seen only in the particular artificial conditions of the experiments, and which of them form some integral part of the normal mitosis-controlling mechanism.

The examples which follow illustrate the range of action of hormones on mitotic activity.

Some hormones appear to have little or no effect in normal animals. Both a glucocorticoid (11-dehydro-17-hydroxycorticosterone-21-acetate) and a mineralocorticoid (deoxycorticosterone acetate) may cause a depression of epidermal mitotic activity when injected into the intact mouse (Bullough, 1952b). However, in both cases milligrams of hormones must be injected to produce an effect and it is doubtful that the endogenous corticoid hormones are ever normally present in such high concentrations. Similarly, the antimitotic effects of pituitary growth hormone are seen only when given in very high concentrations (Bullough, 1955b).

There are hormones, such as insulin, which may exert a marginal effect on mitotic activity in normal animals. With an insufficiency of insulin, cells become starved for glucose, since insulin stimulates the hexokinase system to facilitate the uptake of glucose from the blood. Some tissues seem to be very sensitive to the normal, relatively slight variations in the insulin content of the blood. It has been suggested that the epidermis of the mouse may normally be partly starved for glucose because of the relative sluggishness of the glucokinase reaction (Bullough, 1955a), and that in these circumstances relatively slight increases in the content of blood insulin may lead to significant increases in mitotic rate. A similar mechanism could be responsible for the mitotic stimulus which accompanies the response of the vaginal epithelium to estrone when insulin is administered (Claringbold, 1954). Conversely, estrogens may act with insulin to prevent diabetes (Houssay, 1951).

There are hormones that play a specific role in controlling the mitotic rate in particular tissues of normal animals. The hormones best known for their stimulating influence on mitosis are the estrogens in their action on the vaginal and uterine epithelia (Bullough, 1946); these hormones, however, also exert a variety of other influences. Their action on mitosis may be due partly to a direct stimulus to the basic mitotic control mechanism, and partly to the mobilization of raw materials of various kinds. In this latter connection estrogens are believed (a) to induce the transfer of glucose from the liver to the tissues (Janes and Nelson, 1940), thus assisting the deposition of glycogen in the vaginal and uterine epithelia (Robertson et al., 1930; Walaas, 1952a, b); (b) to stimulate both glycolysis and respiration in the uterus

(Kerly, 1940; Carrol, 1942; Roberts and Szego, 1953), possibly acting primarily on the hexokinase reaction (Walaas, 1952a, b; Bullough, 1955a); (c) and to increase the uterine content of ATP and creatine phosphate (Menkes and Csapo, 1952) which may be related to the energy stores required to support active mitotic activity.

Although estrogens influence mitotic activity in a wide variety of tissues (Bullough, 1946), their action is strongest in such organs as the vagina and the uterus, which have been called "target organs." Evidently, during differentiation the vaginal and uterine tissues acquire some extra degree of sensitivity to these steroids.

We must conclude that the only hormones which in physiological concentrations *in vivo* have an obvious stimulating effect on at least some adult tissues are the estrogens, androgens, and possibly insulin. Of those hormones which are known to inhibit mitotic activity, the only significant one appears to be adrenaline, although in continuous stress its action could be augmented by glucocorticoids (Bullough, 1952a, 1955b). Lettré (1942; Lettré and Albrecht, 1941) first published evidence that adrenaline inhibits mitosis, by testing its actions on chick fibroblasts *in vitro*. In this, as in other similar experiments *in vitro*, it is possible that the active agents are the adrenochromes, the oxidation products of adrenaline, which may inhibit such enzymes as hexokinase (Meyerhof and Randall, 1948; Bacq, 1949). In the intact animal the metabolic destruction of adrenaline follows a different pathway and adrenochromes are not produced *in vivo* (Bacq, personal communication). Both *in vitro* and *in vivo* experiments have shown that adrenaline itself has a powerful antimitotic action (Bullough, 1952b, 1955b). The action of adrenaline may prove to be the basis of the antimitotic effects of stress. In mice crowded together in a small space, the adrenal glands increase in size and the epidermal mitotic rate falls by about 60% (Bullough, 1952b).

Recently, in the epidermis of adult male mice, the antimitotic effect of adrenaline has been confirmed *in vitro*, at concentrations less than 1 μg per milliliter and *in vivo*, at concentrations less than 19 μg per mouse. These inhibitions are fully reversible after the adrenaline has been washed from the affected tissue; the inhibition induced by stress can also be washed out.

Relation of Structure and Function

The proteinous-lipid product of the epidermis, the stratum corneum, is tailored in every detail to protect the body against its environment. The architecture, the rates of wear and replacement, the physical and chemical properties of the stratum corneum are all geared to keep agents from penetrating the skin. Although some substances can pass through the living skin (Blank *et al.*, 1958; Scott and Kalz, 1956; Witten *et al.*, 1951), their portal of entry is probably both through the orifices of the pilary canals and those of the sweat glands and through the intact epidermis.

An electronegatively charged horizontal field between the stratum granulosum and the stratum corneum is believed to repel anions, and to prevent cations from penetrating deeper (Rein, 1924). This field, a layer one or two cells deep, is thought to be the physical and psysiological barricade against the penetration of substances and to be the "barrier layer" of the epidermis (Szakall, 1951; Blank, 1959; Mali, 1956). Skin with an intact barrier has a low electrical conductivity; that with an injured barrier has a high conductivity. Thus, when the barrier is injured, its rate of repair can be followed by making repeated measurements of the conductivity in the injured site (Griesemer, 1959).

However, it may be misleading to refer to a single structure as the barrier layer, since the entire epidermis is a bulwark against penetration. The cutaneous surface is coated with a complex layer of lipids and organic salts, liberated by the keratinizing cells and secreted by the sebaceous and sweat glands (some of the organic acids are probably liberated from the hydrolysis of precursor substances). This layer, which has a pH of 4.5 to 6.0, is called the "acid mantle," and is said to have antifungal and antibacterial properties. Such a property, often attributed to the acid pH, could be due to some of the organic salts (Blank, 1959). The acid mantle, then, is the first barrier against potential invading agents. If agents should get past it, they must get through the stratum corneum, which is an effective filtering system in its own right; since the interstices between its cells become progressively smaller in the deeper parts, they probably serve as physical and chemical traps. The interstices between the cells of the barrier layer are presumably the smallest of all, and injury to it could allow a freer passage of large molecules, microorganisms, or particulate substances which would normally be arrested. Once through the barrier layer, substances are in contact with the living cells of the epidermis between which they diffuse readily. If microorganisms should pass through the barrier layer, the living epidermis is equipped with agents which often arrest their progress.

These are among the most important considerations of the function of the epidermis. Certainly, however, there are other subtle adaptations of structure and function.

REFERENCES

Achten, G. 1959. Recherches sur la Kératinisation de la Cellule épidermique chez l'Homme et le Rat. *Arch. biol.* (*Liège*) **70**: 1-119.

Adachi, B. 1903. Hautpigment beim Menschen und bei den Affen. *Z. Morphol. Anthropol.* **6**: 1-131.

Adachi, K. and W. Montagna. 1961. Histology and cytochemistry of human skin. XXII. Sites of leucine aminopeptidase (LAP). *J. Invest. Dermatol.* (In press.)

Adolph, W. E., R. F. Baker and G. M. Leiby. 1951. Electron microscope study of epidermal fibers. *Science* **113**: 685-686.

Allen, A. C. 1949. A reorientation on the histogenesis and clinical significance of cutaneous nevi and melanomas. *Cancer* **2**: 28-56.

Allen, A. C. and S. Spitz. 1954. Pigment and pigment tumors; histogenesis and clinicopathologic correlation of nevi and malignant melanomas; current status. *Arch. Dermatol. and Syphilol.* **69**: 150-171.

Amberson, W. R. 1928. The influence of oxygen tension upon the respiration of unicellular organisms. *Biol. Bull.* **55**: 79-91.

Andrew, W. and N. V. Andrew. 1949. Lymphocytes in the normal epidermis of the rat and of man. *Anat. Record* **104**: 217-241.

Argaud, R. 1914. Sur les filaments d'Herxheimer. *Compt. rend. soc. biol.* **77**: 61-62.

Argyris, T. S. 1952. Glycogen in the epidermis of mice painted with methylcholanthrene. *J. Natl. Cancer Inst.* **12**: 1159-1165.

Argyris, T. S. 1956. Succinic dehydrogenase and esterase activities of mouse skin during regeneration and fetal development. *Anat. Record* **126**: 1-13.

Astbury, W. T. 1933. The X-ray interpretation of fibre structure. *Science Progr.* **28**: 210-228.

Astbury, W. T. and H. J. Woods. 1930. The X-ray interpretation of structure and elastic properties of hair keratin. *Nature* **126**: 913-914.

Bacq, Z. M. 1949. Metabolism of adrenaline. *J. Pharmacol. Exptl. Therap.* **95**, Part 2, pp. 1-26.

Baker, J. R. 1944. The structure and chemical composition of the Golgi element. *Quart J. Microscop. Sci.* **85**: 1-71.

Baker, J. R. 1946. The histochemical recognition of lipine. *Quart. J. Microscop. Sci.* **87**: 441-470.

Baker, J. R. 1949. Further remarks on the Golgi element. *Quart. J. Microscop. Sci.* **90**: 293-307.

Baker, R. V., M. S. C. Birbeck, H. Blaschko, T. B. Fitzpatrick and M. Seiji. 1960. Melanin granules and mitochondria. *Nature* **187**: 392-394.

Barnicot, N. A. and M. S. C. Birbeck. 1958. The electron microscopy of human melanocytes and melanin granules. In "The Biology of Hair Growth" (W. Montagna and R. A. Ellis, eds.), pp. 239-253. Academic Press, New York.

Barnicot, N. A., M. S. C. Birbeck and F. W. Cuckow. 1955. The electron microscopy of human hair pigment. *Ann. Human Genet.* **19**: 231-249.

Barr, M. L. and E. G. Bertram. 1949. A morphological distinction between neurones of the male and female, and the behavior of the nucleolar satellite during accelerated nucleoprotein synthesis. *Nature* **163**: 676-677.

Barr, M. L. and E. G. Bertram. 1951. The behavior of nuclear structures during depletion and restoration of Nissl material in motor neurones. *J. Anat.* **85**: 171-181.

Barr, M. L., L. F. Bertram and H. A. Lindsay. 1950. The morphology of the nerve cell nucleus, according to sex. *Anat. Record* **107**: 283-297.

Barrnett, R. J. 1952. The distribution of esterolytic activity in the tissues of the albino rat as demonstrated with indoxyl acetate. *Anat. Record* **114**: 577-599.

Barrnett, R. J. 1953. The histochemical distribution of protein-bound sulfhydryl groups. *J. Natl. Cancer Inst.* **13**: 905-925.

Barrnett, R. J. and A. M. Seligman. 1952. Histochemical demonstration of protein-bound sulfhydryl groups. *Science* **116**: 323-327.

Becker, S. W., Sr. 1927. Melanin pigmentation: systematic study of pigment of human skin and upper mucous membranes, with special consideration of pigmented dendritic cells. *Arch. Dermatol. and Syphilol.* **16**: 259-290.

Becker, S. W., Sr. 1930. Cutaneous melanoma, a histologic study directed toward the study of melanoblasts. *Arch. Dermatol. and Syphilol.* **21**: 818-835.

Becker, S. W., Sr. 1933. Vitiligo, a clinical and histologic study, with a consideration of pinta. *Arch. Dermatol. and Syphilol.* **28**: 497-507.

Becker, S. W., Sr. 1934. Origin and nature of pigmented nevi (Schwannomans). *Arch. Dermatol. and Syphilol.* **30**: 779-784.

Becker, S. W., Sr. 1942. Cutaneous melanoblasts as studied by the paraffin dopa technique. *J. Invest. Dermatol.* **5**: 463-471.

Becker, S. W., Sr. 1949. Diagnosis and treatment of pigmented nevi. *Arch. Dermatol. and Syphilol.* **60**: 44-61.

Becker, S. W., Sr. 1954. Critical evaluation of the so-called 'junction nervus.' *J. Invest. Dermatol.* **22**: 217-223.

Becker, S. W., Jr., and A. A. Zimmermann. 1955. Further studies on melanocytes and melanogenesis in the human fetus and newborn. *J. Invest. Dermatol.* **25**: 103-112.

Becker, S. W., Jr., T. B. Fitzpatrick and H. Montgomery. 1952. Human melanogenesis: cytology and histology of pigment cells (melanodendrocytes). *Arch. Dermatol. and Syphilol.* **65**: 511-523.

Beerman, H., R. A. G. Lane and B. Shaffer. 1955. Pigmented nevi and malignant melanoma of the skin; survey of some of the recent literature. *Am. J. Med. Sci.* **229**: 444-465; 583-600.

Belanger, Leonard F. 1956. Autoradiographic visualization of the entry and transit of S[35] methionine and cystine in the soft and hard tissues of the growing rat. *Anat. Record* **124**: 555-572.

Bennett, H. S. and D. A. Yphantis. 1948. 1-(4-Chloromercuriphenylazo)-naphthol-2. *J. Am. Chem. Soc.* **70**: 3522.

Bern, H. A. 1954. Histology and chemistry of keratin formation. *Nature* **174**: 509-512.

Bern, H. A., D. R. Harkness and S. M. Blair. 1955. Radioautographic studies of keratin formation. *Proc. Natl. Acad. Sci. U.S.* **41**: 55-60.

Bernard, C. 1859. De la matière glycogène considérée comme condition de développement de certain tissus, chez le foetus, avant l'apparition de la fonction glycogènique du foie. *Compt. rend. acad. sci.* **48**: 673-684.

Bernard, C. 1878. Leçons sur les phénomènes de la vie communs aux animaux et aux végètaux. **2**: 73-74. Librarie J. B. Baillière et Fils, Paris.

Billingham, R. E. 1948. Dendritic cells. *J. Anat.* **82**: 93-109.

Billingham, R. E. 1949. Dendritic cells in pigmented human skin. *J. Anat.* **83**: 109-115.

Billingham, R. E. and P. B. Medawar. 1948a. Pigment spread and cell heredity in guinea-pigs' skin. *Heredity* **2**: 29-47.

Billingham, R. E. and P. B. Medawar. 1948b. 'Infective' transformation of cells. *Brit. J. Cancer* **2**: 126-131.

Billingham, R. E. and P. B. Medawar. 1950. Pigment spread in mammalian skin: serial propagation and immunity reactions. *Heredity* **4**: 141-164.

Billingham, R. E. and P. B. Medawar. 1953. A study of the branched cells of the mammalian epidermis with special reference to the fate of their division products. *Phil. Trans. Roy. Soc.* **B237**: 151-171.

Billingham, R. E. and W. K. Silvers. 1960. The melanocytes of mammals. *Quart. Rev. Biol.* **35**: 1-40.

Birbeck, M. S. C. and Barnicot, N. A. 1959. Electron microscope studies on pigment formation in human hair follicles. *In* "Pigment Cell Biology" (M. Gordon, ed.), pp. 549-561. Academic Press, New York.

Birbeck, M. S. C. and E. H. Mercer. 1957a. The electron microscopy of the human hair follicle. I. Introduction and the hair cortex. *J. Biophys. Biochem. Cytol.* **3**: 203-214.

Birbeck, M. S. C. and E. H. Mercer. 1957b. The electron microscopy of the human hair follicle. *J. Biophys. Biochem. Cytol.* **3**: 203-230.

Birbeck, M. S. C., E. H. Mercer and N. A. Barnicot. 1956. The structure and function of pigment granules in human hair. *Exptl. Cell Research* **10**: 505-514.

Bischitz, P. G. and R. S. Snell. 1959a. A study of the melanocytes and melanin in the skin of the male guinea-pig. *J. Anat.* **93**: 233-245.

Bischitz, P. G. and R. S. Snell. 1959b. The effect of testosterone on the melanocytes and melanin in the skin of the intact and orchidectomised male guinea-pig. *J. Invest. Dermatol.* **33**: 299-306.

Bizzozero, G. 1871. Sulla struttura degli epiteli pavimentosi stratificati (abstract). *Zentr. med. Wochschr.* **9**: 482-483.

Blank, I. H. 1959. Protection against the invasion of bacteria and fungi. *In* "The Human Integument" (S. Rothman, ed.). Am. Assoc. Advance Sci. Publ. No. 54, Washington, D. C.

Blank, I. H., R. D. Griesemer and E. Gould. 1958. The penetration of an anticholinesterase agent (sarin) into skin. II. Autoradiographic studies. *J. Invest. Dermatol.* **30**: 187-191.

Bloch, B. 1917. Das Problem der Pigmentbildung in der Haut. *Arch. Dermatol. u. Syphilis* **124**: 129-208.

Bloch, B. 1929. The problem of pigment formation. *Am. J. Med. Sci.* **177**: 609-618.

Block, R. J. and H. B. Vickery. 1931. The basic amino acids of proteins. A chemical relationship between various keratins. *J. Biol. Chem.* **93**: 113-117.

Blumenfeld, C. M. 1939. Periodic mitotic activity in the epidermis of the albino rat. *Science* **90**: 446-447.

Born, S. 1921. Zur Frage der epidermalen Basalmembran. *Dermatol. Z.* **34**: 324-331.

Boyd, J. D. 1949a. Argentophil cells in foetal ectodermal epithelia. *J. Anat.* **83**: 74.

Boyd, J. D. 1949b. Argentaffin dendritic cells in urogenital epithelium of male mammalian embryos. *J. Anat.* **83**: 83.

Boyd, J. D. 1950. Argentaffin dendritic cells in hair follicles. *J. Anat.* **84**: 62.

Bradfield, J. R. G. 1951. Glycogen of vertebrate epidermis. *Nature* **167**: 40-42.

Branca, A. 1899. Recherches sur la cicatrisation épithéliale (épitheliums cylindriques stratifiés). La tracheé et sa cicatrisation. *J. anat. physiol. norm. pathol. de l'homme et des anim. Paris.* **35**: 764-807.

Branca, A. 1907. Recherches sur la kératinisation. II. Le diamant du canardi. *J. Anat. Physiol.* **43**: 433-446.

Braun-Falco, O. 1956a. Über die Fähigkeit der menschlichen Haut zur Polysaccharidsynthese, ein Beitrag zur Histotopochemie der Phosphorylase. *Arch klin. u. exptl. Dermatol.* **202**: 163-170.

Braun-Falco, O. 1956b. Zur histochemischen Darstellung von Glukose-6-Phosphatase in normaler Haut. *Dermatol. Wochschr.* **134**: 1252-1257.

Braun-Falco, O. 1956c. Zur Histotopographie der β-Glucuronidase in normaler menschlicher Haut. *Arch klin. u. exptl. Dermatol.* **203**: 61-67.

Braun-Falco, O. 1956d. Beitrag zum histochemischen Nachweis von Esterasen in normaler und psoriatischer Haut. *Arch. klin. u. exptl. Dermatol.* **202**: 153-162.

Braun-Falco, O. 1957. Zur Histotopographie der Aminopeptidase·bei Pemphigus vulgaris. *Dermatol. Wochschr.* **135**: 93-96.

Braun-Falco, O. and B. Rathjens. 1955. Über die histochemische Darstellung der Kohlensäureanhydratase in normaler Haut. *Arch. klin. u. exptl. Dermatol.* **201**: 73-82.

Braun-Falco, O. and K. Salfeld. 1957. Leucine aminopeptidase activity in mast cells. *Nature* **183**: 51-52.

Breathnach, A. S. 1957. Melanocyte counts on human forearm skin. *J. Invest. Dermatol.* **29**: 181-184.

Breathnach, A. S. 1959. An attempt to induce "pigment spread" in freckled human skin. *J. Invest. Dermatol.* **33**: 193-201.

Breathnach, A. S. 1960. Melanocyte pattern of regenerated human epidermis. *Proc. Anat. Soc. J. Anat.* **94** (In press).

Broders, A. C. and W. B. Dublin. 1939. Rhythmicity of mitosis in epidermis of human beings. *Proc. Staff Meetings Mayo Clinic* **14**: 423-425.

Brody, I. 1959. An ultrastructure study on the role of the keratohyalin granules in the keratinization process. *J. Ultrastruct. Research* **3**: 84-104.

Brunet, P. C. J. 1960. Melanogenesis. *In* "Progress in the Biological Sciences in Relation to Dermatology" (A. Rook, ed.), pp. 15-27. Cambridge Univ. Press, London and New York.

Bullough, W. S. 1946. Mitotic activity in the adult female mouse, *Mus musculus* L. A study of its relation to the oestrus cycle in normal and abnormal conditions. *Phil. Trans. Roy. Soc.* **B231**: 453-516.

Bullough, H. F. 1947. Epidermal thickness following oestrone injections in the mouse. *Nature* **159**: 101-103.

Bullough, W. S. 1948a. Mitotic activity in the adult male mouse, *Mus musculus* L. The diurnal cycles and their relation to waking and sleeping. *Proc. Roy. Soc.* **B135**: 212-233.

Bullough, W. S. 1948b. The effects of experimentally induced rest and exercise on the epidermal mitotic activity of the adult male mouse, *Mus musculus* L. *Proc. Roy. Soc.* **B135**: 233-242.

Bullough, W. S. 1949a. Epidermal mitosis in relation to sugar and phosphate. *Nature* **163**: 680.

Bullough, W. S. 1949b. The relation between the epidermal mitotic activity and the blood-sugar level in the adult male mouse. *Mus musculus* L. *J. Exptl. Biol.* **26**: 83-99.

Bullough, W. S. 1949c. Age and mitotic activity in the male mouse, *Mus musculus* L. *J. Exptl. Biol.* **26**: 261-286.

Bullough, W. S. 1949d. The action of colchicine in arresting epidermal mitosis. *J. Exptl. Biol.* **26**: 287-291.

Bullough, W. S. 1949e. The effect of a restricted diet on mitotic activity in the mouse. *Brit. J. Cancer* **3**: 275-282.

Bullough, W. S. 1950a. Epidermal mitotic activity in the adult female mouse. *J. Endocrinol.* **6**: 340-349.

Bullough, W. S. 1950b. The mitogenic actions of androgenic and oestrogenic hormones. *Acta Physiol. et Pharmacol. Neerl.* **1**: 357-358.

Bullough, W. S. 1952a. The energy relations of mitotic activity. *Biol. Revs.* **27**: 133-168.

Bullough, W. S. 1952b. Stress and epidermal mitotic activity. I. The effects of the adrenal hormones. *J. Endocrinol.* **8**: 265-274.

Bullough, W. S. 1953. Oestrogens, carbohydrate metabolism, and mitosis. *Ciba Foundation Colloq. Endocrinol.* **6**: 278-294.

Bullough, W. S. 1954a. A study of the hormonal relations of epidermal mitotic activity *in vitro*. I. Technique. *Exptl. Cell Research* **7**: 176-185.

Bullough, W. S. 1954b. A study of the hormonal relations of epidermal mitotic activity *in vitro*. II. Insulin and pituitary growth hormone. *Exptl. Cell Research* **7**: 186-196.

Bullough, W. S. 1955a. Hormones and mitotic activity. *Vitamins and Hormones* **13**: 261-292.

Bullough, W. S. 1955b. A study of the hormonal relations of epidermal mitotic activity *in vitro*. III. Adrenalin. *Exptl. Cell Research* **9**: 108-115.

Bullough, W. S. and F. J. Ebling. 1952. Cell replacement in the epidermis and sebaceous glands of the mouse. *J. Anat.* **86**: 29-34.

Bullough, W. S. and E. A. Eisa. 1950. The effects of a graded series of restricted diets on epidermal mitotic activity in the mouse. *Brit. J. Cancer* **4**: 321-328.

Bullough, W. S. and H. N. Green. 1949. Shock and mitotic activity in mice. *Nature* **164**: 795.

Bullough, W. S. and M. Johnson. 1951. The energy relations of mitotic activity in adult mouse epidermis. *Proc. Roy. Soc.* **B138**: 562-575.

Bullough, W. S. and E. B. Laurence. 1957a. A technique for the study of small epidermal wounds. *Brit. J. Exptl. Pathol.* **38**: 273-277.

Bullough, W. S. and E. B. Laurence. 1957b. The energy relations of epidermal mitotic activity adjacent to small wounds. *Brit. J. Exptl. Pathol.* **38**: 278-283.

Bullough, W. S. and E. B. Laurence. 1958. The mitotic activity of the follicle. *In* "The Biology of Hair Growth" (W. Montagna and R. A. Ellis, eds.), pp. 171-186. Academic Press, New York.

Bullough, W. S. and G. J. Van Oordt. 1950. The mitogenic actions of testosterone propionate and of oestrone on the epidermis of the adult male mouse. *Acta. Endocrinol.* **4**: 291-305.

Burstone, M. S. 1956. Histochemical demonstration of proteolytic activity in human neoplasms. *J. Natl. Cancer Inst.* **16**: 1149-1161.

Burstone, M. S. 1959. New histochemical technique for the demonstration of tissue oxidase (cytochrome oxidase). *J. Histochem. and Cytochem.* **7**: 112-122.

Burstone, M. S. 1960. Histochemical demonstration of cytochrome oxidase with new amine reagents. *J. Histochem. and Cytochem.* **7**: 63-70.

Burstone, M. S. and J. E. Folk. 1956. Histochemical demonstration of aminopeptidase. *J. Histochem. and Cytochem.* **4**: 217-226.

Busacca, A. 1922. Ueber das Verhalten der sogenannten Basalmembran als Bindemittel zwischen Epidermis und Cutis. *Arch. Dermatol. u. Syphilis* **141**: 88-95.

Cain, A. J. 1947. Demonstration of lipine in the Golgi apparatus in gut cells of *Glossiphonia. Quart. J. Microscop. Sci.* **88**: 151-157.

Cain, A. J. 1949. Recent research in cytoplasmic cytology. *Oxford Sci.* **2**: 30-40.

Cajal, S. R. 1914. Algunas variaciones fisiologicas y patológicas del aparato reticular de Golgi. *Trabajos lab. invest. biol.* **12**: 127-227.

Carleton, A. 1934. A rhythmical periodicity in the mitotic division of animal cells. *J. Anat.* **68**: 251-263.

Carrol, W. R. 1942. Influence of estrogen on respiration of rat uterine tissue. *Proc. Soc. Exptl. Biol. Med.* **49**: 50-52.

Carruthers, C., W. C. Quevedo, Jr. and D. L. Woernley. 1959. Influence of hair growth cycle on cytochrome oxidase and DPNH-cytochrome C reductase in mouse epidermis. *Proc. Soc. Exptl. Biol. Med.* **101**: 374-376.

Cedercreutz, A. 1907. Ueber die Verhornung der Epidermis beim menschlichen Embryo. *Arch. Dermatol. u. Syphilis* **84**: 173-178.

Chambers, R. and G. S. Renyi. 1925. The structure of the cells in tissues as revealed by microdissection. I. The physical relationships of the cells in epithelia. *Am. J. Anat.* **35**: 385-402.

Champetier, G. and A. Litvac. 1939. Structures histologiques et structures moléculaires au cours de la kératinisation épidermique. *Arch. anat. microscop.* **35**: 65-76.

Chase, H. B. 1949. Greying of hair. I. Effects produced by single doses of x-rays on mice. *J. Morphol.* **84**: 57-80.

Chase, H. B. 1951. Number of entities inactivated by x-rays in greying of hair. *Science* **113**: 714-716.

Chase, H. B., H. Rauch and V. W. Smith. 1951. Critical stages of hair development and pigmentation in the mouse. *Physiol. Zoöl.* **24**: 1-10.

Chase, H. B., W. Montagna and J. D. Malone. 1953. Changes in the skin in relation to the hair growth cycle. *Anat. Record* **116**: 75-81.

Chavin, W. 1959. Pituitary hormones in melanogenesis. *In* "Pigment Cell Biology" (M. Gordon, ed.) pp. 63-83. Academic Press, New York.

Chessick, R. D. 1953. Histochemical study of the distribution of esterases. *J. Histochem. and Cytochem.* **1**: 471-485.

Chévremont, M. and J. Frederic. 1943. Une nouvelle méthode histochimique de mise en évidence des substances à fonction sulfhydrile. Application à l'épiderme, au poil et à la levure. *Arch. biol. (Liège)* **54**: 589-605.

Chlopin, G. 1932. Über einige Wachstums—und Differenzierungsercheinungen an der embryonalen menschlichen Epidermis in Explantat. *Wilhelm Roux' Arch. Entwicklungsmech. Organ.* **126**: 69-89.

Claringbold, P. J. 1954. The effect of insulin and phloridzin on the intravaginal action of oestrone. *J. Endocrinol.* **11**: 36-43.

Clark, W. H., R. G. Hibbs and M. Watson. 1958. Electron microscope studies of the human epidermis. The clear cell of Masson (dendritic cells or melanocyte). *J. Biophys. Biochem. Cytol.* **4**: 679-684.

Cleffmann-Brenner, R. 1959. Die Reizwirkung des Methycholanthrens auf die Melanocyten der Haut bei verschiedenen Mausestämmen. *Z. Zellforsch. u. mikroskop. Anat.* **49**: 525-530.

Clowes, G. H. A. and M. E. Krahl. 1940. Studies on cell metabolism and cell division. III. Oxygen consumption and cell division of fertilized sea urchin eggs in the presence of respiratory inhibitors. *J. Gen. Physiol.* **23**: 401-411.

Cooper, Z. K. 1939. Mitotic rhythm in human epidermis. Introduction and review of literature. *J. Invest. Dermatol.* **2**: 289-300.

Cooper, Z. K. and A. Schiff. 1938. Mitotic rhythm in human epidermis. *Proc. Soc. Exptl. Biol. Med.* **39**: 323-324.

Cooper, Z. K. and H. C. Franklin. 1940. Mitotic rhythm in the epidermis of the mouse. *Anat. Record* **78**: 1-8.

Cowdry, E. V. and G. H. Scott. 1928. Études cytologiques sur le paludisme. III. Mitochondries, granules corables au tough neutre et appareil de Golgi. *Arch. inst. Pasteur Tunis* **17**: 233-252.

Cowdry, E. V. and H. C. Thompson, Jr. 1944. Localization of maximum cell division in epidermis. *Anat. Record.* **88**: 403-409.

Da Fano, C. 1921. On Golgi's apparatus of transplantable tumor cells. *Sci. Repts. Cancer Research Foundation London* **7**: 67-91.

Dalton, A. J. 1951. Observations of the Golgi substance within the electron microscope. *Nature* **168**: 244-247.

Dalton, A. J. and D. M. Felix. 1953. Phase contrast and electron micrography of the Cloudman S91 mouse melanoma. *In* "Pigment Cell Growth" (M. Gordon, ed.) pp. 267-274. Academic Press, New York.

Danneel, R. and G. Cleffmann. 1954. Die Einwanderung der Pigmentzellen in die Haut und die Haare bei Nagetieren. *Biol. Zentr.* **73**: 414-428.

Danneel, R. and N. Weissenfels. 1953. Die Herkunft der Melanoblasten in den Haaren des Menschen und ihr Verbleib beim Haarwechsel. *Biol. Zentr.* **72**: 630-643.

Deineka, D. 1912. Der Netzapparat von Golgi in einigen Epithel—und Bindegewebszellen während der Ruhe und während der Teilung derselben. *Anat. Anz.* **41**: 289-309.

Dempsey, E. W., H. M. Singer and G. B. Wislocki. 1950. The increased basophilia of tissue proteins after oxidation with periodic acid. *Stain Technol.* **25**: 73-80.

Derksen, J. C. and G. C. Heringa. 1936. Cited from Derksen *et al.* (1938).

Derksen, J. C., G. C. Heringa and A. Weidinger. 1938. On keratin and cornification. *Acta Neerl. Morphol.* **1**: 31-37.

Dick, J. C. 1947. Observations on the elastic tissue of the skin with a note on the reticular layer at the junction of the dermis and epidermis. *J. Anat.* **81**: 201-211.

DuBuy, H. G., M. W. Woods, D. Burk and M. D. Lackey. 1949. Enzymatic activities of isolated amelanotic and melanotic granules of mouse melanomas and a suggested relationship to mitochondria. *J. Natl. Cancer Inst.* **9**: 325-336.

Durward, A. and K. M. Rudall. 1958. The vascularity and patterns of growth of hair follicles. *In* "The Biology of Hair Growth" (W. Montagna and R. A. Ellis, ed.), pp. 189-217. Academic Press, New York.

Du Shane, G. P. 1943. The embryology of vertebrate pigment cells. I. Amphibia. *Quart. Rev. Biol.* **18**: 109-127.

Du Shane, G. P. 1944. The embryology of vertebrate pigment cells. II. Birds. *Quart. Rev. Biol.* **19**(2): 98-117.

Eartly, H., B. Grad and C. P. Leblond. 1951. The antagonistic relationship between testosterone and thyroxine in maintaining the epidermis of the male rat. *Endocrinology* **49**: 677-686.

Ebling, F. J. 1954. Changes in the sebaceous glands and epidermis during the oestrous cycle of the albino rat. *J. Endocrinol.* **10**: 147-154.

Ehrmann, S. 1885. Untersuchungen über die Physiologie und Pathologie des Haut-pigmentes. I. *Arch. Dermatol. u. Syphilis* **17**: 507-532.

Eisen, A. Z., W. Montagna and H. B. Chase. 1953. Sulfhydryl groups in the skin of the mouse and guinea pig. *J. Natl. Cancer Inst.* **14**: 341-353.

Ellis, R. A. and W. Montagna. 1958. Histology and cytochemistry of human skin. XV. Sites of phosphorylase and amylo-1, 6-glucosidase activity. *J. Histochem. and Cytochem.* **6**: 201-207.

Ernst, P. 1896. Studien über normale Verhornung mit Hülfe der Grams'chen Methode. *Arch. mikroskop. Anat. u. Entwicklungsmech.* **47**: 669-706.

Fand, S. B., H. J. Levine and H. L. Erwin. 1959. A reappraisal of the histochemical method for carbonic anhydrase. *J. Histochem. and Cytochem.* **7**: 27-33.

Farber, E. and C. D. Louviere. 1956. Histochemical localization of specific oxidative enzymes. IV. Soluble oxidation-reduction dyes as aids in the histochemical localization of oxidative enzymes with tetrazolium salts. *J. Histochem. and Cytochem.* **4**: 347-356.

Favre, M. 1920a. Topographie et répartition des filaments spiralés de l'épiderme. *Compt. rend. soc. biol.* **83**: 349-350.

Favre, M. 1920b. Signification morphologique et fonctionelle des filaments spiralés de l'épiderme. *Compt. rend. soc. biol.* **83**: 351-352.

Favre, M. 1924. Faits histologiques concernant la signification des nodules dits de Bizzozero. *Compt. rend. soc. biol.* **91**: 1220-1222.

Favre, M. 1946. Le nodule de Bizzozero dans l'épiderme normal et dans les épidermes pathologiques. *Ann. dermatol. syphilig.* **6**: 537-546.

Favre, M. 1950. Le chondriome de l'épiderme normal et des épidermes pathologiques. Ortho et parakératinisations. *Ann. dermatol. syphilig.* **10**: 241-262.

Favre, M. and C. Regaud. 1910a. Sur certains filaments ayant probablement la signification de mitochondries, dans la couche génératrice de l'épiderme. *Compt. rend. acad. sci.* **150**: 560-562.

Favre, M. and C. Regaud. 1910b. Sur la nature des fibres d'Herxheimer ou filaments bassaux de l'épiderme. *Lyon méd.* **114**: 1132-1138.

Findlay, G. H. 1955. The simple esterases of human skin. *Brit. J. Dermatol.* **67**: 83-91.

Firket, H. 1951. Recherches sur la régénération de la peau de mammifère. Deuxième partie: etude histochimique. *Arch. biol.* (*Liège*) **62**: 335-351.

Firket, J. 1911. Recherches sur la genèse des fibrilles épidermiques chez le poulet. *Anat. Anz.* **38**: 537-549.

Fischer, A. 1946. "Biology of Tissue Cells," 1st ed. Cambridge Univ. Press, London and New York.

Fishman, W. H. and J. R. Baker. 1956. Cellular localization of β-glucuronidase in rat tissues. *J. Histochem. and Cytochem.* **4**: 570-587.

Fitzpatrick, T. B. 1952. Human melanogenesis; the tyrosinase reaction in pigment cell neoplasms, with particular reference to the malignant melanoma: preliminary report. *Arch. Dermatol. and Syphilol.* **65**: 379-391.

Fitzpatrick, T. B. 1959. Zur Rolle der Tyrosinase bei der Säugetier-Melanogenese. *Hautarzt* **10**: 520-525.

Fitzpatrick, T. B. and A. Kukita. 1956. A histochemical autoradiographic method for demonstration of tyrosinase in human melanocytes, nevi and malignant melanoma. *J. Invest. Dermatol.* **26**: 173-183.

Fitzpatrick, T. B. and A. Kukita. 1959. Tyrosinase activity in vertebrate melanocytes. *In* "Pigment Cell Biology" (M. Gordon, ed.) pp. 489-524. Academic Press, New York.

Fitzpatrick, T. B. and A. B. Lerner. 1953. Terminology of pigment cells. *Science* **117**: 640.

Fitzpatrick, T. B., S. W. Becker, Jr., A. B. Lerner and H. Montgomery. 1950. Tyrosinase in human skin: demonstration of its presence and its role in human melanin formation. *Science* **112**: 223-225.

Fitzpatrick, T. B., P. C. J. Brunet and A. Kukita. 1958. The nature of hair pigment. *In* "Biology of Hair Growth" (W. Montagna and R. A. Ellis, eds.), pp. 255-303. Academic Press, New York.

Flemming, W. 1884. Zur Kenntniss der Regeneration der Epidermis beim Säugetier. *Arch. mikroskop. Anat. u. Entwicklungsmech.* **23**: 148-154.

Flesch, P., D. A. Roe and E. C. J. Esoda. 1960. The gram-staining material of human epidermis. *J. Invest. Dermatol.* **34**: 17-29.

Formisano, V. and W. Montagna. 1954. Succinic dehydrogenase activity in the skin of the guinea pig. *Anat. Record* **120**: 893-906.

Foster, M. 1951. Enzymatic studies of pigment forming abilities in mouse skin. *J. Exptl. Zool.* **117**: 211-246.

Foster, M. 1952. Manometric and histochemical demonstration of tyrosinase in foetal guinea-pig skin. *Proc. Soc. Exptl. Biol. Med.* **79**: 713-715.

Foster, M. 1956. Effects of melanocyte crowding on melanin formation. *Anat. Record* **125**: 622-623.

Foster, M. 1959. Physiological studies of melanogenesis. *In* "Pigment Cell Biology" (M. Gordon, ed.) pp. 301-314. Academic Press, New York.

Foster, M. and R. Cook. 1953. Melanocyte population density and tyrosinase activity in mammalian skin. *Genetics* **38**: 662.

Foster, M. and R. Cook. 1954. Tyrosinase in frozen sections and fragments of mouse skin. *Proc. Soc. Exptl. Biol. Med.* **85**: 120-123.

Foster, M., R. Cook and T. A. Stamas. 1956. *In vitro* studies of the effects of melanocyte population density on melanin formation. *J. Exptl. Zool.* **132**: 1-23.

Frederic, J. and M. Chévremont. 1952. Recherches sur les chondriosomes de cellules vivantes par la microscopie et la microcinématographie en contraste de phase. *Arch. biol.* (*Liége*) **63**: 109-131.

Frieboes, W. 1920. Beiträge zur Anatomie und Biologie der Haut. II. Basalmembran: Bau des Deckepithels (1.-Physiologische und pathologische Ausblicke). *Dermatol. Z.* **31**: 57-83.

Frieboes, W. 1921. Beiträge zur Anatomie und Biologie der Haut. III. Bau des Deckepithels (11) Epithelregeneration. Atrophien und Hypertrophien des Deckepithels. Sklerodermie. *Dermatol. Z.* **32**: 1-11.

Frieboes, W. 1922. Beiträge zur Anatomie und Biologie der Haut. IX. Nochmals epidermale Basalmembran.—Eine Entgegnung gegen Herxheimer und Sophie Born. *Arch. Dermatol. u. Syphilis.* **140**: 201-207.

Fruton, J. S. 1946. On the proteolytic enzymes of animal tissues. V. Peptidases of skin, lung, and serum. *J. Biol. Chem.* **166**: 721-738.

Gelfant, S. 1959. A study of mitosis in mouse ear epidermis *in vitro*. II. Effects of oxygen tension and glucose concentration. *Exptl. Cell Research* **18**: 494-503.

Gelfant, S. 1960a. A study of mitosis in mouse ear epidermis *in vitro*. III. Effects of glucolytic and Krebs cycle intermediates. *Exptl. Cell Research* **19**: 65-72.

Gelfant, S. 1930b. A study of mitosis in mouse ear epidermis *in vitro*. IV. Effects of metabolic inhibitors. *Exptl. Cell Research* **19**: 72-82.

Gessler, A. E., C. E. Grey, M. C. Schuster, J. J. Kelsch and M. N. Richter. 1948. Notes on the electron microscopy of tissue sections. II. Neoplastic tissue. *Cancer Research* **8**: 549-573.

Giroud, A. and H. Bulliard. 1934. Mise en évidence des substances à fonction sulf-hydryle. *Bull. histol. appl. physiol. et pathol. et tech. microscop.* **11**: 169-172.

Giroud, A. and H. Bulliard. 1935. Les substances à fonction sulfhydryle dans l'épiderme. *Arch. anat. microscop.* **31**: 271-290.

Giroud, A. and C. P. Leblond. 1951. The keratinization of epidermis and its de-rivatives, especially the hair, as shown by X-ray diffraction and histochemical studies. *Ann. N.Y. Acad. Sci.* **53**: 613-626.

Giroud, A., H. Bulliard and C. P. Leblond. 1934. Les deux types fondamentaux de kératinisation. *Bull. histol. appl. physiol. et pathol. et tech. microscop.* **11**: 129-144.

Giroud, A., C. P. Leblond and R. Ratsimamanga. 1935a. La vitamine C (acide as-corbique) dans la peau. *Compt. rend. soc. biol.* **118**: 321-322.

Giroud, A., C. P. Leblond and R. Ratsimamanga. 1935b. La vitamine C dans l'organisme. Accumulation-élimination. *Compt. rend. assoc. anat. Montpelier*, pp. 1-8.

Glenner, C. G., H. J. Burtner and G. W. Brown, Jr. 1957. The histochemical demon-stration of monoamine oxidase activity by tetrazolium salts. *J. Histochem. and Cytochem.* **5**: 591-600.

Gomori, G. 1948. Histochemical demonstration of sites of phosphamidase activity. *Proc. Soc. Exptl. Biol. Med.* **69**: 407-409.

Gomori, G. 1952. "Microscopic Histochemistry. Principles and Practice." Univ. of Chicago Press, Chicago, Illinois.

Grand, C. O., R. Chambers and G. Cameron. 1935. Neoplasm studies. I. Cells of melanoma in tissue culture. *Am. J. Cancer* **24**: 36-50.

Gray, M., H. Blank and G. Rake. 1952. Electron microscopy of normal human skin. *J. Invest. Dermatol.* **19**: 449-457.

Griesemer, R. D. 1959. Protection against the transfer of matter through the skin. *In* "The Human Integument" (S. Rothman, ed.), Am. Assoc. Advance. Sci., Publ. No. 54, Washington, D. C.

Gustavson, K. H. 1949. Some protein-chemical aspects of tanning processes. *Advances in Protein Chem.* **5**: 353-421.

Hale, C. W. 1946. Histochemical demonstration of acid polysaccharides in animal tissues. *Nature* **157**: 802.

Harkness, D. R. and H. A. Bern. 1957. Radioautographic studies of hair growth in the mouse. *Acta Anat.* **31**: 35-45.

Hawk, P. B., B. L. Oser and W. H. Summerson. 1947. "Practical Physiological Chemistry." McGraw-Hill, New York.

Hawkins, J. 1952. The localization of amine oxidase in the liver cells. *Biochem. J.* **50**: 577-581.

Hellmann, K. 1955. Cholinesterase and amine oxidase in the skin: a histochemical investigation. *J. Physiol. (London)* **129**: 454-463.

Herxheimer, K. 1889. Ueber eigenthuemliche Fasern in der Epidermis und im Epithel gewisser Schleimhaeute des Menschen. *Arch. Dermatol. u. Syphilis* **21**: 645-656.

Herxheimer, K. 1916. Ueber die epidermale Basalmembran. *Dermatol. Z.* **23**: 129-134.

Herxheimer, K. and H. Müller. 1898. Ueber die Deutung der sogenannten Epidermis-spiralen. *Arch. Dermatol. u. Syphilis* **36**: 93-110.

Hibbs, R. G. and W. H. Clark. 1959. Electron microscope studies of the human epidermis. The cell boundaries and topography of the stratum malpighi. *J. Biophys. Biochem. Cytol.* **6**: 71-76.

Hirsch, G. C. 1939. Form- und stoffwechsel der Golgi-körper. *Protoplasma Monographien No.* **18**.

Hochster, R. M. and J. H. Quastel. 1949. Diethyl stilboestrol as a competitive intracellular hydrogen carrier. *Nature* **164**: 865-867.

Hoepke, H. 1927. Die Haare. *In* "Handbuch der mikroskopischen Anatomie des Menschen" (W. V. Möllendorff, ed.), Vol. 3, Part 1, pp. 67-88. Springer, Berlin.

Hogeboom, G. H. and M. H. Adams. 1942. Mammalian tyrosinase and dopa oxidase. *J. Biol. Chem.* **145**: 273-279.

Holmes, R. L. 1953. Patterns of cutaneous pigmentation: rodents. *J. Anat.* **87**: 163-168.

Holmgren, H. 1940. Studien über Verbreitung und Bedeutung der chromotropen Substanz. *Z. mikroskop.-anat. Forsch.* **47**: 489-521.

Horstmann, E. 1952. Über den Papillarkörper der menschlichen Haut und seine regionalen Unterschiede. *Acta Anat.* **14**: 23-42.

Horstmann, E. 1957. Die Haut. *In* "Handbuch der mikroskopischen Anatomie des Menschen" (W. V. Möllendorff, ed.), Vol. 3, Part 3, pp. 1-488. Springer, Berlin.

Horstmann, E. and A. Knoop. 1958. Elektronmikroskopische Studien an der Epidermis. I. Rattenpfote. *Z. Zellforsch. u. mikroskop. Anat.* **47**: 348-362.

Houssay, B. A. 1951. Action of sex hormones on experimental diabetes. *Brit. Med. J.* **2**: 4730.

Hsu, T. C. and T. Y. Lou. 1959. Nuclear extrusion in cells of Cloudman melanoma *in vitro*. *In* "Pigment Cell Biology" (M. Gordon, ed.) pp. 315-325. Academic Press, New York.

Hu, F. 1959. Cytological studies of human pigment cells in tissue culture. *In* "Pigment Cell Biology" (M. Gordon, ed.) pp. 147-158. Academic Press, New York.

Hu, F., R. J. Staricco, H. Pinkus and R. P. Fosnaugh. 1957. Human melanocytes in tissue culture. *J. Invest. Dermatol.* **28**: 15-32.

Hunter, R., H. Pinkus and C. H. Steele. 1956. Examination of the epidermis by the strip method. III. The number of keratin cells in the human epidermis. *J. Invest. Dermatol.* **27**: 31-34.

Janes, R. C. and W. O. Nelson. 1940. Effect of stilboestrol on certain phases of carbohydrate metabolism. *Proc. Soc. Exptl. Biol. Med.* **43**: 340-342.

Jarrett, A., and G. Szabó. 1956. The pathological varieties of vitiligo and their response to treatment with meladinine. *Brit. J. Dermatol.* **68**: 313-326.

Jarrett, A., A. Bligh and J. A. Hardy. 1956. Fluorescent microscopy of the human skin. *Brit. J. Dermatol.* **68**: 111-119.

Jarrett, A., R. I. Spearman and J. A. Hardy. 1959. The histochemistry of keratinization. *Brit. J. Dermatol.* **71**: 277-295.

Kaye, M. 1924. Observations on the behavior of a substance giving the nitro-prusside reaction in skin and in hair. *Biochem. J.* **18**: 1289-1293.

Kerly, M. 1940. The effect of oestrone on the metabolism of rat uterus. *Biochem. J.* **34**: 814-819.

King, L. S. 1949. Effects of podophyllin on mouse skin. III. A study of epidermal fibrils. *J. Natl. Cancer Inst.* **10**: 689-709.

Kollmann, M. and L. Papin. 1914. Étude sur la kératinisation. L'épithélium corné de l'oesophage de quelques mammifères. *Arch. anat. microscop.* **16**: 193-260.

Kooyman, D. J. 1932. LXI.—Lipids of the skin. Some changes in the lipids of the epidermis during the process of keratinisation. *Arch. Dermatol. Syphilol.* **25**: 444-450.

Kromayer, E. 1892. Die Protoplasmafaserung der Epithelzelle. *Arch. mikroskop. Anat. u. Entwicklungsmech.* **39**: 141-150.

Kurata, Y. 1953. Histochemical demonstration of carbonic anhydrase activity. *Stain Technol.* **28**: 231.

Kvorning, S. A. 1949. Investigations into the pharmacology of skin fats and ointments. IV. Investigations into the composition of the lipids on the skin of normal individuals. *Acta Pharmacol. Toxicol.* **5**: 383-396.

Laden, E. L., I. Linden, J. O. Erickson and D. Armen. 1953. Electron microscopic study of epidermal basal cells and epidermal dermal junction. *J. Invest. Dermatol.* **21**: 37-41.

Laguesse, E. 1919a. Sur la structure des papilles et de la couche superficielle du derme chez l'homme. *Compt. rend. soc. biol.* **82**: 435-438.

Laguesse, E. 1919b. Sur la membrane vitrée basale sous-épidermique. *Compt. rend. soc. biol.* **82**: 438-441.

Laidlaw, G. F. 1932. Melanoma studies I. The dopa reaction in general pathology. *Am. J. Pathol.* **8**: 477-490.

Laidlaw, G. F. and M. R. Murray. 1933. Melanoma studies III. Theory of pigmented moles. Their relation to the evolution of hair follicles. *Am. J. Pathol.* **9**: 827-838.

Langerhans, P. 1868. Ueber die Nerven der menschlichen Haut. *Virchow's Arch. pathol. Anat. u. Physiol.* **44**: 325-337.

Langerhans, P. 1873. Ueber Tastkörperchen und rete Malpighii. *Arch. mikroskop. Anat. u. Entwicklungsmech.* **9**: 730-744.

Laser, H. 1933. Der Stoffwechsel von Gewebekulturen und ihr Verhalten in der Anaerobiose. *Biochem. Z.* **264**: 72-86.

Leblond, C. P. 1950. Distribution of periodic acid-reactive carbohydrates in the adult rat. *Am. J. Anat.* **86**: 1-49.

Leblond, C. P. 1951. Histological structure of hair, with a brief comparison of other epidermal appendages and epidermis itself. *Ann. N.Y. Acad. Sci.* **53**: 464-475.

Lerner, A. B. 1959. Mechanism of hormone action. *Nature* **184**: 674-677.

Lerner, A. B. and J. D. Case. 1959. Pigment cell regulatory factors. *J. Invest. Dermatol.* **32**: 211-221.

Lerner, A. B. and T. H. Lee. 1955. Isolation of homogenous melanocyte stimulating hormone from hog pituitary gland. *J. Am. Chem. Soc.* **77**: 1066-1067.

Lerner, A. B., K. Shizume and I. Bunding. 1954. The mechanism of endocrine control of melanin pigmentation. *J. Clin. Endocrinol. and Metabolism* **14**: 1463-1490.

Lerner, A. B., J. D. Case and R. V. Heinzelman. 1959. Structure of melatonin. *J. Am. Chem. Soc.* **81**: 6084-6085.

Lettré, H. 1942. Mitosegifte und ihre Beziehungen zu Naturstoffen. *Naturwissenschaften* **30**: 34-40.

Lettré, H. and M. Albrecht. 1941. Zur Wirkung von β-Phenyläthylaminen auf in vitro gezüchtete Zellen. *Z. physiol. Chem. Hoppe-Seyler's* **271**: 200-207.

Leuchtenberger, C. and H. Z. Lund. 1951. The chemical nature of the so-called keratohyalin granules of the stratum granulosum of the skin. *Exptl. Cell Research* **2**: 150-152.

Lewis, M. R. and W. H. Lewis. 1915. Mitochondria (and other cytoplasmic structures) in tissue cultures. *Am. J. Anat.* **17**: 339-401.

Lison, L. 1935. Études sur la métachromasie. Colorants métachromatiques et substances chromotropes. *Arch. biol.* (*Liège*) **46**: 599-668.

Litvac, A. 1939. Sur la kératinisation épithéliale *in vitro. Arch. anat. microscop.* **35**: 55-63.

Lobitz, W. C., Jr., and J. B. Holyoke. 1954. The histochemical response of the human epidermis to controlled injury; glycogen. *J. Invest. Dermatol.* **22**: 189-198.

Lombardo, C. 1907. Il glicogeno della cute. *Giorn. ital. mal. vener.* **42**: 448-464.

Lombardo, C. 1934. Il glicogeno in alcuni derivati epidermici della cute umana. *Giorn. ital. dermatol. e sifilol.* **75**: 185-186.

Ludford, R. J. 1924. Cell organs during keratinization in normal and malignant growth. *Quart. J. Microscop. Sci.* **69**: 27-57.

Ludford, R. J. 1925. The cytology of tar tumors. *Proc. Roy. Soc.* **B98**: 557-577.

Malaty, H. A. and G. H. Bourne. 1955. The histochemistry of simple esterases. *Acta Anat.* **24**: 347-350.

Mali, J. W. H. 1956. The transport of water through the human epidermis. *J. Invest. Dermatol.* **27**: 451-469.

Markert, C. L. and W. K. Silvers. 1956. The effect of genotype and cell environment on melanoblast differentiation in the house mouse. *Genetics* **41**: 429-450.

Martinotti, L. 1914a. Ricerche sulla fine struttura dell' epidermide umana in rapporto alla sua funzione eleidocheratinica. Comunicazione preventiva.

Martinotti, L. 1914b. Ricerche sulla fine struttura dell'epidermide umana normale in rapporto alla sua funzione eleidocheratinica. Nota I. Il corpo malpighiano e la produzione fibrillare dell'epidermide. *Arch. Zellforsch.* **12**: 457-484.

Martinotti, L. 1915. Ricerche sulla fine struttura dell'epidermide umana normale in rapporto alla sua funzione eleidocheratinica. Nota II. Lo strato granuloso e la funzione cheratojalinica. *Arch. Zellforsch.* **13**: 446-458.

Martinotti, L. 1921. Ricerche sulla fine struttura dell'epidermide umana normale in rapporto alla sua funzione eleidocheratinica. Nota IV. Lo strato corneo e la formazione della cheratina. *Arch. Zellforsch.* **15**: 377-392.

Martinotti, L. 1924. Tecnica per lo studio del processo della corneificazione della cute allo stato normale e patologica. *Z. wiss. Mikroskop.* **41**: 202-237.

Mason, H. S. 1959. Structure of melanins. *In* "Pigment Cell Biology" (M. Gordon, ed.), pp. 563-581. Academic Press, New York.

Masson, P. 1926. Les naevi pigmentaires, tumeurs nerveuses. *Ann. anat. pathol.* **3**: 417-453, 657-696.

Masson, P. 1948. Pigment cells in man. *In* "Biology of Melanomas" (R. W. Miner, ed.), N.Y. Acad. Sci. Spec. Publ. Vol. 4. New York.

Masson, P. 1951. My conception of cellular nevi. *Cancer* **4**: 9-38.

Matoltsy, A. G. 1958. The chemistry of keratinization. *In* "The Biology of Hair Growth" (W. Montagna and R. A. Ellis, eds.), pp. 135-165. Academic Press, New York.

Matoltsy, A. G. and M. N. Matoltsy. 1961. A study of morphological and chemical properties of keratohyalin granules. *J. Invest. Dermatol.* (In press.)

Medawar, P. B. 1941. Sheets of pure epidermal epithelium from human skin. *Nature* **148**: 783.

Medawar, P. B. 1947. The behaviour of mammalian skin epithelium under strictly anaerobic conditions. *Quart. J. Microscop. Sci.* **88**: 27.

Medawar, P. B. 1953. The micro-anatomy of the mammalian epidermis. *Quart. J. Microscop. Sci.* **94**: 481-506.

Menkes, J. H. and A. Csapo. 1952. Changes in the adenosine triphosphate and creatine phosphate content of the rabbit uterus throughout sexual maturation and after ovulation. *Endocrinology* **50**: 37-50.

Mercer, E. H. 1958. The electron microscopy of keratinized tissues. *In* "The Biology of Hair Growth" (W. Montagna and R. A. Ellis, eds.), pp. 91-110. Academic Press, New York.

Mescon, H. and P. Flesch. 1952. Modification of Bennett's method for the histochemical demonstration of free sulfhydryl groups in skin. *J. Invest. Dermatol.* **18**: 261-266.

Meyer, J. and J. P. Weinmann. 1955. A modification of Gomori's method for the demonstration of phosphamidase in tissue sections. *J. Histochem. and Cytochem.* **3**: 134-140.

Meyer, J. and J. P. Weinmann. 1957. Occurrence of phosphamidase activity in keratinizing epithelia. *J. Invest. Dermatol.* **29**: 393-405.

Meyer, K. 1947. The biological significance of hyaluronic acid and hyaluronidase. *Physiol. Revs.* **27**: 335-359.

Meyer, K. and E. Chaffee. 1941. The mucopolysaccharides of skin. *J. Biol. Chem.* **138**: 491-499.

Meyer, K. and M. M. Rapport. 1951. The mucopolysaccharides of the ground substance of connective tissue. *Science* **113**: 596-599.

Meyerhof, O. and L. O. Randall. 1948. Inhibitory effects of adrenochrome on cell metabolism. *Arch. Biochem.* **17**: 171-182.

Mohn, M. P. 1958. The effects of different hormonal states on the growth of hair in rats. *In* "The Biology of Hair Growth" (W. Montagna and R. A. Ellis, eds.), pp. 336-393. Academic Press, New York.

Montagna, W. 1950. Perinuclear sudanophil bodies in mammalian epidermis. *Quart. J. Microscop. Sci.* **91**: 205-208.

Montagna, W. 1955. Histology and cytochemistry of human skin. IX. The distribution of non-specific esterases. *J. Biophys. Biochem. Cytol.* **1**: 13-16.

Montagna, W. 1957. Histology and cytochemistry of human skin. XI. The distribution of β-glucuronidase. *J. Biophys. Biochem. Cytol.* **3**: 343-348.

Montagna, W. and H. B. Chase. 1950. Redifferentiation of sebaceous glands in the mouse after total extirpation with methylcholanthrene. *Anat. Record* **107**: 82-92.

Montagna, W. and R. A. Ellis. 1958. L'histologie et la cytologie de la peau humaine. XVI. Repartition et concentration des estérases carboxyliques. *Ann. histochim.* **3**: 2-17.

Montagna, W. and R. A. Ellis. 1959. The skin of primates. I. The skin of the potto (*Perodicticus potto*) *Am. J. Phys. Anthropol.* **17**: 137-162.

Montagna, W. and V. Formisano. 1955. Esterase activity in the skin of mammals. *J. Anat.* **89**: 425-429.

Montagna, W. and J. B. Hamilton. 1949. The sebaceous glands of the hamster. II. Some cytochemical studies in normal and experimental animals. *Am. J. Anat.* **84**: 365-395.

Montagna, W., C. R. Noback and F. G. Zak. 1948. Pigment, lipids and other substances in the glands of the external auditory meatus of man. *Am. J. Anat.* **83**: 409-436.

Montagna, W., H. B. Chase and H. P. Melaragno. 1951. Histology and cytochemistry of human skin. I. Metachromasia in the mons pubis. *J. Natl. Cancer Inst.* **12**: 591-597.

Montagna, W., H. B. Chase and W. C. Lobitz, Jr. 1952. Histology and cytochemistry of human skin. II. The distribution of glycogen in the epidermis, hair follicles, sebaceous glands and eccrine sweat glands. *Anat. Record* **114**: 231-248.

Montagna, W., A. Z. Eisen, A. H. Rademacher and H. B. Chase. 1954. Histology and cytochemistry of human skin. VI. The distribution of sulfhydryl and disulfide groups. *J. Invest. Dermatol.* **23**: 23-32.

Moretti, G. and H. Mescon. 1956. A chemical-histochemical evaluation of acid phosphatase activity in human skin. *J. Histochem. and Cytochem.* **4**: 247-253.

Nachlas, M. M., D. T. Crawford and A. M. Seligman. 1957. The histochemical demonstration of leucine aminopeptidase. *J. Histochem. and Cytochem.* **5**: 264-278.

Nachlas, M. M., B. Monis, D. Rosenblatt and A. M. Seligman. 1960. Improvement in the histochemical localization of leucine aminopeptidase with a new substrate, 1-leucyl-4-methoxy-2-naphthylamide. *J. Biophys. Biochem. Cytol.* **7**: 261-264.

Nichols, S. E. Jr. and W. M. Reams, Jr. 1960. The occurrence and morphogenesis of melanocytes in the connective tissues of the PET/MCV mouse strain. *J. Embryol. Exptl. Morphol.* **8**: 24-32.

Nicolaides, N. and G. C. Wells. 1957. On the biogenesis of the free fatty acids in human skin surface fat. *J. Invest. Dermatol.* **29**: 423-433.

Odland, G. F. 1950. The morphology of the attachment between the dermis and the epidermis. *Anat. Record* **108**: 399-413.

Odland, G. F. 1958. The fine structure of the interrelationship of cells in the human epidermis. *J. Biophys. Biochem. Cytol.* **4**: 529-538.

Odland, G. F. 1960. A submicroscopic granular component in human epidermis. *J. Invest. Dermatol.* **34**: 11-15.

Opdyke, D. L. 1952. Observations on the chemical morphology of the keratohyalin granules. Thesis. Washington Univ., St. Louis, Missouri.

Oppenheimer, J. M. 1949. A typical pigment cell differentiation in embryonic teleostean grafts and isolates. *Proc. Natl. Acad. Sci. U.S.* **35**: 709-712.

Ortiz-Picón, J. M. 1933. Über Zellteilungsfrequenz und Zellteilungsrhythmus in der Epidermis der Maus. *Z. Zellforsch. u. mikroskop. Anat.* **19**: 488-509.

Ottenstein, B., N. Boncoddo, A. Walker and F. M. Thurmon. 1952. Experiments on the choline content of the skin and sebum. *J. Invest. Dermatol.* **19**: 105-108.

Ottolenghi-Lodigiani, F. 1957. Le idrolasi della cute umana. *Giorn. ital. dermatol.* **2**: 105-128.

Palade, G. E. 1952. The fine structure of mitochondria. *Anat. Record* **114**: 427-451.

Palade, G. E. 1953. An electron microscope study of the mitochondrial structure. *J. Histochem. and Cytochem.* **1**: 188-211.

Palade, G. E. 1955. Studies on the endoplasmic reticulum. II. Simple disposition in cells in situ. *J. Biophys. Biochem. Cytol.* **1**: 59.

Palade, G. E. and A. Claude. 1949a. The nature of the Golgi apparatus. I. Parallelism between intracellular myelin figures and Golgi apparatus in somatic cells. *J. Morphol.* **85**: 35-69.

Palade, G. E. and A. Claude. 1949b. The nature of the Golgi apparatus. II. Identification of the Golgi apparatus with a complex of myelin figures. *J. Morphol.* **85**: 71-111.

Parat, M. 1928. Contribution à l'étude morphologique et physiologique du cytoplasme. Chondriome, vacuole (appareil de Golgi), enclaves, etc.; pH, oxidases, peroxidases, rH de la cellule animale. *Arch. anat. microscop.* **24**: 73-357.

Patzelt, V. 1926. Zum Bau der menschlichen Epidermis. *Z. mikroskop.-anat. Forsch.* **5**: 371-462.

Patzelt, V. 1954. Über Tonofibrillen, Keratohyalin, Glykogen und Verhornung in der Epidermis. *Acta Anat.* **21**: 349-356.

Pearce, R. H. and E. M. Watson. 1949. The mucopolysaccharides of human skin. *Cancer J. Research* **E27**: 43-57.

Pease, D. C. 1951. Electron microscopy of human skin. *Am. J. Anat.* **89**: 469-498.

Pepper, F. J. 1954. The epithelial repair of skin wounds in the guinea-pig with special reference to the participation of melanocytes. *J. Morphol.* **95**: 471-499.

Pinkus, H. 1938. Notes on structure and biological properties of human epidermis and sweat gland cells in tissue culture and in the organism. *Arch. exptl. Zellforsch. Gewebezücht.* **22**: 47-52.

Pinkus, H. 1951. Examination of the epidermis by the strip method of removing horny layers. I. Observations on thickness of the horny layer, and on mitotic activity after stripping. *J. Invest. Dermatol.* **16**: 383-386.

Pinkus, H. 1952. Examination of the epidermis by the strip method. II. Biometric data on regeneration of the human epidermis. *J. Invest. Dermatol.* **19**: 431-447.

Pinkus, H. 1958. Embryology of hair. In "Biology of Hair Growth" (W. Montagna and R. A. Ellis, eds.), pp. 1-32. Academic Press, New York.

Pomerat, C. M. and E. N. Willmer. 1939. Studies on the growth of tissues *in vitro*. VII. Carbohydrate metabolism and mitosis. *J. Exptl. Biol.* **16**: 232-249.

Porter, K. R. 1954. Observation on the fine structure of animal epidermis. *Proc. 3rd Intern. Conf. Electron Microscopy, London*, p. 539.

Quevedo, W. C., Jr. and H. B. Chase. 1957. Histological observations on the silvering process in the Champagne d'Argent rabbit. *Anat. Record* **129**: 87-96.

Quevedo, W. C., Jr. and D. Grahn. 1958. Effect of daily gamma-irradiation on the pigmentation of mice. *Radiation Research* **8**: 254-264.

Quevedo, W. C., Jr. and J. E. Isherwood. 1958. "Dopa oxidase" in melanocytes of x-irradiated quiescent hair follicles. *Proc. Soc. Exptl. Biol. Med.* **99**: 748-750.

Rabl, H. 1897. Haut. *Merkel-Bonnets Ergeb.* **8**: 339-400.

Radaeli, G. 1953. Improvement of dopa reaction. *Arch. Dermatol. and Syphilol.* **68**: 668-671.

Ranvier, L. 1879. Nouvelles recherches sur le mode d'union des cellules du corps muqueux de Malpighi. *Compt. rend. soc. biol.* **89**: 667-669.

Ranvier, L. 1898. Histologie de la peau. I. La matière grasse de la couche cornée de l'épiderme chez l'homme et les mammifères. *Arch. anat. microscop.* **2**: 510-514.

Raper, H. S. 1926. The tyrosinase-tyrosine reaction. V. Production of 1 (−) 1–3:4-dihydroxyphenylalanine from tyrosine. *Biochem. J.* **20**: 735-742.

Raper, H. S. 1928. The aerobic oxidases. *Phys. Rev.* **8**: 245-282.

Raper, H. S. 1932. Tyrosinase. *Ergeb. Enzymforsch.* **1**: 270-279.

Rawles, M. E. 1940. The development of melanophores from embryonic mouse tissues grown in the coelom of chick embryos. *Proc. Natl. Acad. Sci. U.S.* **26**: 673-680.

Rawles, M. E. 1947. Origin of pigment cells from the neural crest in the mouse embryo. *Physiol. Zoöl.* **20**: 248-266.

Rawles, M. E. 1953. Origin of the mammalian pigment cell and its role in the pigmentation of hair. In "Pigment Cell Growth" (M. Gordon, ed.), pp. 1-12. Academic Press, New York.

Reams, W. M., Jr., S. E. Nichols, Jr. and H. G. Hager, Jr. 1959. Chemical evocation of melanocyte branching in the chick embryo. *Anat. Record* **134**: 667-676.

Reed, S. C. 1938. Determination of hair pigments. II. Transplantation results in mice, rats and guinea-pigs. *J. Exptl. Zool.* **79**: 331-336.

Reed, S. C. and J. M. Henderson. 1940. Pigment cell migration in mouse epidermis. *J. Exptl. Zool.* **85**: 409-418.

Reed, S. C. and G. Sander. 1937. Time of determination of hair pigments in the mouse. *Growth* **1**: 194-200.

Regaud, C. and M. Favre. 1912. Nouvelles recherches sur les formations mitochondriales de l'épiderme humain, à l'état normal et pathologique. *Compt. rend. soc. biol.* **72**: 328-331.

Rein, H. 1924. Experimentelle Studien ueber Elektrondosmose an ueberlebender menschlicher Haut. *Z. Biol.* **81**: 125-140.

Riehl, G. 1884. Zur Kenntnis des Pigmentes im menschlichen Haar. *Arch. Dermatol. u. Syphilis* **11**: 33-39.

Reynolds, J. 1954. The epidermal melanocytes of mice. *J. Anat.* **88**: 45-58.

Roberts, S. and C. M. Szego. 1953. The influence of steroids on uterine respiration and glycolysis. *J. Biol. Chem.* **201**: 21-30.

Robertson, D. C., W. P. Maddux and E. Allen. 1930. Ovarian hormone effects in ovariectomized monkeys. *Endocrinology* **14**: 77-88.

Rogers, G. E. 1953. The localization of dehydrogenase activity and sulphydryl groups in wool and hair follicles by the use of tetrazolium salts. *Quart. J. Microscop. Sci.* **94**: 253-268.

Rosenstadt, B. 1910. Über die Protoplasmafasern in den Epidermiszellen. *Arch. mikroskop. Anat. u Entwicklungsmech.* **75**: 659-688.

Rothman, S. 1954. "Physiology and Biochemistry of the Skin." Univ. of Chicago Press, Chicago, Illinois.

Rudall, K. M. 1946. The structure of epidermal protein. *Fibrous Proteins* (*Soc. Dyers Colourists*), *Proc. Symposium Univ. Leeds* pp. 15-23.

Rudall, K. M. 1947. X-ray studies on the distribution of protein chain types in the vertebrate epidermis. *Biochim. et Biophys. Acta* **1**: 549-562.

Rudall, K. M. 1953. Elastic properties and the α-β-transformation of fibrous proteins. *Proc. Roy. Soc.* **B141**: 39-45.

Ryder, M. L. 1959. Studies of sulfur, phosphorus, and some metals in skin follicles. *J. Histochem. and Cytochem.* **7**: 133-138.

Sasakawa, M. 1921. Beiträge zur Glykogenverteilung in der Haut unter normalen und pathologischen Zuständen. *Arch. Dermatol. u. Syphilis* **134**: 418-443.

Saunders, J. W., Jr., W. C. Quevedo, L. Pierro and F. E. Morbeck. 1955. The effects of tyrosine and phenylalanine on the synthesis of pigment in melanocytes of embryonic chick skin cultured *in vitro*. *J. Natl. Cancer Inst.* **16**: 475-487.

Schäfer, E. A. 1912. Text-book of microscopic anatomy. *In* "Quain's Elements of Anatomy," 11th ed., Vol. 2, Part 1. Longmans, Green, London.

Schaffer, J. 1933. "Lehrbuch der Histologie und Histogenese," pp. 333-355. Englemann, Leipzig.

Schmidt, W. J. 1937. Neuere polarisationsoptische Arbeiten auf dem Gebiete der Biologie. I. Teil. *Protoplasma* **29**: 300-312.

Scothorne, R. J. and A. W. Scothorne. 1953. Histochemical studies on human skin autografts. *J. Anat.* **87**: 22-29.

Scott, A. and F. Kalz. 1956. The penetration and distribution of C^{14}-hydrocortisone in human skin after its topical application. *J. Invest. Dermatol.* **26**: 149-158.

Seiji, M., T. B. Fitzpatrick and M. S. C. Birbeck. 1960. The melanosome: A distinctive subcellular particle of mammalian melanocytes and the site of melanogenesis. *J. Invest. Dermatol.* **36**: 243-252.

Selby, C. C. 1955. An electron microscope study of the epidermis of mammalian skin in thin sections. I. Dermo-epidermal junction and basal cell layer. *J. Biophys. Biochem. Cytol.* **1**: 429-444.

Selby, C. C. 1956. Fine structure of human epidermis. *J. Soc. Cosmetic Chemists* **7**: 584-599.

Seligman, A. M. and A. M. Rutenburg. 1951. The histochemical demonstration of succinic dehydrogenase. *Science* **113**: 317-320.

Seligman, A. M., H. H. Chauncey and M. M. Nachlas. 1950. Effect of formalin fixation on the activity of five enzymes of rat liver. *Stain Technol.* **26**: 19-23.

Seligman, A. M., K. C. Tsou, S. H. Rutenburg and R. B. Cohen. 1954. Histochemical demonstration of β-D-glucuronidase with a synthetic substrate. *J. Histochem. Cytochem.* **2**: 209-229.

Serra, J. A. 1946. Histochemical tests for proteins and amino acids; the characterization of basic proteins. *Stain Technol.* **21**: 5-18.

Serri, F. 1955a. Note de enzimologia cutanea. I. Stato attuale della nostre conoscenze. *Giorn. ital. dermatol. e sifilol.* **3**: 1-14.

Serri, F. 1955b. Note di enzimologia cutanea. II. Ricerche bio ed istochimiche sull'attività succinodeidrasica della cute umana normale. *Boll. soc. medi-chir. Pavia* **3-4**: 1-19.

Shapiro, B. 1924. On the epithelial fibres in the skin of mammals. *Quart. J. Microscop. Sci.* **68**: 101-145.

Shelley, W. B., S. B. Cohen and G. B. Koelle. 1955. Histochemical demonstration of monamine oxidase in human skin. *J. Invest. Dermatol.* **24**: 561-565.

Silvers, W. K. 1956a. Pigment cells: occurrence in hair follicles. *J. Morphol.* **99**: 41-46.

Silvers, W. K. 1956b. Pigment cell migration following transplantation. *J. Exptl. Zool.* **132**: 539-554.

Silvers, W. K. 1957a. A histological and experimental approach to determine the relationship between gold-impregnated dendritic cells and melanocytes. *Am. J. Anat.* **100**: 225-240.

Silvers, W. K. 1957b. Melanoblast differentiation secured from different mouse genotypes after transplantation to adult mouse spleen or to chick embryo coelom. *J. Exptl. Zool.* **135**: 221-238.

Silvers, W. K. 1958a. Origin and identity of clear cells found in hair bulbs of albino mice. *Anat. Record* **130**: 135-144.

Silvers, W. K. 1958b. An experimental approach to action of genes at the agouti locus in the mouse. II. Transplants of newborn aa ventral skin to aᵗa, Aʷa and aa hosts. *J. Exptl. Zool.* **137**: 181-188.

Silvers, W. K. 1958c. Pigment spread in mouse skin. *J. Exptl. Zool.* **139**: 443-458.

Silvers, W. K. and E. S. Russell. 1955. An experimental approach to action of genes at the agouti locus in the mouse. *J. Exptl. Zool.* **130**: 199-220.

Snell, R. S. and P. G. Bischitz. 1959. A study of the effect of orchidectomy on the melanocytes and melanin in the skin of the guinea-pig. *Z. Zellforsch. u. mikroskop. Anat.* **50**: 825-834.

Snell, R. S. and P. G. Bischitz. 1960. A study of the melanocytes and melanin in the skin of the immature, mature and pregnant female guinea-pig. *Z. Zellforsch. u. mikroskop. Anat.* **51**: 225-242.

Snessarew, P. 1929. Ueber die Pigmentzellen piae matris beim Menschen, ihren Zusammenhang mit den Nervenfasern, ihre Genese und Funktion. Z. Zellforsch u. mikroskop. Anat. 9: 683-693.

Staricco, R. J. and H. Pinkus. 1957. Quantitative and qualitative data on the pigment cells of adult human epidermis. J. Invest. Dermatol. 28: 33-45.

Stearner, S. P. 1946. Pigmentation studies in salamanders, with special reference to the changes at metamorphosis. Physiol. Zoöl. 19: 375-404.

Steigleder, G. K. 1957. Die Histochemie der Epidermis und ihrer Anhangsgebilde. Arch. klin. u. exptl. Dermatol. 206: 276-317.

Steigleder, G. K. 1958. Morphologische und histochemische Befunde in pathologischer Hornschicht, insbesondere bei Parakeratose. Arch. klin. u. exptl. Dermatol. 207: 209-229.

Steigleder, G. K. and H. Elschner. 1959a. Eine neue Methode zum Nachweis von Esterasen auf der Haut. Sond. klin. Wochschr. 37: 104-105.

Steigleder, G. K. and H. Elschner. 1959b. Die Fähigkeit der Hautoberfläche zur Esterspaltung. Arch. klin. u. exptl. Dermatol. 208: 489-501.

Steigleder, G. K. and K. Schultis. 1957a. Zur Histochemie der Esterasen der Haut. Arch. klin. u. exptl. Dermatol. 205: 196-211.

Steigleder, G. K. and K. Schultis. 1957b. Die Bedeutung des Nachweiss unspezifischer Esterasen in Bindegewebszellen der Haut. Arch. klin. u. exptl. Dermatol. 204: 448-456.

Storey, W. F. and C. P. Leblond. 1951. Measurement of the rate of proliferation of epidermis and associated structures. Ann. N.Y. Acad. Sci. 53: 537-545.

Swanbeck, G. 1959. Macromolecular organization of epidermal keratin. An X-ray diffraction study of the horny layer from normal, ichthyotic and psoriatic skin. Acta Dermato.-Venereol. 29 (Suppl. 43): 37 pp.

Swann, M. M. 1957. The control of cell division: a review. I. General mechanisms. Cancer Research 17: 727-757.

Sylvén, B. 1941. Über des Vorkommen von hochmolekularen Esterschwefelsäuren im Granulationsgewebe und bei der Epithelregeneration. Acta Chir. Scand. 86 (Suppl. 66): 1-151.

Sylvén, B. 1950. The qualitative distribution of metachromatic polysaccharide material during hair growth. Exptl. Cell Research 1: 582-589.

Szabó, G. 1954. The number of melanocytes in human epidermis. Brit. Med. J. I: 1016-1017.

Szabó, G. 1957. Tyrosinase in the epidermal melanocytes of white human skin. A.M.A. Arch. Dermatol. 76: 324-329.

Szabó, G. 1959. Quantitative histological investigations on the melanocyte system of the human epidermis. In "Pigment Cell Biology" (M. Gordon, ed.), pp. 99-125. Academic Press, New York.

Szakall, A. 1951. Hautphysiologische Forschung und Gesunderhaltung der Haut. Fette, Seifen, Anstrichmittel 53: 399-405.

Szakall, A. 1955. Über die Eigenschaften, Herkunft und physiologischen Funktionen der die H-Ionen-Konzentration bestimmenden Wirkstoffe in der verhornten Epidermis. Arch. klin. u. exptl. Dermatol. 201: 331-360.

Szily, A. v. 1911. Ueber die Enstehung des melanotischen Pigmentes im Auge der Wirbeltierembryonen und in Choroidsarkomen. Arch. mikroskop. Anat. u. Entwicklungsmech. 77: 87-156.

Takeuchi, T. 1958. Histochemical demonstration of branching enzyme (amylo-1,-4→ 1,6-transglucosidase) in animal tissues. J. Histochem. and Cytochem. 6: 208-216.

Takeuchi, T. and H. Kuriaki. 1955. Histochemical demonstration of phosphorylase in animal tissues. *J. Histochem. and Cytochem.* **3**: 153-160.

Tello, J. F. 1913. El reticulo de Golgi en las cellulas de algunos tumores y en las del granuloma experimental producido por el kieselgur. *Trabajos lab. invest. biol.* **11**: 145-161.

Tello, J. F. 1923. Genèse des terminaisons motrices et sensitives. II. Terminaisons dans les poils de la souris blanche. *Trabajos lab. invest. biol.* **21**: 255-384.

Thomas, O. L. 1948. A study of the spheroid system of sympathetic neurons with special reference to the problem of neurosecretion. *Quart. J. Microscop. Sci.* **89**: 333-335.

Thuringer, J. M. 1924. Regeneration of stratified squamous epithelium. *Anat. Record* **28**: 31-43.

Thuringer, J. M. 1928. Studies on cell division in the human epidermis. II. A. Rate of cell division in the prepuce. B. Influence of various factors on cell division. *Anat. Record* **40**: 1-13.

Unna, P. G. 1889. Die Fortschritte der Hautanatomie in den letzten fünf Jahren. IV. Der Nagel. *Monatshr. prakt. Dermatol.* **8**: 79.

Unna, P. G. and L. Golodezt. 1909. Die Hautfette. *Biochem. Z.* **20**: 469-502.

Van Scott, E. and P. Flesch. 1954. Sulfhydryl and disulfide in keratinization. *Science* **119**: 70-71.

Walaas, O. 1952a. Effect of oestrogens on the glycogen content of the rat uterus. *Acta Endocrinol.* **10**: 175-191.

Walaas, O. 1952b. Effect of Oestrogens on the Glycogen Content of the Rat Liver. *Acta Endocrinol.* **10**: 193-199.

Waldeyer, W. 1882. Untersuchungen über die Histogenese der Horngebilde, besonders Haare und Federn. *Beitr. Anat. Embryol. Henle-Festgabe.* Cited from Hoepke (1927).

Walker, E. 1925. The sulphydryl reaction of skin. *Biochem. J.* **19**: 1085-1087.

Weidenreich, F. 1900. Ueber Bau und Verhornung der menschlichen Oberhaut. *Arch. mikroskop. Anat.* **56**: 169-229.

Weiss, P. and W. Ferris. 1954a. Electron microscopic study of the texture of the basement membrane of larval amphibian skin. *Proc. Natl. Acad. Sci. U.S.* **6**: 528-540.

Weiss, P. and W. Ferris. 1954b. Electron micrograms of larval amphibian epidermis. *Exptl. Cell Research* **6**: 546-549.

Weissenfels, N. 1956. Licht-, Phasenkontrast- und elektronenmikroskopische Untersuchungen über die Entstehung der Propigmentgranula in Melanoblastenkulturen. *Z. Zellforsch u. mikroskop. Anat.* **45**: 60-73.

Wellings, S. R. and B. V. Siegel. 1960. Electron microscopy of human malignant melanoma. *J. Natl. Cancer Inst.* **24**: 437-461.

Wheatley, V. R. 1952. The chemical composition of sebum. "Libre jubilaire 1901-1951," Societe belge de Dermatologie et de Syphiligraphie, pp. 90-102. Imprimerie medicale et scientifique, Bruxelles.

Wicks, L. F. and V. Suntzeff. 1942. Reduction of total lipid-protein nitrogen ratio of mouse epidermis by a single application of methylcholanthrene. *J. Natl. Cancer Inst.* **3**: 221-226.

Wilkerson, V. A. 1934. The chemistry of human epidermis. I. Amino acid content of the stratum corneum and its comparison to other human keratins. *J. Biol. Chem.* **107**: 377-381.

Wilkerson, V. A. 1935. The chemistry of human epidermis. II. The isoelectric points of the stratum corneum, hair, and nails as determined by electrophoresis. *J. Biol. Chem.* **112**: 329-335.

Willmer, E. N. 1954. "Tissue Culture," 2nd ed. Methuen, London.

Wislocki, G. B., H. Bunting and E. W. Dempsey. 1947. Metachromasia in mammalian tissues and its relationship to mucopolysaccharides. *Am. J. Anat.* **81**: 1-37.

Wislocki, G. B., D. W. Fawcett and E. W. Dempsey. 1951. Staining of stratified squamous epithelium of mucous membranes and skin of man and monkey by the periodic acid-Schiff method. *Anat. Record* **110**: 359-576.

Witten, V. H., M. S. Ross, E. Oshry and A. B. Hyman. 1951. Studies of thorium X applied to human skin. I. Routes and degree of penetration and sites of deposition of thorium X in selected vehicles. *J. Invest. Dermatol.* **17**: 311-322.

Wolf, J. 1939. Die innere Struktur der Zellen des Stratum desquamans der menschlichen Epidermis. *Z. mikorskop.-anat. Forsch.* **46**: 170-202.

Wolf, J. 1940. Das Oberflächenrelief der menschlichen Haut. *Z. mikroskop-anat. Forsch.* **47**: 351-400.

Wolf, J. 1944. Neue Verwendungen der Adhäsions (Mikrorelief) Methode in der Hauthistologie. *Z. wiss. Mikroskop.* **59**: 246-251.

Worley, L. G. 1944. Studies of the vitally stained Golgi apparatus. III. The methylene blue technique and some of its implications. *J. Morphol.* **75**: 261-289.

Worley, L. G. 1946. The Golgi apparatus—an interpretation of its structure and significance. *Ann. N.Y. Acad. Sci.* **47**: 1-56.

Zimmerman, A. A. and S. W. Becker, Jr. 1959. Melanoblasts and melanocytes in fetal negro skin. *Illinois Monograph Med. Sci.* **6**(3): 1-59.

CHAPTER 3

The Dermis

Introduction

The epidermis and the cutaneous appendages grow upon the *dermis,* and take nourishment from it. In addition, their growth and differentiation seem to be guided and controlled by it. Being a connective tissue, the dermis is unstable and undergoes change, breakdown, and renewal.

The dermis is thicker in men than in women, and thicker on the dorsal surface and extensory surfaces of the extremities than on the ventral and flexor areas of the same individual. It is the thickest on the nape and on the palms and soles of men and women. Being continuous with the tela subcutanea, the dermis lacks exact boundaries and its thickness cannot be measured accurately.

The dermis has a superficial *papillary layer* or *body* and a deep *reticular layer.* A well-developed papillary body is one of the most characteristic features of the skin of man. In many mammals the distinction between papillary and reticular layers is not clear. In the papillary body, widely separated delicate collagenous, elastic, and reticular fibers, enmeshed with superficial capillaries, are surrounded by abundant, viscous *ground substances.* The surface of the papillary body, which bears the negative imprint of the underside of the epidermis, is molded into intricate valleys, ridges, and papillae (Fig. 1). The cutaneous appendages that extend into the dermis pierce the reticular layer, and are accompanied by the papillary body throughout their length. Around hair follicles the papillary body forms the connective tissue sheath.

In the reticular layer of the skin of the aureola and nipple of the breast, the penis, the scrotum, and perineum are found variable numbers of oriented smooth muscle fibers. When these muscle fibers contract, the skin becomes wrinkled. The fibrous reticular layer is composed of dense, coarse, branching collagenous fiber bundles, which in spite of an apparent haphazard distribution, form layers mostly directed parallel to the surface. Alternate layers are at an angle to each other. A few perpendicularly directed fibers can be traced down to the *tela subcutanea,* where they branch loosely, become incorporated into the framework of the fatty layer, and form the *retinacula cutis* that separate the fat into lobules. Flattened rhomboidal meshes between the collagenous fibers more or less indicate the direction of extensibility of the skin. Loose networks of elastic fibers between the collagenous fibers are more closely woven around the cutaneous appendages. Around the blood vessels and nerves the connective tissue fibers are always delicate and more widely spaced than they are elsewhere.

Connective tissue cells, more of them in the papillary layer than in the reticular layer, are sparsely distributed among the fibers. In normal skin, fibroblasts are the most numerous cells with *mast cells* next in abundance. Histiocytes, or macrophages, common under certain

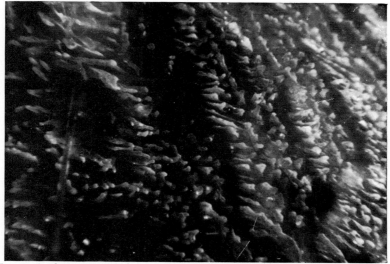

FIG. 1. Surface view of the papillary body from the skin from the anal region of a 49-year-old woman. This is the negative image of the underside of the epidermis. (Courtesy of Dr. E. Hortsmann.)

conditions, can be recognized only when they display phagocytic activity. Pigment-bearing cells, melanocytes and macrophages, sparingly distributed in the dermis of normal skin, are numerous in nevi, moles, and in some heavily pigmented areas. There are also variable numbers of lymphocytes and some extravasated leucocytes.

Development

The dermis of 2-month-old human embryos is only a bed of closely packed mesenchymal cells, surrounded by ground substance, with no visible fibers. Argyrophil fibrils are formed from the second to the fourth month, delicate ones first, and coarse ones later. A superficial papillary layer is first distinguished from the reticular layer below it in the fourth month. In the papillary layer are delicate, horizontally arranged fibers; in the reticular layer are fine and coarse collagenous bundles with no particular orientation, at first, but horizontal later. Most elastic fibers are formed after birth, and increase in numbers during subsequent maturation. As the fibers are formed and mature, the cells become increasingly widely separated. In the late fetal months the dermis resembles that of the adult, although the fibers are widely spaced by comparison, and there are many more fibroblasts. Even in the infant, the papillary body has a much higher population of cells than the reticular layer has. Large blood vessels, composed at first only of endo-thelium, run through the embryonic dermis. The characteristic connec-tive tissue tunics of the vessels and the major patterns of the cutaneous vascular beds develop late in fetal life.

During the second period of fetal life a loose bed of tissue rich in cells that are characteristically clustered around the blood vessels, and poor in fibers, becomes the fatty layer beneath the dermis. Although every cell in this tissue represents a potential fat cell, this property is actually shared by every undifferentiated connective tissue cell.

Up to the second fetal month, the underside of the epidermis is smooth and the dermoepidermal junction is a relatively straight line. As hair follicles, and later sweat glands begin to form, ridges and papillae also develop on the underside of the epidermis, and the dermis is molded around them. When intrinsic growth folds develop in the skin, some of them probably as the result of the movement of the limbs, the connective tissue fibers in their path attain a special orientation.

Collagenous fibers are always formed in the same way, whether in the embryo or the adult, in young scar tissue or in tissue culture. Histo-logically, they develop first as delicate argyrophil, periodic acid-Schiff (PAS)-positive fibrils in the amorphous ground substance near fibro-blasts. The fibrils fuse, become coarser, and then arrange themselves in parallel, wavy bundles. The mature fiber bundles are no longer argyro-phil or PAS-positive.

Preliminary histochemical studies have been carried out on the skin of human embryos in our laboratories. These studies, far from complete, are now being continued by others, and their results should be fruitful.

The abundant ground substance in the dermis of the fetus does not stain well with toluidine blue, azure A, or other metachromatic dyes. Late in fetal life, faint metachromatic and orthochromatic staining ap-pears around the cutaneous appendages and in the papillary body. In contrast, the mesenchymal cells, and later the fibroblasts, stain intensely basophilically. The fibroblasts retain this property during fetal life and during early postnatal years.

The embryonic dermis has large amounts of glycogen. The mesenchymal cells, and later the fibroblasts, occasionally have some granules of glycogen in their cytoplasm, but the ground substance of the differentiating dermis abounds in glycogen. The appearance of glycogen in granules and plaques in the intercellular spaces is probably brought about by the fixative. Abundant in the first 4 fetal months, glycogen is much reduced at birth. Glycogen is always more concentrated in the embryonic papillary body; in the presumptive fatty layer all of the differentiating fat cells contain appreciable glycogen. Even during the early postnatal years fat cells retain glycogen. Later glycogen is found only in the polylocular fat, particularly copious in the skin of the cheeks and the upper trunk.

The embryonic fibroblasts always contain globules of sudanophil lipids. Naturally, those of the presumptive fatty layer are richer in lipids even during the early fetal months.

Embryonic fibroblasts are strongly reactive for cytochrome oxidase, monoamine oxidase, amylophosphorylase, β-glucoronidase, esterases, and aminopeptidase. None of them, except those that become accumulated at the base of the primary hair germs, contain appreciable quantities of phosphatases. During the postnatal years amylophosphorylase activity can no longer be demonstrated in the fibroblasts except during wound healing. The fibroblasts in the dermis of the infant and the adult all show variable β-glucuronidase reactivity, the reaction being more intense in the cells of the papillary body. In the dermis of the infant all of the fibroblasts are reactive for aminopeptidase, but in that of the adult only those in the papillary layer show this property.

The Ground Substance

For a thorough account on the nature of the ground substance, see Gersh and Catchpole (1960), Dorfman and Schiller (1958), Schiller (1959), and Schiller and Dorfman (1957). The ground substance of the dermis is a semifluid, nonfibrillar, amorphous substance that fills the spaces between the fibers and cells. There is proportionately more of it in the papillary than in the reticular layer. The chemical properties and the significance of this substance have been intensely studied and it is not possible to give here even a brief review of it.

The ground substance, which is digestible with pancreatin but not with pepsin (Bensley, 1934), contains acid mucopolysaccharides, neutral heteropolysaccharides, proteins, soluble collagens, enzymes, immune bodies, metabolites, and many other substances (Meyer and Rapport, 1951; Stearns, 1940a; Schiller and Dorfman, 1957; Schiller, 1959; Gersh and Catchpole, 1960). It stains weakly with the PAS technique, suggesting that it may contain glycoproteins (Gersh and Catchpole, 1949), groups of proteins that contain less than 4% hexosamine, in contrast with mucoids, which contain more than 4% (Meyer, 1945). A thermostable fraction of testicular hyaluronidase, chondromucase, digests that ground substance which stains metachromatically, suggesting that it is a chrondromucin (Lillie *et al.*, 1951). The total amount of ground substance and the proportions of its component substances vary from region to region and at different times (Bunting, 1950; Duran-Reynals *et al.*, 1950).

Under scrupulously controlled conditions, metachromatic staining with toluidine blue indicates the presence of acid mucopolysaccharides. If, however, the concentration of the dye is too high and the pH is above 5.0, all semblance of specificity of metachromasia is lost. In normal skin, extracellular metachromatic staining may be obtained in the papillary body (Wislocki *et al.*, 1947), in the loose connective tissue layers around the sebaceous glands, sweat glands, blood vessels, and the hair follicles. Around the follicles metachromasia is often concentrated around the bulge of the outer root sheath, the connective tissue sheath in the lower part of the follicles, and the dermal papilla of active follicles (Montagna *et al.*, 1951). With the exception of that in the dermal papilla, neither its presence nor the amount is predictable. During catagen, the transition of the follicles from active to quiescent, the connective tissue sheath around the lower half of the follicle becomes vividly metachromatic, but this subsides as soon as the metamorphosis of the follicle is completed.

The intercellular spaces of the reticular layer of normal skin occasionally show some metachromatic staining, particularly in edematous skin and in granulation tissues (Bensley, 1934; Bunting, 1950; Sylvén, 1941). Acid mucopolysaccharides in connective tissue may be concerned with the regulation of the nucleation and growth of fibrils, and thus help to determine their rate of formation and final size. Differences in the content of mucopolysaccharides in different tissues could be related to the variations of fibrillar width from tissue to tissue (Wood, 1959). In regenerating connective tissue the metachromatic material resembles that of the embryonal mesenchyme (Lansing *et al.*, 1952; Romanini, 1951; Wislocki *et al.*, 1947). During the reparation of damage, connective tissues resemble the embryonal mesenchymatous tissue and contain increased amounts of ground substance. Mucopolysaccharides extracted from granulation tissue and dialyzed to remove low molecular substances inhibit the growth of fibroblasts *in vitro* (Balazs and Holmgren, 1950). Similar extracts from young wounds, however, act as growth promoters. Obviously, not all metachromatically staining substances in the ground substance are the same. Some of them, like those in the dermal papilla and around the bulb of hair follicles, are not affected by digestion with testicular hyaluronidase (Montagna *et al.*, 1951), but those in granulation tissue are abolished by the enzyme (Bunting, 1950; Wislocki *et al.*, 1947).

The ground substance must play many physiological roles. Metachromatically staining material in wounds diminishes as the scars mature, indicating that mucopolysaccharides may be tied up with the formation of collagenous fibers (Bunting, 1950; Meyer, 1945; Sylvén, 1941). Hyaluronic acid in connective tissues occurs in greatly hydrated gels and may be involved in water binding. The ground substance contains no free fluid, and even water is bound to hyaluronic acid. Sulfate mucopolysaccharides and their protein complexes do not bind water, but they could act as cationic exchange resins (Meyer, 1947).

When fluids tagged with vital dye indicators are injected into the skin, they can be seen going through the dermis between or upon the connective tissue fibers. This spreading can be greatly enhanced by the action of hyaluronidase. Since the ground substance is in the form of a gel, fluids may not actually mix with it but move along the fibers in very thin layers or films. Although such fluids would not become a part of the ground substance, they would still be able to transport ions and to diffuse (McMaster and Parsons, 1950). Considering the large number of fibers, the thin films of fluid upon them could amount to a great deal and account for all the extravascular fluid which comprises about 30% of all body fluid.

The Collagenous Fibers

A brief summary of a subject about which so much has been written is of necessity inadequate. Those who wish to know more can consult some of the thorough accounts of the biological and biophysical properties of collagen (Bear, 1952; Schmitt, 1959; Gustavson, 1956).

So-called because upon boiling they yield glue, collagenous, or white, fibers are found everywhere in animal tissues. They consist of branching, wavy bands one to 15 μ in width. The fibers are colorless and show faint longitudinal striations. Under the dark-field microscope, it is evident that each fiber is a bundle of parallel fibrils. The fibrils are embedded in, and held together by, a cementing substance which forms a membrane at the surface of each fiber. The fibrils do not branch, and the branching of the fibers simply separates the fibrils into smaller bundles. In transverse sections, the shapes of collagenous fibers reflect the degree of compactness of the tissue. Weak acids and alkalies swell the fibers and make them transparent. Strong acids and alkalies destroy or macerate them. Collagenous fibers are digested by pepsin but are unaffected by trypsin. Tannic acid and the salts of heavy metals combine with collagen and form leather, a tough insoluble substance.

Collagenous fibers are stainable with some acid dyes. They avidly pick up acid fuchsin and aniline blue. Thus, they can be stained well with Van Gieson's and Mallory's stains. When tissues are stained with basic dyes buffered below pH 5.0, collagenous fibers remain unstained, but at higher pH values they are stained progressively more intensely.

Collagenous fibers are faintly reactive to the PAS technique. When they are treated with "collagenase," which disperses the interfibrillar substance and leaves the bundles of fibrils intact, the "freed" fibrils are strongly reactive to the PAS method. This might indicate that the fibrils contain glycoproteins, said to be found also in the ground substance (Gersh and Catchpole, 1949).

In microincinerated sections of human skin, collagenous fibers leave a considerable amount of blue ash residue, indicating the presence of sodium and potassium. They leave no white ash of calcium and/or magnesium. No detectable changes in the ash residue have been noted with aging (MacCardle *et al.*, 1943).

When frozen sections of human skin are fragmented by teasing, microblending, or by sonic oscillations, the collagenous fibrils are released from the cementing substance and are dispersed in water either singly or in bundles. Under the dark-field microscope, the fibrils from adult skin appear long, unbranched, straight, and smooth. They are in the lower limits of, or just below, the resolution of the microscope (Gross, 1950a; Gross and Schmitt, 1948). In the dermis of infants the fibrils are more cohesive, apparently shorter, finer, and contorted and are frequently clumped after fragmentation.

Seen under the electron microscope, the collagenous fibrils are surrounded by various amounts of an amorphous substance, greater in the skin of infants than in that of adults (Fig. 2). In the skin of aged people the amount of amorphous substance is very small. This substance can be removed by centrifuging collagen fragments in distilled water. The amorphous substance is said to be composed of acid polysaccharides and protein (Gross, 1950a, b). Studies with the electron microscope reveal a homogeneous matrix which might be composed of filaments measuring less than 50 Å.

The widths of collagen fibrils range from 700 to 1400 Å, the majority being around 1000 Å (Gross and Schmitt, 1948). The fibrils tend to be finer in infants than in adults. The fibrils are characteristically cross-

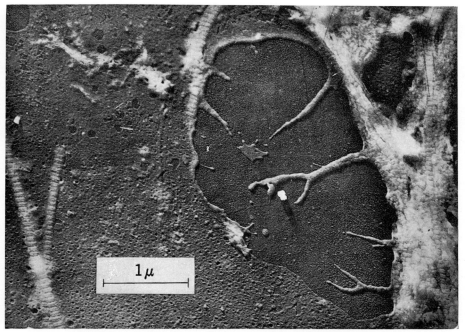

FIG. 2. Electron micrograph of unwashed, teased connective tissue from the skin of a human newborn. The collageneous fibrils are embedded in an amorphous ground substance. From Gross (1950a). (Reproduced by permission of the author and the New York Academy of Sciences.)

striated by evenly spaced bands about 700 Å apart (Fig. 3). Between these bands is found a number of additional bands and interbands of characteristic density and position. Fibers are relatively thicker across the bands than in the spaces between them. Bundles of closely adhering fibrils show that the cross bands are usually in almost perfect correspondence (Fig. 3). The fibrils are composed of still finer filaments, or protofibrils, which are aligned parallel to the axis of the fibril. The protofibrils may extend longitudinally over a number of bands, and they are as thin as individual polypeptide molecules (Bear, 1952).

Collagenous fibers, when placed in 0.01% acetic acid, swell and dissociate into submicroscopic filaments, the smallest of which may be below the resolving power of the electron microscope. If neutral salts are added to the acid solution, or if the pH of the solution is raised from 4.8 to 6.8, needle-shaped crystals are formed which under the electron microscope show cross striation. These crystals come together and form fibrils which have the periodicity of collagen. In the smaller fibrils the

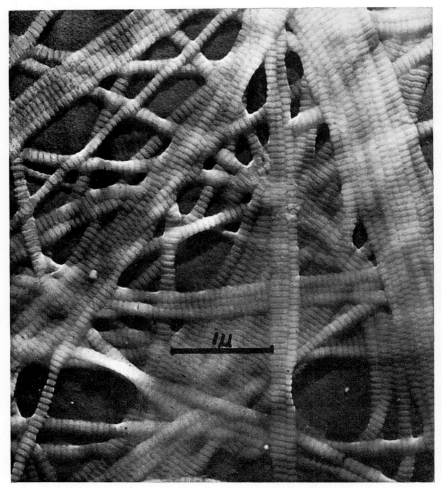

FIG. 3. Electron micrograph of a bundle of teased collagenous fibrils from the dermis of an aged man. Shadowed with chromium. Magnification: × 29,000. (Courtesy of Dr. Jerome Gross.)

striations are spaced at 210 Å, but with continued growth they attain the characteristic distance of approximately 640 Å (Vanamee and Porter, 1951).

Collagen can be characterized by its amino acid composition, its X-ray diffraction pattern, and its periodicity in the electron microscope. Collagen proteins are unique in that they contain the amino acids hydroxyproline and hydroxylysine. About one third of the amino acid residues is glycine; proline and hydroxyproline make up about another third, and other amino acids make up the final third. Thus, a determination of the hydroxyproline and glycine of a given tissue gives an adequate estimate of its collagen content. Physically, one of the most distinctive features of collagen is its large X-ray diffraction pattern, which reflects the organization of the collagen macromolecule. These diffractions are now interpreted in terms of a macromolecule containing three chains, coiled in helical fashion about each other to form a triple-stranded coil. In addition to the large-angle X-ray pattern that presumably arises from the three-coiled macromolecule, collagen also shows a small angle X-ray pattern that consists of many orders of large axial repeat (see Schmitt, 1959).

Histological preparations of fetal and infant skin contain numerous argyrophil reticular fibers. Electron microscope studies of specimens from these same tissues show no obvious morphological differences between reticular and collagenous fibrils (Fig. 4). Reticular fibrils, however, are between one third and one half as wide as collagenous fibrils (Gross, 1950a; Gross and Schmitt, 1948). With aging there is a continuous increase in the number of thicker fibrils. Whether or not collagenous fibrils and fibers are actually formed from these argyrophil fibers, collagenous fibers develop by the coming together of very small unit fibrils.

Kölliker (1861) considered the fibrous part of the connective tissue mere filler, and the cells the essential elements. He believed that the ground substance and the collagenous fibers are formed under the influence of cells, and that these substances could be formed within the cells, be secreted by them, and subsequently become consolidated. A depression of fibroblast growth *in vitro* stops the growth of collagen (Hass and McDonald, 1940). Observations through a transparent chamber in the ear of the rabbit show that during wound healing, just preceding rapid fiber formation, the fibroblasts acquire numerous refractile granules, or their surfaces may be covered with "bubbles" (Stearns, 1940a, b), the secretion of which could be related to the formation of fibers.

Porter and Pappas (1959) have shown that the collagen fibrils form in close association with the surface of the fibroblasts. The unit fibrils organize out of, or polymerize from a material that is at the surface of the cell, whence they are shed or spun into the intercellular spaces. Once shed, the unit fibrils expand in diameter by an accretion of mate-

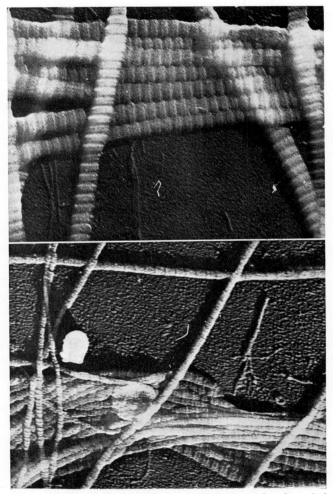

FIG. 4. Electron micrographs of collagenous fibrils from the skin of the rat. The *upper* figure, of a 90-day-old rat, shows fibrils treated with trypsin and shadowed with chromium. Magnification: × 24,000. The lower figure, from the skin of a 2-day-old rat, shows "reticulin" fibrils treated with trypsin and shadowed with chromium. Magnification: × 28,000. From Gross (1954). (Reproduced by permission of the author and the Josiah Macy, Jr. Foundation, New York.)

rial from the ground substance. These two sites are the templates for the initiation of the polymerization of collagen (Porter and Pappas, 1959). The surface of the cell is the primary site of formation. The partly formed fibrils grow at the expense of the monomeric collagen in the tissue medium. The monomeric collagen, probably secreted by the fibroblasts, is induced to polymerize by the enzymes that form a part of the templates at the surface of the cells or on the formed fibrils.

The Reticular Fibers

So-called because they branch and form a network, reticular fibers are found throughout the connective tissue. They make up about 0.38% of the dry weight of skin. A dense bed of them found in the upper part of the papillary layer, underneath the epidermis, either forms the basement membrane or is a component part of it. Reticular fibers are numerous around sweat glands and in the connective sheath of hair follicles, from where they seem to penetrate the glassy membrane. The greatest preponderance of reticular fibers is in the papillary layer and in its extensions around the cutaneous appendages. In the reticular layer, reticular fibers are numerous only around blood vessels. In the fatty layer, reticular fibers are well developed around blood vessels and they form basketlike capsules around each fat cell. The fibers are of different thicknesses, and at least the larger ones seem to consist of bundles of finer fibrils.

Reticular fibers are argyrophil, reducing ammoniacal silver nitrate. They are reactive to the PAS technique. They stain poorly or not at all with most connective tissue stains. With acid aniline dyes, they stain like collagenous fibers. Paper chromatographic analyses of reticular fibers show large concentrations of galactose, glucose, and mannose and a smaller amount of fucose (Glegg et al., 1953). Reticulin, a substance which reticular fibers yield on boiling, probably consists of a carbohydrate-protein complex. The four sugars mentioned above are also present in collagen but in much smaller amounts. These findings explain the behavior of reticular fibers toward the PAS technique and the ammoniacal silver nitrate methods. The aldehyde groups liberated after the tissues have been treated with an oxidizing agent react to both the Schiff reagent and ammoniacal silver nitrate.

Evidence suggests that reticular fibers are probably "precollagenous" elements and do not constitute a separate type of fiber. The physical and chemical properties of reticulin and collagen are similar. Reticular fibers often seem to continue into collagenous fibers. The fibroglia of

mesenchyme have the properties of reticular fibers, and they are replaced by collagenous fibers. The dermis of embryos contains only
reticulin (Yuditskaya, 1949). Nearly all of the fibers in the dermis of
2-day-old rats are argyrophilic, but they are gradually replaced by
collagenous fibers in progressively older animals (Gross, 1950a). During
wound healing the first formed fibers are argyrophilic and indistinguishable from reticular fibers. They are replaced by or transformed
into true collagen. With the electron microscope the fibrils of reticular
fibers are shown to have a periodicity identical to that of collagenous
fibrils (Gross, 1950a). Wide angle X-ray diffraction patterns of fibers
from the dermis of newborn rats are like those of the collagen of adults
(Bensley, 1934). These facts suggest that reticulin' is a precursor of
collagen and that its presence denotes a primitive condition in the
tissue.

The Elastic Fibers

When skin is boiled in 0.1 N sodium hydroxide and collagen is
destroyed, a residue called elastin (Lowry *et al.*, 1941) is left which is

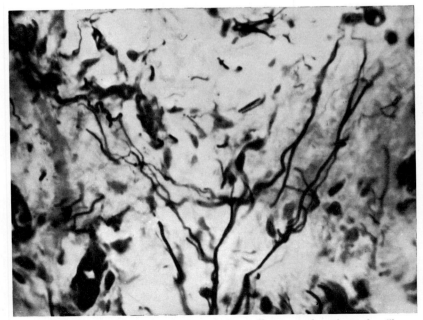

Fig. 5. Elastic fibers in the dermis of the axilla, stained with Verhoeff's stain.
These perpendicularly oriented fibers are in the vicinity of a hair follicle, not shown
here.

composed largely of albuminoids and scleroproteins. Under steam pressure, collagen can be converted into gelatin by hydrolysis with water, but elastin remains apparently intact (Neuman and Logan, 1950). Elastin makes up only 2% of the dry weight of human skin, and knowledge of its chemistry is not as advanced as that of collagen. Elastic fibers in the dermis are coarse, branching, cylindrical, or flat ribbons entwined among the collagenous fibers; they do not appear fibrillar when stained (Figs. 5 and 6). The diameter of the fibers ranges in size from barely resolvable with the light microscope to several micra in width. Elastic fibers can be stained selectively with orcein or resorcinfuchsin. Gomori (1950) stained them somewhat specifically with aldehyde-fuchsin, a dye formed by the conjugation of paraldehyde and basic fuchsin in acid solution. They become basophilic when treated with chromates (Lillie, 1952). Actually, elastic fibers are relatively chromophobic. They have little affinity for basic or acid dyes. They stain weakly with acid dyes buffered to pH 2.0 and with basic dyes buffered to pH 8.5. Variations in the pH of the staining solutions beyond these

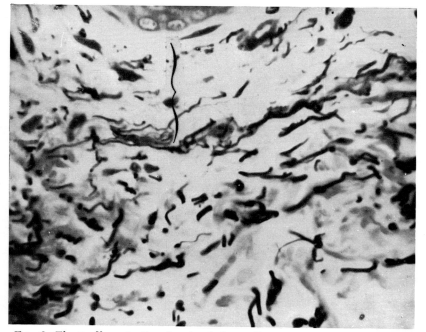

FIG. 6. Elastic fibers in the dermis of the axilla, stained with Verhoeff's stain. The fibers are much more delicate in the papillary body (bracket) than in the reticular layer.

limits have no effect on their stainability (Drennan, 1951). They can be stained with Verhoeff's stain, with basic fuchsin, Victoria blue, Congo red, and Nile blue sulfate. The fibers of rodents, but not those of man, recolorize the Schiff reagent without the intervention of chromic acid or periodic acid, and they are positive to the Seligman-Ashbel carbonyl reaction. Since both of these reactions can be blocked by previously treating the tissue with phenylhydrazine, elastic fibers may contain aldehyde and/or carbonyl groups (Herman and Dempsey, 1951). The fibers stain clearly with the methods used to show —S—S— groups.

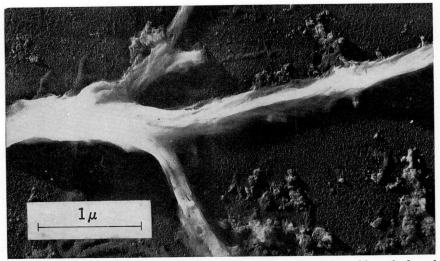

Fig. 7. Electron micrograph of elastic fibers from the aorta of a rabbit. Shadowed with chromium. Magnification: × 27,000. (Courtesy of Dr. Jerome Gross.)

Elastic fibers are unaffected by alcohol, dilute acid, and alkali and salt solutions. They can be digested with trypsin, but only slightly with pepsin. Acids and alkalies swell elastic fibers slightly on transverse and longitudinal planes. Fibers are also swollen by exposure to formamide, formic acid, thioglycolic acid, acetic acid, and fused phenol (Lloyd et al., 1946). Because of its relative insolubility, elastin is usually prepared by boiling or by digestion with dilute acid or alkali. Purified trypsin has no effect on elastin, but commercial grades of the enzyme attack it. Elastase, an enzyme isolated from crude pancreatin, seems to attack elastin fairly specifically (Lansing et al., 1952). Since elastic fibers are osmiophilic and sudanophilic, elastin might contain lipoproteins (Lansing, 1951).

Studies of elastic fibers with the electron microscope have yielded controversial results. Gross (1949) first reported that digestion with crystalline trypsin releases delicate threads, the largest number of which are evenly and tightly coiled double helices. These are formed from at least two interlacing filaments which measure 120 Å in width. Lansing et al. (1952), who also studied elastic fibers with the electron microscope, after heating them with elastase, concluded that the coiled fibrils of elastic fibers are embedded in a homogeneous matrix, the physical and chemical properties of which are nearly identical with those of the fibrils. The existence of helically coiled threads has been discounted on the grounds that they were residues of digested bacteria in the trypsin solution (Friberg et al., 1951; Gross, 1951). Figure 7 shows a fragment of elastin from the aorta of the rabbit with no visible fibrillar structure. There is, however, some reluctance to abandon this idea, since partial digestion with elastase removes only the matrix, leaving intact fibrils which appear like twisted threads (Lansing et. al., 1952). Longer action by the enzyme digests both matrix and fibrils. Elastic fibers are isotropic but begin to show uniaxial birefringence when stretched 100 to 150% of their original length. This suggests that elastin molecules lie in a randomly crumpled position, or a position of maximum entrophy, and when pulled tend to go back to this position.

The Fibroblasts

Fibroblasts are ubiquitous. In surface view, they have an ameboid shape, with processes of varying lengths stretching out from the body of the cell; in profile they appear spindle-shaped. Their shape is determined by their environment. In the reticular layer of the dermis, they are usually very thin, long, and compressed; in the papillary layer they are larger and resemble mesenchymal cells. The large oval nucleus is stippled with very delicate chromatin particles and contains one or more large nucleoli. The cytoplasm of the living fibroblast is amorphous under ordinary light, but under the phase-contrast or dark-field illumination it is seen to contain numerous mitochondria, granules, and vacuoles of varying sizes. Mitochondria in the form of rodlets and filaments almost completely encircle the nucleus, but only a few of them are seen in the cytoplasmic processes.

The cytoplasm of dermal fibroblasts stains a very pale color with basic dyes buffered in the acid range. The fibroblasts in the papillary layer are more basophil. The cytoplasm usually stains a homogeneous color, but in some cells it contains variable numbers of discrete basophil granules. This basophilia, which is removed with ribonuclease, must contain ribonucleic acid. Occasional small granules stain metachromatically with toluidine blue. During wound healing the cytoplasm of the fibroblasts becomes vacuolated, more strongly basophil, and acquires more basophilic granules.

The nuclei of fibroblasts are intensely Feulgen-reactive. Although nuclei in mitosis are not encountered too frequently, Chu (1960) has discovered a diurnal mitotic activity in the skin of the mouse. He finds that the rate of mitotic activity in connective tissue cells is 21 times higher than that of the epidermis. It is not known whether or not the fibroblasts in the dermis of the skin of man also divide in rhythmic diurnal cycles, but one may infer from this that they do.

Numerous mitochondria are easily demonstrated in preparations stained with phosphotungstic acid-hematoxylin or acid fuchsin-methyl green. The appearance, distribution, and number of mitochondria resemble those seen in fresh tissues under the phase-contrast microscope. During wound healing, fibroblasts have a greater number of mitochondria, and even their cytoplasmic processes may contain some of them. Under the electron microscope, the mitochondria show the typical arrangements of cristae seen in other cells (Fig. 8).

The cytoplasm of fibroblasts, itself PAS-negative, may contain PAS-reactive granules near the nucleus. In some cells, particularly during wound healing, the granules may be large. Since during wound repair the ground substance may also be PAS-reactive, the granules within the fibroblasts could be the precursors of the glycoproteins found in the ground substance (Gersh and Catchpole, 1949). However, although the ground substance stains metachromatically and is PAS-reactive, the granules in the fibroblasts are PAS-reactive but not metachromatic. Thus, either the degree of polymerization of the same substance in the two places is different, or the two substances are different.

Nearly every dermal fibroblast has delicate clusters of sudanophil lipid granules in the cytoplasm at one or both poles of the cell, corresponding in position to the Golgi apparatus. In tissues exposed to X-rays, in sites of irritation, infection, and wound healing, there is a pronounced increase in the number and size of lipid granules. In fact, many of these cells may become indistinguishable from very young fat cells.

All dermal fibroblasts contain cytochrome oxidase, succinic dehydrogenase, and monoamine oxidase, demonstrable only in fresh, unfixed tissues. Fibroblasts have no amylophosphorylase, but during wound healing they attain a strong reactivity. Fibroblasts also contain β-glucuronidase and a number of esterases. The cells in the papillary layer

of the dermis, those in the connective tissue sheath of the hair follicles
and around sweat glands always show greater activity of these enzymes
than the fibroblasts in the reticular layer do. This is particularly con-

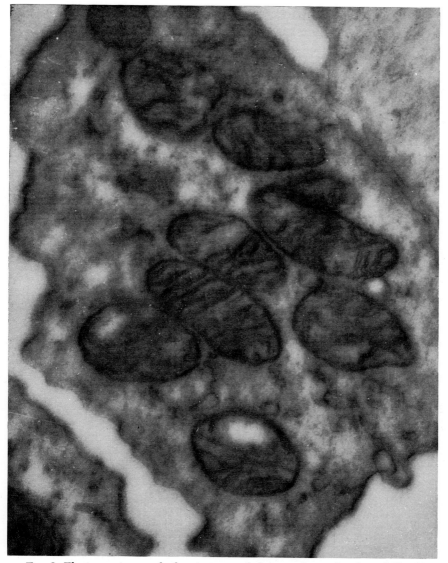

FIG. 8. Electron micrograph showing part of the cytoplasm of a dermal fibroblast
with a cluster of mitochondria. (Courtesy of Dr. G. Odland.)

spicuous with aminopeptidase which, though strong in the cells of the papillary body, is absent in those of the reticular layer (Adachi and Montagna, 1961). Alkaline phosphatase activity can be demonstrated only in the fibroblasts around sites of wound healing.

The function of the fibroblast has been an enigma, but, as has already been demonstrated, the electron microscopist has made a substantial contribution. Circumstantial evidence points to the fibroblast as the progenitor of other connective tissue cells and all of the fibers, but there is no unequivocal proof. Fibroblasts may secrete acid mucopolysaccharides and a "globular native protein," precollagen (Meyer, 1950). The precollagen would then be precipitated and denatured onto the polysaccharide fibrils by local acid production by the cells, forming the fibrous proteins of the reticulum. "The regularly spaced acidic group of the polysaccharide chain would form the template . . . on which the fibrous proteins are built up. The mucopolysaccharides which first form a sheath on the fibrils would then be removed by enzymatic digestion" (Meyer, 1950).

When one searches for subtle changes and differences in the fibroblasts of the dermis, he is impressed by the many cells which could be intermediate between fibroblasts and histiocytes, and between fibroblasts and mast cells. Perhaps the fibroblast is the stem cell from which arise all other cells in connective tissue. There has been a great deal of unnecessary controversy on this point. The common belief that there are within the connective tissue mesenchymal, or embryonic, cells which can repopulate both fibroblasts and other cells is only a hypothesis, and one which should perhaps be cast aside. Connective tissue cells arise from fibroblast-like stem cells, and no one has effectively denied that these are in fact fibroblasts that can modulate in response to demands.

The Histiocytes

Histiocytes are described as cells which, though resembling fibroblasts, are stellate or fusiform with a granular, and usually vacuolated cytoplasm, with the nucleus more compact and smaller than that of fibroblasts. This characterization is of little help in identifying quiescent histiocytes in the dermis. A search for histiocytes, or macrophages, in normal, healthy skin, is likely to be futile. If, however, particulate matter has been injected into the skin, the histiocytes can be recognized easily by their capacity for ingesting the particles. Organic particles are digested intracellularly, but inorganic ones may remain within the same cell or be passed on to others. Two general types, large and small histiocytes can be recognized in the dermis. The large cells phagocytose large and small particles, and the small cells, only the small particles. When the particles are too large to be engulfed, several cells may gather around them and become fused into multinucleated, plasmodium-like masses called foreign-body giant cells. These cells become very numerous in the dermis that contains degenerating cutaneous adnexa, and are predictably found in such conditions as alopecia areata. The histological features of histiocytes, then, are applicable only to cells during the process of phagocytosis. This poses the question of what happens to histiocytes when they are not active.

Histiocytes arise from a variety of different cells, such as fibroblasts, lymphocytes, skeletal muscle, and Schwann cells. In tissue culture, skeletal muscle and subcutaneous tissue are readily transformed into histiocytes (Chèvremont, 1948). Some authors believe that histiocytes belong to a specific group of cells, the reticulo-endothelial system, composed of undifferentiated cells, which allegedly have become arrested, or which have returned to the embryonal state. Chèvremont (1948), however, argues that histiocytes do not comprise a cellular system and do not belong to a specific genetic line of undifferentiated cells. They are cells characterized not by form but by a particular functional state, and they arise from widely different and differentiated types of cells. For this reason, Chèvremont insists that these cells, rather than morphological entities, are physiological expressions shared by many cells, and he calls this condition l'état histiocytaire.

"Histiocytic" changes are observed often in vitro. The addition of blood serum of normal rabbits to explants of 18-day-old chick embryos induces the formation of large numbers of macrophages (Pomerat et al., 1949). This serum contains a thermolabile, alcohol- and acetone-insoluble macrophage-promoting factor. Histiocytic changes in tissue culture may be evoked by irritants, intoxicants, and infections. Arsenic or atropine sulfate added to culture media bring about histiocytic changes readily. A surprisingly high number of macrophages appears spontaneously in cultures of skeletal muscle or of subcutaneous connective tissue (Chèvremont, 1948). The type of plasma, the amount of nutrient, the reduction in oxygen tension, or modifications of the pH seem to have no effect on this transformation, although embryonic extract enhances it. The size of the explant and the quantity of the tissue in an individual culture are directly related to it. When the explants are large (one or more millimeters), or if the tissues are crowded in the same flask, abundant transformation of muscle fibers to macrophages takes place, but transformation is rare in the reverse situation. If a small fragment is cultured alongside a large one, transformation takes place in both of them. If the liquid media from a culture in which transformation has been abundant is added to a culture which shows little or no transformation, histiocytic transformation becomes pronounced in the recipient culture. The inducing factor, then, is diffusible and transmissible by a liquid. The liquid media of all cultures rich in histiocytic transformation contain choline. If choline is extracted from the liquid, transformation ceases; when it is added to the media, transformation begins. Transformation is inhibited when choline oxidase, which selectively destroys choline, is added to cultures. The addition of inactivated choline oxidase has no effect. If chemically pure choline is added to cultures which show scant or no transformation, abundant transformation takes place. The conclusions are inescapable that *in vitro* choline is liberated by the tissue and that choline induces histiocytic transformations.

These observations make less tenable the belief that histiocytes are cells derived from a single lineage. Fazzari (1951), who has long studied the stroma, favors *l'état histiocytaire* of Chèvremont. He also denies the existence of specific cells which are permanently active histiocytes, and believes that every connective tissue cell can assume histiocytic functions.

Chromaffin Cells

A new system of cells in the dermis has been recently described by Swedish investigators (Adams-Ray and Nordenstam, 1956; Nordenstam and Adams-Ray, 1957). These *chromaffin* cells are said to contain granules which have the same histochemical properties for adrenaline and noradrenaline as those found in the adrenal medulla (using the method of Hillarp and Hökfelt, 1955). These cells are distributed mostly in the cutaneous perivascular and perineural tissue. The granules in these cells are argentaffin, reduce ferriferricyanide and have a yellow autofluorescence when viewed under near ultraviolet light (3660 Å). The granules are smaller than mast granules; the chromaffin cells are smaller than mast cells, and their general shape is said to be different. These authors further state that "There is correlation between the amount of chromaffine substance on one hand and the vascular tonus and amount of cathecols in different regions of the skin on the other" (Adams-Ray and Nordenstam, 1956, p. 129). A description of new types of cells in rather well-known organ systems always stirs a certain amount of excitement. Still, diligent search for chromaffin cells in human skin in our laboratory and in the laboratories of our American colleagues does not confirm their existence. Cells in the perivascular tissue often contain granules that are argentaffin and autofluorescent, but these granules are pigmented in unstained preparations. We wonder if the granules may not be some sort of wear-and-tear pigment phagocytosed by histiocytes. If chromaffin cells are present in the skin, they will have to be documented better than they have been until now.

Mast Cells

Paul Ehrlich, who first saw granular cells in "nutritive" connective tissue, named them *mast cells.*

Any connective tissue cell containing cytoplasmic granules that stain metachromatically with toluidine blue is a mast cell. Thus, many cells indistinguishable from a fibroblast in size and shape but containing from few to many metachromatic granules could be considered mast cells. "Typical" mast cells, however, are large and rounded, with one, rarely two, small nuclei, and a cytoplasm filled with coarse basophil granules that stain metachromatically with toluidine blue, azure B, thyronine, etc. In ordinary preparations, the staining properties of mast cells is unpredictable. With hematoxylin and eosin, for example, they usually stain blue but may stain red. They may or may not stain with iron hematoxylin. The granules stain readily and fairly selectively with toluidine blue, pinacyanol erythrosinate, methyl green, etc. (Bensley, 1952). They may be stained supravitally with neutral red. Under the phase-contrast microscope mast granules are highly refractive. The intergranular cytoplasm is usually homogeneous but may have some vacuoles. Generalizations about the mast cells in other animals cannot be made readily since there are enormous species differences (Riley, 1959).

Mast cells may be found anywhere in the dermis and adipose layer. They are most numerous around the walls of small blood vessels where they are arranged in concentric circles as if they arose from perivascular cells indistinguishable from fibroblasts. Stem cells could be located in the walls of the blood vessels and then migrate into the surrounding connective tissue as they become matured; or perhaps the stimulus for differentiation could radiate from the blood vessels into the surrounding tissue (Fawcett, 1953; Montagna et al., 1954). Mast cells in human dermis are polymorphic, and many of them look like fibroblasts. However, it is difficult to be sure that all of the fibroblast-like cells that contain metachromatic granules are really mast cells, since histiocytes can phagocytose the granules released by mast cells.

The number of mast cells in the skin increases under certain conditions (Bates, 1935). Their population increases in the skin of mice during experimental carcinogenesis (Asboe-Hansen, 1954). In skin carcinoma of man and animals, mast cells are abundant even at some distance from the tumor, and they seem to form a barrier between the tumor and the normal tissue. Mast cell tumors, mastocytomas, have been found in the dog, mouse, horse, and man (Bloom, 1942, 1952). Urticaria pigmentosa, a disease of the skin, is characterized by great local increases in the number of mast cells.

When the skin of man is stained with toluidine blue, the granules in the mast cells in some specimens are mostly colored a dark lilac blue, those in others a reddish purple. Many mast cells look like fibroblasts. Around small blood vessels, the more peripheral cells contain the coarsest granules, and these also stain most intensely metachromatically. The granules in the cells immediately around the blood vessels stain orthochromatically with a faint metachromatic tinge. With toluidine blue buffered to pH 2.3, most of the coarse granules stain metachromatically; the very small granules and some of the large ones stain a pale blue or remain unstained (Montagna and Melaragno, 1953). At pH 3.0 and 4.0 there are more granules that stain metachromatically, and at pH 5.0 all of the granules stain metachromatically. In addition to a variable complement of mast granules, each of the fibroblastic mast cells contains fine granules which stain orthochromatically. At pH 6.0 and above, all granules, whether they stain orthochromatically or metachromatically, and the intergranular cytoplasm stain more intensely but the cytoplasm is never stained metachromatically. In contrast some authors state that the granules are stained orthochromatically and the cytoplasm metachromatically (Glick and Sylvén, 1951; Julén et al., 1949; Sylvén, 1950, 1951), but this is a misinterpretation.

After digestion with ribonuclease and subsequent staining with toluidine blue buffered from pH 3.0 to 5.0, the mast granules appear red or reddish purple, clearly outlined against the unstained background of the cytoplasm. None of the orthochromatically staining granules seen in control sections are stained at these pH ranges. Above pH 5.0, however, some of the granules and the intergranular cytoplasm once more stain orthochromatically. The metachromatic granules appear more blue than at lower pH values. Thus, some of the granules and the intergranular cytoplasm contain ribonucleic acid. The material stainable with toluidine blue buffered above pH 5.0 after digestion with ribonuclease may represent the protein cytoskeleton.

Treatment of sections of human skin with periodic acid or sulfurous acid before staining with toluidine blue has no influence on the tinctorial behavior of mast granules. Similarly, deparaffinized sections of tissues fixed in Helly's fluid deliberately left in running water for 24 hours show neither a diminution nor an alteration in the stainability of the mast granules (Montagna et al., 1954). Sections can be stained with toluidine blue at any desired pH, photographed, destained with 80% ethanol, and stained again at any other pH. This procedure can be repeated at will and the tissues behave each time as if they had not been stained before.

Some mast granules have a greater affinity for toluidine blue than others (Castiglioni, 1947; Paff et al., 1947). In the dye buffered from pH 2.3 to 3.2, only the coarse granules stain metachromatically, but from pH 4.0 to 5.0, both coarse and fine granules do so. Differences in the staining of granules at low pH values must be due to chemical differences, and may indicate stages in their maturation (Drennan, 1951). It is possible that only the granules which are stained metachromatically at pH 2.3 to 3.2 are mature (Castiglioni, 1947).

Mast granules are moderately PAS-reactive (Friberg et al., 1951; Glegg et al., 1953; Montagna et al., 1954; Wislocki and Fawcett, 1951; Riley, 1959). Since, however, the intergranular cytoplasm is also PAS-reactive, the granulation is poorly discerned. If preparations are studied under light filtered with a combination of green and yellow Wratten filters, the granules in every cell appear sharply demarcated. Only some of the granules in a mast cell are actually Schiff-reactive, although most or all of them stain with toluidine blue. When sections colored with the PAS technique are subsequently stained with toluidine blue buffered to pH 4.0 or above, the mast granules take up the stain as avidly as if they had not been treated with the PAS method. Perhaps the PAS technique and toluidine blue stain two coexistent substances in the mast granules.

Mitochondria, usually difficult to demonstrate because the highly refractile granules tend to obscure them, can nonetheless be shown with the Altmann technique; the granules stain green, and the mitochondria red. These are more numerous in the fibroblast-like mast cells which contain only a few granules, and they resemble those of ordinary fibroblasts. This suggests that (a) mast cells are transformed from fibroblasts, and that (b) mast granules may bear an inverse relation to mitochondria.

A very small Golgi apparatus has been demonstrated only in the mast cells of the hamster (Compton, 1952).

Studies of mast cells with the electron microscope have been reported by Rogers (1956), in the dermis of very young mice, and Smith and Lewis (1957) in that of hamsters. In mice, the metachromatically staining mast granules, under the electron microscope are electron-dense bodies that appear granular and filamentous. Each granule has

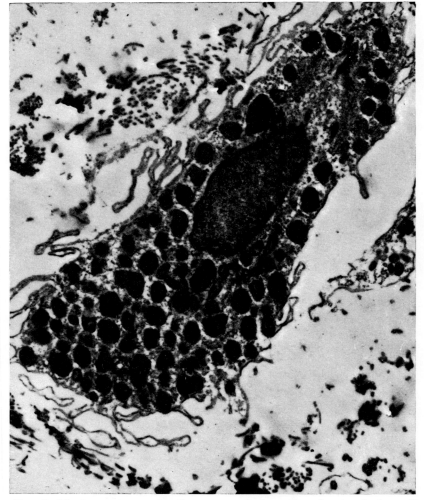

Fɪɢ. 9. Electron micrograph of a mast cell from the dermis of the axilla. Mitochondria and endoplasmic reticula can be seen between the granules. Many narrow and long cytoplasmic processes containing some RNA particles extend from the cell body. A Golgi complex is clearly demarcated at the upper pole of the cell, above the nucleus. (Courtesy of Dr. R. A. Ellis.)

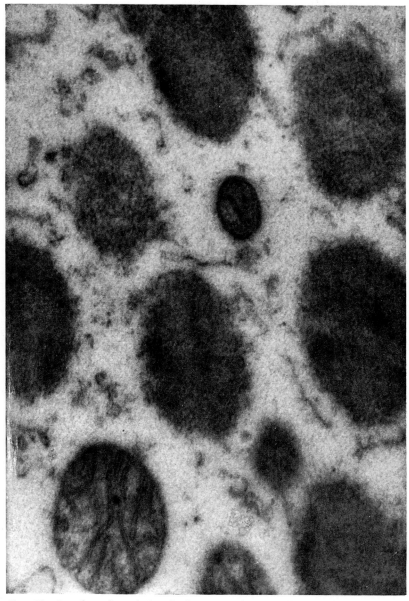

FIG. 10. Greatly enlarged detail of Fig. 9, showing the granular and partially filamentous mast granules. The mitochondrion in the lower left corner has a typical internal structure. (Courtesy of Dr. R. A. Ellis.)

a dense periphery, surrounded by a cytoplasmic "space." Scattered between the granules in the cytoplasm are pleomorphic mitochondria with typical internal structures. In the cytoplasm are also closely packed Golgi membranes and vesicles, but practically no endoplasmic reticulum. In contrast, Smith and Lewis (1957) find in the intergranular cytoplasm of the mast cells of the hamster an architecture that they interpret as endoplasmic reticulum. These authors also find an increase in endoplasmic reticulum as the granules grow farther apart after the animals have been treated with protamine sulfate, stilbamidine, or toluidine blue. After the animals have been X-irradiated, the mast granules seem to coalesce and there is some loss of intragranular substance. Observations of the mast cells in the dermis of the skin of man by my colleague, R. A. Ellis, are in general agreement with the brief descriptions above (see Figs. 9 and 10).

The various histochemical tests applied to mast cells often give different results. This is due to three factors: (a) mast cells are not identical in all of the tissues of the same animal; (b) mast cells from different animals show remarkable species differences; and (c) technical procedure from one laboratory to another may yield different results.

Sudanophil lipid granules can be demonstrated in some mast cells (Rheingold and Wislocki, 1948), but even in the same individual not all cells contain demonstrable lipids. Those from the connective tissue of the abdominal viscera always contain some sudanophil granules, but those in the dermis rarely have them. The mast cells of the dog contain granules reactive to the acid hematein test, indicating the presence of phospholipids (Montagna and Parks, 1948). Mast cells contain alkaline and acid phosphatases and esterases. They are reactive to the benzidine peroxidase technique and sometimes to the M-nadi reagent (Compton, 1952; Montagna and Noback, 1948). The granules may contain aminopeptidase (Braun-Falco and Salfeld, 1959), phosphamidases, and disulfide groups (Montagna et al., 1954). After the injection of S^{35}-sodium sulfate, radioactive sulfur can be demonstrated in some mast cells in the skin of mice and rats but not in others (Asboe-Hansen, 1953; Montagna and Hill, 1957).

An impressive amount of information indicates that mast cells are the source of heparin, or at least an anticoagulant substance similar to heparin. The liver of the ox, for instance, which is rich in mast cells, contains large amounts of an extractable ester of sulfuric acid which is a strong anticoagulant and stains metachromatically (Holmgren and Wilander, 1937). In contrast, the liver of the sheep is sparsely populated with mast cells and contains only traces of an extractable sulfuric acid ester that has no anticoagulating property. Similarly, the aorta of the ox and the horse, in which mast cells are numerous, yields an anticoagulant but the aorta of the pig, which has few mast cells, does not (Jorpes *et al.*, 1937). The content of anticoagulant substances in spontaneous mast cell tumors of the dog composed of mature mast cells was found to be 50 times greater than that of the liver. Tumors composed of immature mast cells with few, delicate granules yielded only 1.7 times more anticoagulant agent than the liver (Oliver *et al.*, 1947). In some clinical hemorrhages, an increased number of mast cells has been found in the bone marrow (Messerschmitt, 1954). In the skin of hemophiliacs, mast cells seem to be more numerous than in the skin of normal subjects, and the dermis shows greater amounts of metachromatic staining (Sjölin, 1951). In elephantiasis the skin contains numerous mast cells and yields as much as 126 mg of heparin per kilogram of tissue (Ehrlich *et al.*, 1949). Certain facts indicate a relation between heparin and mast cells and the lack of thrombosis with an increased number of mast cells. Heparin is fibrinolytic *in vitro* (Halse, 1948). If fibrin or blood clots are implanted under the skin of guinea pigs, mast cells accumulate in the surrounding tissue (Baeckeland, 1950a, b). Mast cells invade, undergo some nuclear and cytoplasmic changes, and finally discharge granules inside of the clot. After this the clot undergoes fibrinolysis. Mast cells seem to contain different types of heparin. The cells with strongly metachromatic and PAS-reactive granules are believed to contain the highly esterified form of anticoagulant, and those with weakly staining granules, the less developed variety, heparin monosulfate (Drennan, 1951). It is assumed that the first type mentioned is the more mature of the two.

Since mast cells increase in number in several itching skin diseases (Asboe-Hansen, 1951), it was suggested that they contain and release histamine. Lesions of urticaria pigmentosa contain two and a half times more histamine than the adjacent uninvolved skin. The liver capsule of the ox and the sheep, and the pleura of the ox, pig, and dog have high concentration of mast cells and histamine. The skin of the mouse shows increases in mast cells and in histamine content with aging and after the application of methylcholanthrene. Mast-cell tumors from the dog and from man yield large quantities of histamine (Riley and West, 1952, 1953; Riley, 1959). Certain pathological tissues rich in mast cells have exceptionally high histamine values. Urticaria pigmentosa in man and mast-cell tumors in domestic animals all yield high values, sometimes measurable in *milligrams* of histamine per gram of tissue (Riley, 1959). Heparin, on the other hand, occasionally fails to show a correspondingly high value, as, for example, in the mast-cell tumors of cats. In dogs it is possible to anticipate histological evidence of mast-cell tumors and metastases by the demonstration of high blood histamine and heparin values (Cass *et al.*, 1954). When a rat is killed by an intravenous dose of a fluorescent histamine liberator, the fluorescence can be seen localized first in the mast cells, and especially in those within the loose areolar tissue around the peritoneum. When later the mast cells break up, the histamine content of the tissue drops (Riley, 1954). Other evidence has come from observations of mast cells in the mesenteries of the rat (Fawcett, 1954a, b). Injection of distilled water into the peritoneal cavity of the rat causes an osmotic disruption of mast cells and a release of small amounts of histamine into the peritoneal cavity. Injection of Tyrode solution containing "Compound 48/80," a strong histamine liberator, causes a release of mast cell granules and the liberation of large amounts of histamine. If mast cells have been destroyed by previous injection of distilled water, the injection of "48/80" causes no release of histamine. Mast cells, then, seem to be as rich in histamine as they are in anticoagulant substances.

It seems that histamine in the mast cells is preformed and ready for release. Histamine is probably held only by loose ionic forces within a phospholipid complex that also contains heparin and proteins rich in basic amino acids. Paper chromatographic analyses of mast cells, or isolated mast granules from rat tissues show that these contain large amounts of phosphatides. These may constitute a "trigger" that releases histamine from the granule.

Concerning their function in releasing heparin, Riley (1959) suggests that mast cells store and release mucopolysaccharides for the connective tissues. A carbohydrate precursor substance probably formed by fibroblasts, becomes a temporary component of the ground substance. At the beginning of fibrillogenesis, excess ground substance is broken down, rebuilt and stored in altered, sulfated form (heparin) in the granules of the tissue mast cells. This could later be released and be again ingested by the cells of the connective tissues. This process may be at work in the embryo, and in adult tissues in response to trauma. Massive releases of stored sulfated mucopolysaccharide could result in its spillage into the blood with consequent manifestation of its anti-coagulant properties.

Various physiologic, pathologic, pharmacologic, and physical factors have profound effects on the morphology of mast cells. Mast cells are large and laden with granules in thyroid deficiency. They become small and their granulation sparse after the administration of thyroxine

(Asboe-Hansen, 1950). Their number increases in guinea pigs after injections of thyrotropic hormones (Asboe-Hansen and Iversen, 1951). A certain amount of degranulation follows treatment with corticotropic hormones and cortisone; what granules remain are uneven in size and clumped; the cells become vacuolated and attain bizarre shapes (Asboe-Hansen, 1952; Videbaek et al., 1950). Some multiple mast-cell tumors rapidly regress and disappear, after treatment with cortisone (Bloom, 1952). Intradermal injections of hyaluronidase cause a partial degranulation of mast cells. This, however, is not a specific effect, and a number of unrelated irritants do the same thing (Sylvén and Larsson, 1948). Exposure of skin to X-irradiation is followed by a degranulation of mast cells and subsequently by an increase in their number (Sylvén, 1940). Mechanical stimuli and other factors also induce degranulation.

Mast cells, particularly those of the mouse and rat, have been found to contain high contents of 5-hydroxytryptamine. The sources of this high content of 5-hydroxytryptamine and its significance are not yet known (Riley, 1959).

Cutaneous Innervation

There are numerous studies of the distribution, the anatomy, and the physiology of the cutaneous nerves. Among them, that of Tamponi (1940), written in Italian, has largely been overlooked. For a fuller account of the structure and function of the cutaneous nerves, the reader is referred to the Ciba Foundation, Study Group No. 1 (Wolstenholme and O'Connor, eds., 1959), on "Pain and Itch"; that of Winkelmann (1960a), on "Nerve Endings in Normal and Pathologic Skin"; that of the Brown University Symposium (Montagna, 1960a), on "Cutaneous Innervation"; and that of Ormea (1961), on "La cute organo di senso."

Most of the studies of the morphology of cutaneous nerves have been guided by the techniques used to demonstrate them. Methylene blue, used as an infravitam dye, perhaps yields the most sensitive results (Tamponi, 1938; Arthur and Shelley, 1959; Miller et al., 1958), but these methods require more art than science. The recent silver impregnation method of Richardson (1960) is very good and deserves to be widely tried out. The account that follows mentions in a general way only the highlights of our knowledge of the cutaneous nerves. The innervation of the various cutaneous appendages is described separately in the chapters that deal with them.

Our standard concept of the distribution of the cutaneous sensory nerves is that there is a *deep cutaneous plexus* in the panniculus adi-

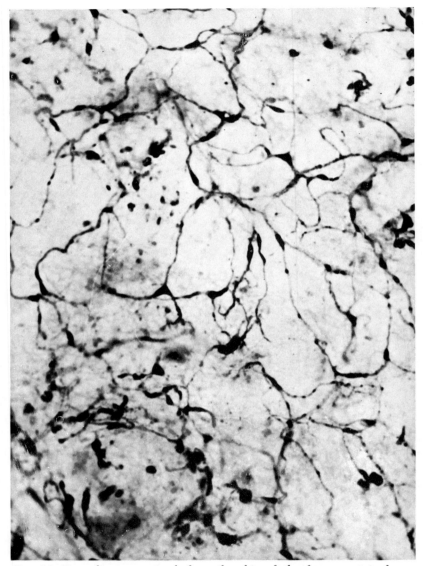

FIG. 11. Dermal nerve network from the skin of the forearm, stained supra-vitally with methylene blue. This being a thick, freehand section, is focused only at the surface, but shows some of the other nerve meshes at lower levels. (Courtesy of Dr. F. Allegra and Professor M. Tamponi.)

posus, from which tortuous fibers traverse the dermis to the papillary body, where they form a *superficial cutaneous nerve plexus,* less complex than the deep one. Many fibers from the deep plexus are also thought to go directly to the papillary ridges of the epidermis. A third, nonmyelinated subpapillary plexus, just underneath the dermoepidermal

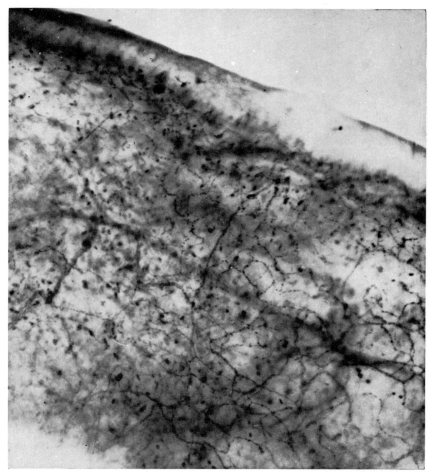

Fig. 12. Dorsum of toe of a 14-year-old girl, the distal phalanx, near the nail groove, perfused with methylene blue. The level of focus is near the dermo-epidermal junction. Note the profusion of freely ending fibers. While the branches of any one fiber may form a few anastomoses before ending freely, the branches of one fiber do not fuse with those of another. There are no other types of endings in this area. (Courtesy of Drs. M. R. Miller and M. Kasahara.)

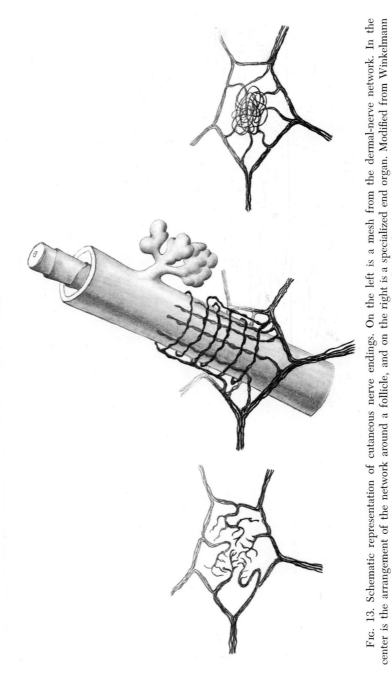

FIG. 13. Schematic representation of cutaneous nerve endings. On the left is a mesh from the dermal-nerve network. In the center is the arrangement of the network around a follicle, and on the right is a specialized end organ. Modified from Winkelmann (1960). (Reproduced by permission of the author and the Pergamon Press Ltd., London.)

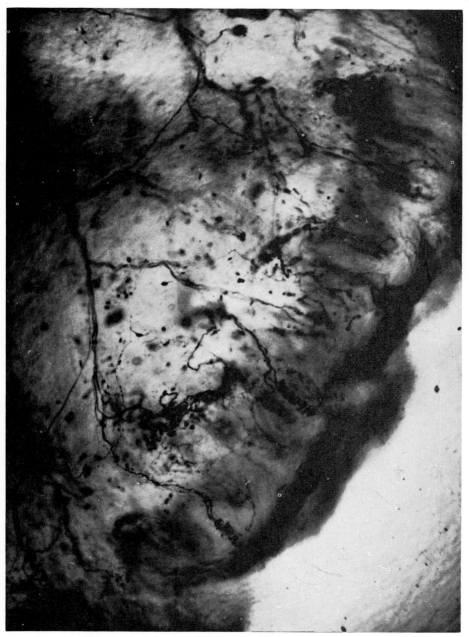

FIG. 14. This vertical section of the volar skin of the toe of a 14-year-old girl, perfused with methylene blue, shows the free, expanded-tip and encapsulated types of endings. (Courtesy of Dr. M. R. Miller.)

junction is said to form large, irregular meshes. As we shall see, this is an oversimplification of the patterns of nerve fibers in the dermis.

Tamponi (1940) first described numerous, superimposed nerve nets throughout the dermis, that extend far beyond the simple pattern just described above. Tamponi points out that the distinction between a deep and superficial plexus, with a "diaphragm" poor in nerves between them, is erroneous. The reticular dermis, an allegedly nerve-poor tissue, contains many characteristic nerve meshes that become progressively denser in higher levels (Figs. 11 and 12).

Sensory nerves emerge from a wide variety of morphologically "different" end organs, for each of which a physiologic function has been hypothesized. Gradually, however, we are beginning to emphasize the similarities rather than the dissimilarities of these end organs. Similarities, for example, are evident during development, in adult tissues, in histochemical and functional properties, and even in phylogeny (Winkelmann, 1960b).

Cutaneous sensory nerves have a simple basic pattern (Walshe, 1942; Winkelmann, 1960a, b). The nerve fibers of the neurons in the dorsal root ganglia come together in the dermis, where they form intricate, interconnected networks. A stimulus applied at any point on the skin evokes not one, but a *pattern* of responses (Fig. 13). Since this network of nerve fibers is present in all skin, it is probably its principal sensory end organ (Tamponi, 1940; Winkelmann, 1960a, b). There are no end organs found in mucous membranes—only a network of nerve fibers. In body skin the networks that surround the hair follicles have a plan or arrangement similar to that found in glabrous skin, except that the end-organ fibers are associated with the outer root sheath of the follicle (Winkelmann, 1960a) (Fig. 13). Special end organs, such as those in the mucocutaneous tissue and the friction surfaces, have a similar arrangement (Figs. 14, 15, and 16). The filaments within these structures are rolled into balls or coils, rather than being associated loosely with an epithelial structure.

Fig. 15. An off-center lengthwise section through a papillary ridge of the fingertip of a 66-year-old woman, perfused with methylene blue. In the upper mid-portion of the photograph is a tuft of fibers ending freely within a dermal papilla; although not clearly shown here, some of these fibers extend into the epidermis. In the left mid-lower portion of the photograph is a group of Merkel's discs ending near the cells of the stratum germinativum in the region of the intermediate ridge. To the right of the middle of the photograph is a Meissner corpuscle, and a few free fibers in a dermal papilla. From Miller *et al.* (1960). (Reproduced by permission of the authors and the Pergamon Press Ltd., London.)

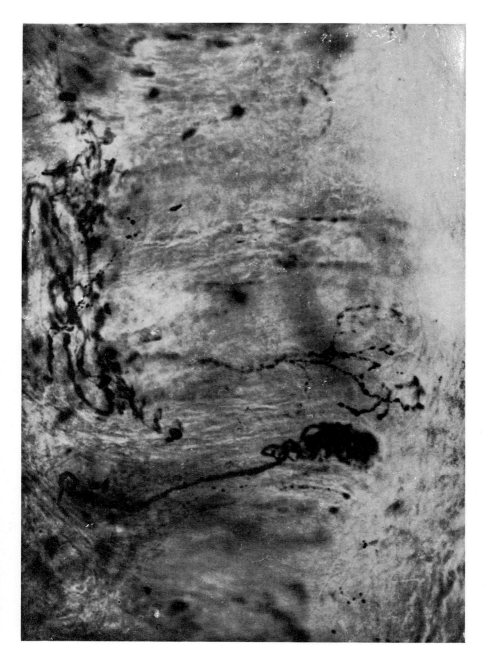

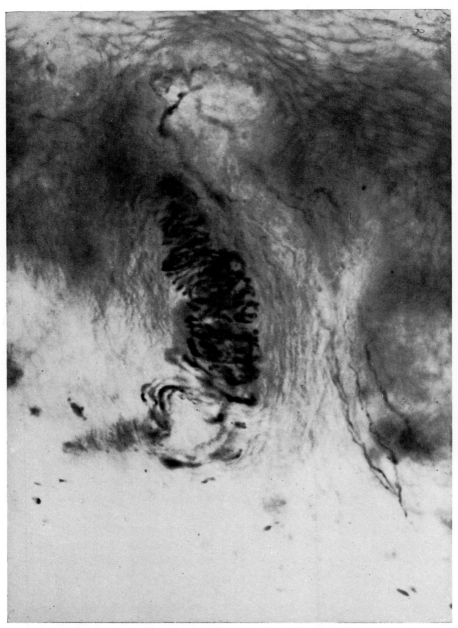

FIG. 16. A Meissner corpuscle in a dermal papilla of the fingertip of a 66-year-old woman, perfused with methylene blue. Freely ending fibers are seen to the right and in the cupola of the papilla. From Miller *et al.* (1960). (Reproduced by permission of the authors and Pergamon Press Ltd., London.)

Of the numerous "end organs" described, only a few have morphologic features that are constant and distinct enough to justify special anatomic assignation. Principal among these are the *dermal nerve networks*, the *hair follicle networks*, the various *mucocutaneous end organs*, the *Meissner corpuscles*, the *hederiform endings*, and the *Vater-Pacini corpuscles* (Winkelman, 1960a, b). Even so, we cannot infer that each of these has a special, physiologically distinct function.

During development, the nerve net is the first ordered structure to appear in the dermis, and may influence the development of cutaneous appendages (Tello, 1923-1924; Winkelmann, 1959a, b; 1960a). The plan of the dermal nerve networks varies with the density of the cutaneous appendages. In regions heavily populated with hair follicles, most of the cutaneous sensory nerves are distributed around them, but where follicles are sparse, the networks are prominent (Winkelmann, 1960a). Smooth muscle, sebaceous glands, sweat glands, and the thickness of the dermis itself, all have a profound influence upon the particular form of the nerve networks (Tamponi, 1940; Winkelmann, 1960a, b).

Specialized, encapsulated end organs are found only underneath the glabrous, cutaneous and mucocutaneous epidermis which has a ridged underside (Winkelmann, 1957, 1959a). The number of hair follicles and the number of specialized endings in skin are in inverse ratio to each other. Proceeding from hairy skin, across the mucocutaneous junctions and to mucous membranes, there is a gradual waning of hair follicles and other appendages with a concomitant appearance of specialized end organs (Winkelmann, 1960a, b).

Mucocutaneous end organs consist of coils, or rolls of fine nerve fibers from which issue myelinated A fibers. Thus, they resemble the networks around the hair follicles, the basic difference being the presence of the follicle (Winkelmann, 1960a, b). Winkelmann states that without the follicle, the nerve net could form a ball, and rise up higher in the dermis, simulating a mucocutaneous end organ (Fig. 13).

Since there are similarities between the mucocutaneous end organs and the hair follicle nerve networks, other end organs may also be similar. The Meissner corpuscles and the hederiform endings under the epidermis of the hands and feet, may appear to be structurally different from the mucocutaneous end organs, but both types are associated with myelinated A fibers, and both contain nonspecific cholinesterase (Winkelmann, 1960b). The unencapsulated hederiform endings are found at the base of the epidermal ridges and not in dermal papillae (Miller *et al.*, 1960); similar, disc-like endings, associated with heavy A fibers, are also found deeper in the dermis (Miller *et al.*, 1958). Furthermore, even the inner bulb of the Vater-Pacini corpuscle, stripped of its surrounding capsule, could resemble the mucocutaneous end organs.

All of the specialized sensory endings in the skin of man contain nonspecific cholinesterase (Cauna, 1960; Winkelmann, 1960b; Montagna, 1960b). The nerves of the dermal nerve network, which in the skin of embryos contain specific cholinesterase (Montagna, 1960b), in adult skin are largely free of it. Some of the nerves of the hair follicle networks contain specific cholinesterase; others do not. The central bulb of the Vater-Pacini corpuscle, like the Meissner corpuscles and mucocutaneous end organs, contain nonspecific cholinesterase. Unfortunately, little is known about the function of cholinesterase in sensory end organs.

Skin perceives so many modalities of sensations that it would be impossible for each of them to be subserved exclusively by an anatomically distinct end organ. This point puzzled even Malpighi, who first studied the cutaneous nerves. Meissner corpuscles, the hederiform ending, and the mucocutaneous end organs all seem to be sensory endings for acute touch, but the principal organ for the perception of touch must be the nerve network around the hair follicle. Touch is also perceived on the surface of the cornea (Lele and Weddell, 1956; Weddell, 1960), where the only nerves present are those of the dermal nerve network. This is also true of mucous membranes.

Since all sensory nerve endings can be related to the sensation of touch, it is difficult to believe that other sensations are transmitted by anatomically different end organs (Weddell, 1960; Miller et al., 1960; Winkelmann, 1960b). Attempts to demonstrate specific sensory perceptions by anatomically distinct nerve endings have failed. If special nerve endings were tailored to perceive only specific sensations, they should be present in more than a few localized regions of the skin. Temperature, pain, and other sensations, therefore, must also be perceived by a variety of apparently "different" receptors. It would seem that the specialized end organs are modified according to the region in which they grow, and not according to the function that they subserve (Winkelmann, 1960a, b; Miller et al., 1960; Ormea, 1961).

The only specialized end organ for which a relationship to a specific sensation is known is the Vater-Pacini corpuscle. Stimulation of this end organ gives the sensation of pressure, but it does not discharge a receptor potential until a definite threshold is reached (Gray and Sato, 1955).

In conclusion, the morphologic differences of the cutaneous end organs are expressions of regional variations of the nerve tissue, and do not necessarily reflect functional differences. The theory of von Frey that specific receptors perceive specific sensation cannot be confirmed (Sinclair *et al.*, 1952).

Cutaneous Blood Vessels

This vast subject, first described in detail by Spalteholtz (1893), has been reviewed by Horstmann (1957). The details of structure and function of the peripheral circulation in man, have been published in a Ciba Foundation Symposium (Wolstenholme, ed., 1954), and more recently in a Brown University Symposium (Montagna and Ellis, eds., 1961). The account that follows deals only with some generalities of cutaneous vascularization in man, an enormously dangerous approach, since inaccuracies are inherent in generalizations.

Those who wish to simplify the concept of cutaneous vascular patterns have relied upon the schemata of Spalteholz. Too liberal acceptances of his summarizing diagrams has given rise to dogmatic and wholly inaccurate versions of his findings. The first important caution here is that together with the differences which occur in the skin over the various regions of the body, differences also occur in nearly every detail of its blood vessels. The thickness of the skin, the types and numbers of cutaneous appendages present, the type of epidermis, the relationship of the skin to the underlying muscle or bone, and other factors all influence the types of vascular patterns present.

Spalteholz recognized two types of cutaneous arteries to the skin: *direct* or *cutaneous* proper, and *indirect,* among them the *musculocutaneous arteries.* There are relatively few *direct* arteries, one of them being the *superficial epigastric* artery. Direct arteries are found in the scalp, the face, and parts of the trunk; indirect arteries are notably present in the appendages. The number and caliber of the arteries varies according to the regions of the body. On the face, for example, vessels are numerous and medium-sized; on the arms and legs the arteries are fewer and larger.

The arteries to the skin anastomose below the hypodermis, where they form the large-meshed "fascial network" of Spalteholz. Arterial branches from this network traverse the hypodermis across the "retinacula cutis" and divide again in the lower limits of the dermis. A second large-meshed, "subdermal" ill-defined arterial network parallel to the deeper one is formed at this level (Spalteholz, 1927). From here on it is more difficult to generalize, since the entire dermis is riddled by a continuous meshwork of anastomosing arterioles and capillaries.

The terminal branching of the arteries has a regular pattern of interconnecting links that is associated with structural changes in the vessels (Zweifach, 1959). As they enter the dermis, the small arteries divide into long arterioles about 50 μ in diameter, which become interconnected to form interarterial networks. Adjacent links in these meshes give off cross-branches that are connected by arterial capillaries. The capillary branches underneath the epidermis come directly from the interanastomosing arteriolar arcades (Zweifach, 1959). Although this is the basic pattern of distribution of the arterial vessels, some vessels outline certain characteristic configurations which merit some attention. Some arterioles seem to run a fairly straight course through the dermis and branch in treelike fashion underneath the epidermis, forming the so-called *candelabra arterioles* of Spalteholz. The hair follicles are accompanied by more or less parallel longitudinal vessels that are interconnected by arteriolar and capillary cross-shunts and anastomoses. The straight portions of the ducts of eccrine sweat glands are also accompanied by similar longitudinally oriented, interconnected arterioles and capillaries, which at the level of the papillary body become connected with the intricate plexus of vessels there (subepidermal plexus of Durward and Rudall, 1958).

The loops of capillaries found in the dermal papillary ridges between the epidermal ridges are most numerous in regions where the underside of the epidermis has the greatest amount of sculpturing. Therefore, they are more numerous and complex in the friction areas. Elsewhere, they show great regional differences.

In close association with the meshwork of large and small arterioles is a series of interconnecting large and small venules (Zweifach, 1959). A prominent venous plexus in the subcutaneous tissue is even more extensive than the associated network of arterial vessels. Between venous and arterial plexuses there are numerous direct intercommunications through which blood is shunted to the venous circulation without having to traverse the capillaries.

It is usual to think of the superficial capillary loops in the papillary body as consisting of an arterial, afferent limb and a venous efferent one. The venous limbs of the capillary arcades drain into a subpapillary venous plexus, which is said to communicate with a second subpapillary venous network underneath the subpapillary arterial plexus. A third venous network, in the middle dermis, is said to be interposed between the second and the deeper cutaneous arterial network (Spalteholz, 1927; Comel, 1933). Veins drain this network into the larger, denser cutaneous venous network in the hypodermis. This, in turn, is drained by the efferent veins that accompany the deep cutaneous arteries. Such neat geometric patterns, however, are difficult to demonstrate and may not always exist. Many of the superficial capillary loops do have one limb that has a larger bore than the other and seems to be venous. In preparations stained for alkaline phosphatase, the arterial limb is always more intensely reactive than the venous limb. I have the impression that some of the papillary capillary loops are entirely arterial and that most arteriovenous capillary connections take place deeper in the dermis.

The dermis and hypodermis are perforated by a continuous arteriovenous meshwork with meshes of different sizes and with various spatial relationships. Every level of the tissue, every cutaneous appendage, is vascularized by vessels coming and going in various directions. Thus, one cannot speak of exact "vascular trees" with progressive (arterioles) or degressive (venules) dichotomous splitting. To speak of specific "plexuses" would imply that only certain levels of the dermis are rich in vessels. It is well to remember that Spalteholz (1893, 1927) and Bellocq (1925) demonstrated the "plexuses" in horizontal sections of injected tissues, a method that may have influenced their judgment. Perhaps the "plexuses" are those levels where the vascular anastomoses are most distinct. Observation of skin injected with radiopaque substances and viewed with an X-ray microscope show an incredible interconnection of macro- and micro-networks (Saunders et al., 1957; Saunders, 1961). From such preparations the cutaneous vascular trees appear to be continuous meshworks composed of vessels of different diameters.

Two general interconnected vascular areas can be recognized: one which includes *all* of the vascular beds of the dermis (Moretti et al., 1959), and the other the perifollicular network. The first vascularizes every entity of the skin and includes the periadnexal networks. The details of the perifollicular vascular network are described in the chapter on the pilary system. The perifollicular network joins the dermal vascular plexus by way of the "vascular units" (Moretti et al., 1959). These vascular baskets surround the hair follicles or groups of them; depending upon the size of the follicles and the specific region, they have greater or lesser diameter and depth. Vascular units resemble inverted cones, the superficial extensions of which are connected with the vessels in the papillary body. Adjacent vascular units are connected by lateral shunts; they are also connected with the plexuses that surround sweat glands (Moretti and Montagna, 1959).

The complex, and sometimes apparently chaotic, distribution of vessels in the dermis is nonetheless well adapted to the various changes and stresses to which the skin is exposed. The major vessels, being more or less serpentine, allow a distention of the skin without appreciably interfering with the circulation of blood (Comel, 1933). This adaptability is particularly evident during the various phases of the hair growth cycles (Montagna and Ellis, 1957; Ellis and Moretti, 1959); in catagen, for example, the hair follicle withdraws upwards, leaving the lower part of the perifollicular vascular basket collapsed below it. When the follicles become active again they must plow their way through these collapsed sleeves of vessels.

Not enough attention has been paid to the differences in the morphology of the vascular beds in different areas. For example, the long, narrow, adjacent dermal papillary ridges in the olecranon and patellar regions and, to an even greater extent, those on the palms and soles contain long and relatively straight capillary loops. The shallower and broader papillary ridges on the trunk, in contrast, have more meandering, less constantly geometric capillary loops (Baccaredda-Boy, et al., 1960).

Little is known about the behavior of cutaneous blood vessels during aging. Some authors (Bellocq, 1925) claim a progressive rarefaction of the cutaneous vessels of the dermal meshwork with aging, but Spalteholz (1927) denies this. On the other hand, a diminution in the number of blood vessels does occur in the balding scalp (Chiale, 1927; Ellis, 1958), where the flattening out of the underside of the epidermis is accompanied by a decimation of the papillary capillary loops and the superficial part of the dermal vascular meshworks (Fig. 17) (Ellis, 1958). This relatively unexplored field should be studied systematically.

Arteriovenous anastomoses are characteristically found in the skin of the fingers and toes. Their morphology need not be described here since it may be found in any textbook of histology. Clara (1959) has reviewed the problem of their presence in the skin elsewhere than on the fingers, and concludes that although arteriovenous anastomoses may be found on the skin of the extremities, their presence elsewhere on the body must be considered accidental. More information is needed here.

Zweifach (1949) has presented a schematic conception of the pattern of terminations of cutaneous vessels (Fig. 18). From terminal arterioles emerge *metarterioles*, or "preferential" thoroughfare channels, which are vessels surrounded by one layer of smooth muscle. The most direct channels from arterial to venous circulation, give off sidebranches called *precapillary sphincters*, which control the flow of blood into the capillaries proper (Fig. 18). The capillaries, consisting only of an endo-

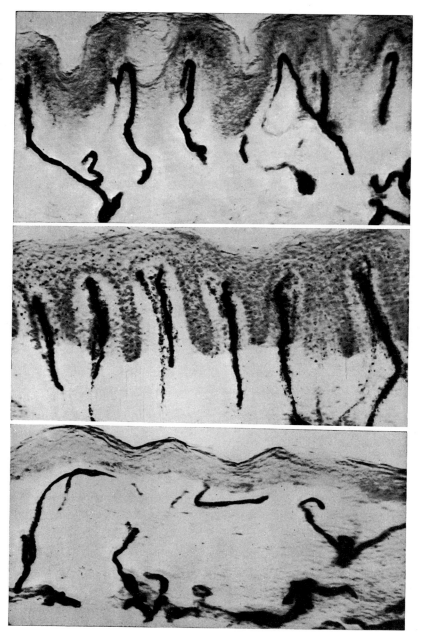

Fig. 17. Aging changes in the superficial capillary loops in the scalp of man, shown with the alkaline phosphatase technique. Above is the scalp of a 3-year-old boy; in the center is that of a man 33 years old, and below the bald scalp of a man 69 years old. From Ellis (1958). (Reproduced by permission of the author and Academic Press, New York.)

165

thelial tube, may anastomose and then join the collecting venules. Thus, capillary blood flow can be regulated by the contraction and dilatation of the venules and the precapillary sphincters. Contraction of only the precapillary sphincters would shunt the blood through a preferential channel, omitting the various lateral capillary networks. Contraction of the metarteriole could shunt the blood through arteriovenous anastomoses directly to muscular venules. The venules in the skin have remarkable ability to contract and dilate, in contrast with those in other tissues (Zweifach, 1959). At least in the digits, great changes in the flow of blood in the skin is brought about by the vasomotor control of arte-

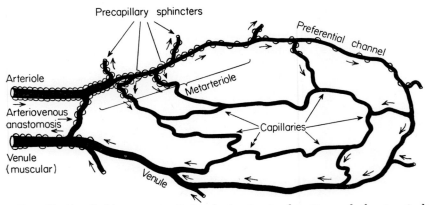

Fig. 18. Zweifach's concept of the basic structural pattern of the terminals of cutaneous vessels. The white humps on the walls of the vessels indicate muscle fibers. From Zweifach (1949). (Reproduced by permission of the author and the Josiah Macy, Jr. Foundation, New York.)

riovenous anastomoses (Burton, 1959). The increase in flow through these shunts does not increase the diffusion from blood to tissue. Thus, if one could close these shunts with some drug there might be a corresponding increase in nutrition of the skin. Closure of the capillaries by a vasoconstrictor agent opens the arteriovenous shunts. These shunts are analogous to the safety valves of a boiler; rises in blood pressure resulting from vasoconstriction opens the shunts automatically, preventing excessive rise in pressure (Burton, 1959). Temperature regulation is the main function of cutaneous vessels, but the function of pressure regulation should also be emphasized.

Since the greater part of the cutaneous vasculature is not associated with the adnexal tissues (Saunders, 1961), the vascularization is developed far out of proportion to its possible usefulness to skin. Its role, therefore, cannot be only that of nutrition (Winkelmann, 1961). As has been mentioned earlier, the major role of the cutaneous vascular meshwork is to regulate heat and blood pressure. Burton (1959) states that ". . . in its blood flow the skin is peculiarly the servant of the whole organism and is less endowed with autonomous control than other tissues. Possibly this view is important in understanding the susceptibility of the skin to ischemia in abnormal conditions, and worth remembering in considering management of disturbed skin function."

REFERENCES

Adachi, K. and W. Montagna. 1961. Histology and cytochemistry of human skin. XXII. Sites of leucine aminopeptidase (LAP). *J. Invest. Dermatol.* (In press.)

Adams-Ray, J. and H. Nordenstam. 1956. Un système de cellules chromaffines dans la peau humaine. *Lyon chir.* **52:** 125-129.

Arthur, R. P. and W. B. Shelley. 1959. The innervation of human epidermis. *J. Invest. Dermatol.* **32:** 397-411.

Asboe-Hansen, G. 1950. The intercellular substance of the connective tissue in myxedema. A morphological and histochemical study. *J. Invest. Dermatol.* **15:** 25-32.

Asboe-Hansen, G. 1951. Om Bindevaevets Mucinøse Substanser. Thesis. Rosenkilde and Bagger, Copenhagen.

Asboe-Hansen, G. 1952. The mast cell. Cortisone action on connective tissue. *Proc. Soc. Exptl. Biol. Med.* **80:** 677-679.

Asboe-Hansen, G. 1953. Autoradiography of mast cells in experimental skin tumors of mice injected with radioactive sulfur (S^{35}). *Cancer Research* **13:** 587-589.

Asboe-Hansen, G. 1954. Hormonal effects on connective tissues. *Trans. 5th Josiah Macy Jr. Conf. on Connective Tissues,* pp. 123-182.

Asboe-Hansen, G. and K. Iversen. 1951. Influence of thyrotrophic hormone on connective tissue. Pathogenetic significance of mucopolysaccharides in experimental exophthalmos. *Acta Endocrinol.* **8:** 90-98.

Baccaredda-Boy, A., G. Moretti and G. Farris. 1930. Varieta topografiche della reazione per la fosfatasi alcalina nel circolo superficiale cutaneo. *Ann. ital. dermatol. e Sifilog.* (In press.)

Baeckeland, E. 1950a. Influence d'implantats sanguins et fibrineux sur le nombre des mastocytes et tactisme de ces cellules. *Compt. rend. soc. biol.* **144:** 1005-1007.

Baeckeland, E. 1950b. Evolution des mastocytes dans la peau du cobaye à la suite d'implantations sanguines et fibrineuses. *Compt. rend. soc. biol.* **144:** 1007-1009.

Balazs, A. and H. Holmgren. 1950. The basic dye-uptake and the presence of a growth-inhibiting substance in the healing tissue of skin wounds. *Exptl. Cell Research* **1:** 206-216.

Bates, E. O. 1935. A quantitative study and interpretation of the occurrence of basophile (mast) cells in the subcutaneous tissue of the albino rat. *Anat. Record* **61:** 231-239.

Bear, R. S. 1952. The structure of collagen fibrils. *Advances in Protein Chem.* **7:** 69-160.

Bellocq, P. 1925. "Etude anatomique des arteres de la peau chez l'homme." Masson, Paris.

Bensley, S. H. 1934. On the presence, properties and distribution of the intercellular ground substance of loose connective tissue. *Anat. Record* **60**: 93-109.

Bensley, S. H. 1952. Pinacyanol erythrosinate as a stain for mast cells. *Stain Technol.* **27**: 269-273.

Bloom, F. 1942. Spontaneous solitary and multiple mast cell tumors ("mastocytoma") in dogs. *Arch. Pathol.* **33**: 661-676.

Bloom, F. 1952. Effect of cortisone on mast cell tumors (mastocytoma) of the dog. *Proc. Soc. Exptl. Biol. Med.* **79**: 651-654.

Braun-Falco, O. and K. Salfeld. 1959. Leucine aminopeptidase activity in mast cells. *Nature* **183**: 51-52.

Bunting, H. 1950. The distribution of acid mucopolysaccharides in mammalian tissues as revealed by histochemical methods. *Ann. N.Y. Acad. Sci.* **52**: 977-982.

Burton, A. C. 1959. Physiology of cutaneous circulation, thermoregulatory functions. *In* "The Human Integument" (S. Rothman, ed.). Am. Assoc. Advance. Sci., Washington, D. C.

Cass, R., J. F. Riley, G. B. West, K. W. Head and S. W. Stroud. 1954. Heparin and histamine in mast-cell tumours from dogs. *Nature* **174**: 318.

Castiglioni, G. 1947. Osservazioni sulla cromotropia delle Mastzellen. Proposta di un metodo di colorazioni. *Ann. biol. normale e pathol.* **1**: 71-76.

Cauna, N. 1960. The distribution of cholinesterase in the cutaneous receptor organs, especially touch corpuscles of the human finger. *J. Histochem. and Cytochem.* **8**: 367-375.

Chèvremont, M. 1948. Le système histiocytaire ou réticulo-endothélial. *Biol. Revs.* **23**: 267-295.

Chiale, C. 1927. Delle modificazioni dei vasi cutanei inerenti all'eta. *Giorn. ital. dermatol. e Sifilol.* **68**: 1625-1645.

Chu, C. H. U. 1960. A study of the subcutaneous connective tissue of the mouse, with special reference to nuclear type, nuclear division and mitotic rhythm. *Anat. Record* **138**: 11-25.

Clara, M. 1959. "Le Anastomosi Arteriovenose. "Casa Ed. Dr. Francesco Vallardi, Milano.

Comel, M. 1933. Fisiologia normale e patologica della cute umana. **1**: 650-675. Treves, Milano.

Compton, A. S. 1952. A cytochemical and cytological study of the connective tissue mast cell. *Am. J. Anat.* **91**: 301-329.

Dorfman, A. and S. Schiller. 1958. Effects of hormones on the metabolism of acid mucopolysaccharides of connective tissue. *Recent Progr. in Hormone Research* **14**: 427-456.

Drennan, J. M. 1951. The mast cells in urticaria pigmentosa. *J. Pathol. Bacteriol.* **63**: 513-520.

Duran-Reynals, F., H. Bunting and G. van Wagenen. 1950. Studies on the sex skin of *Macaca mulatta*. *Ann. N.Y. Acad. Sci.* **52**: 1006-1014.

Durward, A. and K. M. Rudall. 1958. The vascularity and patterns of growth of hair follicles. *In* "The Biology of Hair Growth" (W. Montagna and R. A. Ellis, eds.), pp. 189-217. Academic Press, New York.

Ehrlich, W. E., J. Seifter, H. E. Alburn and A. J. Begany. 1949. Heparin and heparinocytes in elephantiasis scroti. *Proc. Soc. Exptl. Biol. Med.* **70**: 183-184.

Ellis, R. A. 1958. Ageing of the human male scalp. *In* "The Biology of Hair Growth" (W. Montagna and R. A. Ellis, eds.), pp. 469-485. Academic Press, New York.

Ellis, R. A. and G. Moretti. 1959. Vascular patterns associated with catagen hair follicles in the human scalp. *Ann. N.Y. Acad. Sci.* **83**: 448-457.

Fawcett, D. W. 1953. Experimental studies on the regeneration of mast cells (abstract). *Anat. Records* **115**: 305.

Fawcett, D. W. 1954a. Correlated cytological and pharmacological observations on the release of histamine by mast cells (abstract). *Anat. Record* **118**: 297.

Fawcett, D. W. 1954b. Cytological and pharmacological observations on the release of histamine by mast cells. *J. Exptl. Med.* **100**: 217-224.

Fazzari, I. 1951. Il problema dello stroma. *Rass. clin. sci. Ist. biochim. ital.* **27**: 355-361.

Friberg, U., W. Graf and B. Aberg. 1951. On the histochemistry of the mast cells. *Acta Pathol. Microbiol. Scand.* **29**: 197-202.

Gersh, I. and H. R. Catchpole. 1949. The organization of ground substance and basement membrane and its significance in tissue injury, disease and growth. *Am. J. Anat.* **85**: 457-521.

Gersh, I. and H. R. Catchpole. 1960. The nature of ground substance of connective tissue. *Perspectives in Biol. Med.* **3**: 282-319.

Glegg, R. E., D. Eidinger and C. P. Leblond. 1953. Some carbohydrate components of reticular fibers. *Science* **118**: 614-616.

Glick, D. and B. Sylvén. 1951. Evidence for heparin nature of the non-specific hyaluronidase inhibitor in tissue extracts and blood serum. *Science* **113**: 388-389.

Gomori, G. 1950. Aldehyde-fuchsin: new stain for elastic tissue. *Am. J. Clin. Pathol.* **20**: 665-666.

Gray, J. A. B. and M. Sato. 1955. Movement of sodium and other ions in Pacinian corpuscles. *J. Physiol. (London)* **129**: 594-607.

Gross, J. 1949. The structure of elastic tissue as studied with the electron microscope. *J. Exptl. Med.* **89**: 699-708.

Gross, J. 1950a. A study of certain connective tissue constituents with the electron microscope. *Ann. N.Y. Acad. Sci.* **52**: 964-970.

Gross, J. 1950b. A study of the aging of collagenous connective tissue of rat skin with the electron microscope (abstract). *Am. J. Pathol.* **26**: 708.

Gross, J. 1951. Fiber formation in trypsinogen solutions: An electron optical study. *Proc. Soc. Exptl. Biol. Med.* **78**: 241-244.

Gross, J. and F. O. Schmitt. 1948. The structure of human skin collagen as studied with the electron microscope. *J. Exptl. Med.* **88**: 555-568.

Gustavson, K. H. 1956. "The Chemistry and Reactivity of Collagen." Academic Press, New York.

Halse, T. 1948. Zur Wirkung des Heparins auf die Fibrinolyse. *Enzymologia* **13**: 176-181.

Hass, G. and F. McDonald. 1940. Studies of collagen. I. The production of collagen *in vitro* under variable experimental conditions. *Am. J. Pathol.* **16**: 525-548.

Herman, E. and E. W. Dempsey. 1951. The demonstration of compounds containing carbonyl groups in tissue sections. *Stain Technol.* **26**: 185-191.

Hillarp, N. A. and B. Hökfelt. 1955. Histochemical demonstration of noradrenaline and adrenaline in the adrenal medulla. *J. Histochem. and Cytochem.* **3**: 1-5.

Holmgren, H. and O. Wilander. 1937. Beitrag zur Kenntnis der Chemie und Funktion der Ehrlichschen Mastzellen. *Z. mikroskop.-anat. Forsch.* **42**: 242-278.

Horstmann, E. 1957. Die Haut. *In* "Handbuch der mikroskopischen Anatomie des Menschen" (W. v. Möllendorff, ed.), Vol. III, Part 3. Springer, Berlin.

Jorpes, E., H. Holmgren and O. Wilander. 1937. Über das Vorkommen von Heparin in den Gefässwänden und in den Augen. Ein Beitrag zur Physiologie der Ehrlichschen Mastzellen. *Z. mikroskop.-anat. Forsch.* **42**: 279-301.

Juleń, C., O. Snellman and B. Sylvén. 1949. Cytological and fractionation studies on the cytoplasmic constituents of tissue mast cells. *Acta Physiol. Scand.* **19**: 289-305.

Kölliker, A. 1861. Neue Untersuchungen über die Entwicklung des Bindegewebes. *Würzburger naturw. Z.* **2**: 141-170.

Lansing, A. I. 1951. Chemical morphology of elastic fibers. *Trans. 2nd Josiah Macy Jr. Conf. on Connective Tissue* pp. 45-85.

Lansing, A. I., T. B. Rosenthal, M. Alex and E. W. Dempsey. 1952. The structure and chemical characterization of elastic fibers as revealed by elastase and by electron microscopy. *Anat. Record* **114**: 555-575.

Lele, P. P. and G. Weddell. 1956. The relationship between neurohistology and corneal sensibility. *Brain* **79**: 119-154.

Lillie, R. D. 1952. Staining of connective tissue. *A.M.A. Arch. Pathol.* **54**: 220-233.

Lillie, R. D., E. W. Emmart and A. M. Laskey. 1951. Chondromucinase from bovine testis and the chondromucin of the umbilical cord. *A.M.A. Arch. Pathol.* **52**: 363-368.

Lloyd, D. J., M. Dempsey and M. Garrod. 1946. The swelling of protein fibres in organic solvents. *Trans. Faraday Soc.* **42B**: 228-241.

Lowry, O. H., D. R. Gilligan and E. M. Katersky. 1941. The determination of collagen and elastin in tissues, with results obtained in various normal tissues from different species. *J. Biol. Chem.* **139**: 795-804.

MacCardle, R. C., M. F. Engman, Jr. and M. F. Engman, Sr. 1943. XCIV. Mineral changes in neurodermatitis revealed by microincineration. *Arch. Dermatol. and Syphilol.* **47**: 335-372.

McMaster, P. D. and R. J. Parsons. 1950. The movement of substances and the state of the fluid in the intradermal tissue. *Ann. N.Y. Acad. Sci.* **52**: 992-1003.

Messerschmitt, J. 1954. Fréquence des Mastzellen dans les frottis de moelle osseuse chez l'homme. *Rev. hématol.* **9**: 189-197.

Meyer, K. 1945. Mucoids and glycoproteins. *Advances in Protein Chem.* **2**: 249-275.

Meyer, K. 1947. The biological significance of hyaluronic acid and hyaluronidase. *Physiol. Revs.* **27**: 335-359.

Meyer, K. 1950. Chemistry of connective tissue, polysaccharides. *Trans. 1st Josiah Macy Jr. Conf. on Connective Tissues* pp. 88-100.

Meyer, K. and M. M. Rapport. 1951. The mucopolysaccharides of the ground substance of connective tissue. *Science* **113**: 596-599.

Miller, M. R., H. J. Ralston III and M. Kasahara. 1958. The pattern of cutaneous innervation of the human hand. *Am. J. Anat.* **102**: 183-217.

Miller, M. R., H. J. Ralston III and M. Kasahara. 1960. The pattern of cutaneous innervation of the human hand, foot and breast. *In* "Advances in Biology of Skin" Vol. I: "Cutaneous Innervation" (W. Montagna, ed.). Pergamon Press, New York.

Montagna, W. (ed.) 1960a. "Advances in Biology of Skin" Vol. I: "Cutaneous Innervation." Pergamon Press, New York.

Montagna, W. 1960b. Cholinesterases in the cutaneous nerves of man. *In* "Advances in Biology of Skin, Vol. I: Cutaneous Innervation." (W. Montagna, ed.). Pergamon Press, New York.

Montagna, W. and R. A. Ellis. 1957. Histology and cytochemistry of human skin. XIII. The blood supply of hair follicles. *J. Natl. Cancer Inst.* **19**: 451-463.

Montagna, W. and R. A. Ellis (eds.). 1961. "Advances in Biology of Skin," Vol. II: "Blood Vessels and Circulation." Pergamon Press, New York.

Montagna, W. and C. R. Hill. 1957. The localization of S^{35} in the skin of the rat. *Anat. Record* **127**: 163-171.

Montagna, W. and H. P. Melaragno. 1953. Histology and cytochemistry of human skin. III. Polymorphism and chromotropy of mast cells. *J. Invest. Dermatol.* **20**: 257-261.

Montagna, W. and C. R. Noback. 1948. Localization of lipids and other chemical substances in the mast cells of man and laboratory animals. *Anat. Record* **100**: 535-545.

Montagna, W., H. B. Chase and H. P. Melaragno. 1951. Histology and cytochemistry of human skin. I. Metachromasia in the mons pubis. *J. Natl. Cancer Inst.* **12**: 591-597.

Montagna, W., A. Z. Eisen and A. S. Goldman. 1954. The tinctorial behavior of human mast cells. *Quart. J. Microscop. Sci.* **95**: 1-4.

Montagna, W. and H. F. Parks. 1948. A histochemical study of the glands of the anal sac of the dog. *Anat. Record* **100**: 297-317.

Moretti, G. and W. Montagna. 1959. Istologia e citochimica della cute umana. XVIII. Le Unità Vascolari. *Giorn. ital dermatol.* **3**: 242-254.

Moretti, G., R. A. Ellis and H. Mescon. 1959. Vascular patterns in the skin of the face. *J. Invest. Dermatol.* **33**: 103-112.

Neuman, R. E. and M. A. Logan. 1950. The determination of collagen and elastin in tissues. *J. Biol. Chem.* **186**: 549-556.

Nordenstam, H. and J. Adams-Ray. 1957. Chromaffin granules and their cellular location in human skin. *Z. Zellforsch.* **45**: 435-443.

Oliver, J., F. Bloom and C. Mangieri. 1947. On the origin of heparin. An examination of the heparin content and the specific cytoplasmic particles of neoplastic mast cells. *J. Exptl. Med.* **86**: 107-116.

Ormea, F. 1961. "La Cute Organo di Senso." Minerva Medica, Torino, Italy.

Paff, G. H., F. Bloom and C. Reilly. 1947. The morphology and behavior of neoplastic mast cells cultivated *in vitro. J. Exptl. Med.* **86**: 117-124.

Pomerat, C. M., W. Jacobson and M. F. Orr. 1949. A macrophage-promoting factor (MPF) in the blood of rabbits. *Am. J. Anat.* **84**: 1-26.

Porter, K. R. and G. D. Pappas. 1959. Collagen formation by fibroblasts of the chick embryo dermis. *J. Biophys. Biochem. Cytol.* **5**: 153-166.

Rheingold, J. J. and G. B. Wislocki. 1948. Histochemical methods applied to hematology. *Blood* **3**: 641-655.

Richardson, K. C. 1960. Studies on the structure of autonomic nerves in the small intestine, correlating the silver-impregnated image in light microscopy with the permanganate-fixed ultrastructure in electron-microscopy. *J. Anat.* **94**: 458-472.

Riley, J. F. 1954. The riddle of the mast cells. *Lancet* i: 841-844.

Riley, J. F. 1959. "The Mast Cells." E. & S. Livingston Ltd., Edinburgh and London, England.

Riley, J. F. and G. B. West. 1952. Histamine in tissue mast cells. *J. Physiol. (London)* **117**: 72-73.

Riley, J. F. and G. B. West. 1953. The presence of histamine in tissue mast cells. *J. Physiol. (London)* **120**: 528-537.

Rogers, G. E. 1956. Electron microscopy of mast cells in the skin of young mice. *Exptl. Cell Research* **11**: 393-402.

Romanini, M. G. 1951. Contributions à l'étude histochimique des mucopolysaccharides. I° Gelée de Wharton et substance métachromatique des vaisseaux. *Acta Anat.* **13**: 256-288.

Saunders, R. L. De C. H. 1961. Micrographic studies and vascular patterns in skin. In "Advances in Biology of Skin," Vol. II: "Blood Vessels and Circulation" (W. Montagna and R. A. Ellis, eds.). Pergamon Press, New York.

Saunders, R. L. De C. H., J. Lawrence and D. A. Maciver. 1957. Microradiographic studies of the vascular patterns in muscles and skin. In "X-Ray Microscopy and Microradiography" (E. V. Coslett, A. Engström, and H. H. Pattee, Jr., eds.), pp. 539-550. Academic Press, New York.

Schiller, S. 1959. Mucopolysaccharides of the estrogen-stimulated chick oviduct. *Biochim. et Biophys. Acta* **32**: 315-319.

Schiller, S. and A. Dorfman. 1957. The metabolism of mucopolysaccharides in animals. IV. The influence of insulin. *J. Biol. Chem.* **227**: 625-632.

Schmitt, F. O. 1959. Interaction properties of elongate protein macromolecules with particular reference to collagen (tropocollagen). In "Biophysical Science—A Study Program" (J. L. Oncley, ed.), pp. 349-358. Wiley, New York.

Sinclair, D. C., G. Weddell and E. Zander. 1952. The relationship of cutaneous sensibility to neurohistology in the human pinna. *J. Anat.* **86**: 402-411.

Sjölin, K. E. 1951. Mucopolysaccharides in the dermal connective tissue of hemophiliacs. *Acta Pathol. Microbiol. Scand.* **28**: 309-312.

Smith, D. E. and Y. S. Lewis. 1957. Electron microscopy of the tissue mast cell. *J. Biophys. Biochem. Cytol.* **3**: 9-14.

Spalteholz, W. 1893. Die Verteilung der Blutgefässe in der Haut. *Arch. Anat. Entwicklungsgesch.* pp. 1-54.

Spalteholz, W. 1927. Blutgefässe in der Haut. In "Handbuch der Haut und Geschlechtskrankheiten" (J. Jadassohn, ed.). Springer, Berlin.

Stearns, M. L. 1940a. Studies on the development of connective tissue in transparent chambers in the rabbit's ear. I. *Am. J. Anat.* **66**: 133-176.

Stearns, M. L. 1940b. Studies on the development of connective tissue in transparent chambers in the rabbit's ear. II. *Am. J. Anat.* **67**: 55-97.

Sylvén, B. 1940. Studies on the liberation of sulphuric acids from the granules of the mast cells in the subcutaneous connective tissue after exposure to roentgen and gamma rays. *Acta Radiol.* **21**: 206-212.

Sylvén, B. 1941. Über das Vorkommen von hochmolekularen Esterschwefelsäuren im Granulationsgewebe und bei der Epithelregeneration. *Acta Chir. Scand.* **86**: Suppl. 66: 1-151.

Sylvén, B. 1950. The cytoplasm of living tissue mast cells in visual phase-contrast. *Exptl. Cell Research* **1**: 492-493.

Sylvén, B. 1951. On the cytoplasmic constituents of normal tissue mast cells. *Exptl. Cell Research* **2**: 252-255.

Sylvén, B. and L. G. Larsson. 1948. The mast cell reaction in mouse skin to some organic chemicals. III. The early effect of aromatic hydrocarbons. *Cancer Research* **8**: 449-463.

Tamponi, M. 1938. Ricerche di colorazione sopravitale della cute. Nota I. *Arch. ital. dermatol. sifilol. e venereol.* **5**: 499-536.

Tamponi, M. 1940. "Structure Nervose Della Cute Umana." Editore L. Cappelli, Bologna, Italy.

Tello, J. F. 1923-1924. Génése des terminaisons motrices et sensitives. II. Terminaisons dans les poils de la souris blanche. *Trav. lab. recherches biol. univ. Madrid.* **21**: 257-384.

Vanamee, P. and K. R. Porter. 1951. Observations with the electron microscope on the solvation and reconstitution of collagen. *J. Exptl. Med.* **94**: 255-268.

Videbaek, A., G. Asboe-Hansen, P. Astrup, V. Faber, C. Hamburger, K. Schmith, M. Sprechler and K. Brøchner-Mortensen. 1950. Effect of ACTH and cortisone on rheumatic fever. *Acta Endocrinol.* **4**: 245-264.

Walshe, F. M. R. 1942. The anatomy and physiology of cutaneous sensibility: A critical review. *Brain* **65**: 48-112.

Weddell, G. 1960. Studies related to the mechanism of common sensibility. *In* "Advances in Biology of Skin," Vol. I: "Cutaneous Innervation" (W. Montagna, ed.). Pergamon Press, New York.

Winkelmann, R. K. 1957. The mucocutaneous end-organ: The primary organized ending in human skin. *A.M.A. Arch. Dermatol.* **766**: 225-235.

Winkelmann, R. K. 1959a. The erogenous zones: Their nerve supply and its significance. *Proc. Staff Meetings Mayo Clin.* **34**: 39-47.

Winkelmann, R. K. 1959b. The innervation of a hair follicle. *Ann. N.Y. Acad. Sci.* **83**: 400-407.

Winkelmann, R. K. 1960a. "Nerve Endings in Normal and Pathologic Skin." C. C Thomas, Springfield, Illinois.

Winkelmann, R. K. 1960b. Similarities in cutaneous nerve end-organs. *In* "Advances in Biology of Skin" Vol. I: Cutaneous Innervation. (W. Montagna, ed.). Pergamon Press, New York.

Winkelmann, R. K. 1961. Cutaneous vascular patterns. *In* "Advances in Biology of Skin" Vol. II: The Blood Vessels and Circulation of Blood in the Skin (W. Montagna and R. A. Ellis, eds.). Pergamon Press, New York.

Wislocki, G. B. and D. W. Fawcett. 1951. Some histochemical properties of mast cells and tissue eosinophils in stained spreads of normal rat mesentery (abstract). *J. Natl. Cancer Inst.* **12**: 258.

Wislocki, G. B., H. Bunting and E. W. Dempsey. 1947. Metachromasia in mammalian tissues and its relationship to mucopolysaccharides. *Am. J. Anat.* **81**: 1-37.

Wolstenholme, G. E. W. (ed.). 1954. "Peripheral Circulation in Man." Ciba Foundation Symposium. Little, Brown, Boston, Massachusetts.

Wolstenholme, G. E. W. and M. O'Connor (eds.). 1959. "Pain and Itch. Nervous Mechanisms," Ciba Foundation Study Group. No. 1. Little, Brown, Boston, Massachusetts.

Wood, G. C. 1959. The formation of fibrils from collagen solutions. 3. Effect of chondroitin sulfate and some other naturally occurring polyanions on the rate of formation. *Biochem. J.* **75**: 605-612.

Yuditskaya, A. I. 1949. The chemical nature of reticulin. *Chem. Abstr.* **43**: 6263.

Zweifach, B. W. 1949. Basic mechanisms in peripheral vascular homeostasis. *Trans. 3rd Josiah Macy, Jr. Conf. on Factors Regulating Blood Pressure.*

Zweifach, B. W. 1959. Structural aspects and hemodynamics of microcirculation in the skin. *In* "The Human Integument" (S. Rothman, ed.). Am. Assoc. Advance Sci., Washington, D.C.

CHAPTER 4

The Pilary System

Introduction

Since only mammals have hairs, they could be called Pilifera (Bonnet, 1892). Little is known for certain about the phylogenetic origin of hair, and no satisfactory relation has been established between hairs and homologous epidermal appendages in the other vertebrates (de-Meijere, 1894; Pinkus, 1927). Today we know many of the physicochemical properties of hairs, and great progress has been made in the clarification of the structure and function of hair follicles. Most of this knowledge, however, has not been used, and many books still employ obsolete descriptive and illustrative material, perpetuating oversights, omissions, misconceptions, and errors. There is still confusion in the names of the different parts of the hair follicles; such terms as *papilla, hair germ, bulb, matrix,* and *club* are variously defined by different authors.

During the last ten years three monographs have been published on the problems of the growth and composition of hair (Montagna and Ellis, 1958b; New York Academy of Sciences, 1951, 1959). This chapter, therefore, can present only the highlights of our present knowledge of the pilary system; it will describe briefly the architecture of the hair follicle, its histochemical properties, and the patterns of growth and differentiation.

Hairs are dead structures, composed of keratinized cells that are compactly cemented together. They grow out of tubes of epidermis, the hair follicles, sunken into the dermis. Hair follicles, together with the sebaceous glands, that grow from their sides, form the *pilosebaceous systems.*

Hair follicles are among the simplest of biological systems in which to study growth and differentiation. Regardless of their size, only a small mass of cells at the base of hair follicles, the *matrix,* produces the hair. Each hair follicle from the human scalp, for example, produces approximately 0.35 mm of hair per day. The daily metabolic requirement of the germinative tissue to carry on mitotic activity and of the cells which synthesize the complex fibrous proteins to produce this much hair is enormous. Mitotic activity of the germinative cells and the synthesis of proteins go on unceasingly. Follicles periodically cease to produce a hair, the major portion of the bulb disappears and what

174

cells remain in the follicle enter a period of quiescence. After variable intervals of time, the dormant follicle bursts into activity again, and undergoes a period of organogenesis during which a new follicle is formed and the production of a new hair is begun.

Growing hair follicles are said to be *in anagen,* quiescent ones *in telogen,* and the period of transition between the two, *catagen* (Dry, 1926). These terms are convenient and in common usage, and it would be confusing to discard them until less cumbersome terms are suggested.

The descriptions that follow deal primarily with human hair follicles, and although differences occur, the basic structure of the follicles in other mammals is similar.

It is difficult to attain a three dimensional concept of hair follicles from the average histological preparation. The general groupings of follicles, the over-all structure of the follicles, the differences in size of different follicles at different states of activity, etc., can be appreciated best in models reconstructed from serial sections. Though tedious and time consuming, this work yields gratifying results. The illustrations shown here are drawn from models reconstructed in balsa wood by Dr. Eugene Van Scott (Figs. 1–6). These reconstructions were made at identical magnifications, and the differences in size are real; certain distortions due to fixation and the general abuses of histological handling have occurred, but the over-all shape and size are faithfully reproduced. In Fig. 1, the middle follicle contains no hair, and all three follicles share one orifice. In Fig. 2, two follicles from the upper back share a pilary canal. The small follicle on the left, just under the sebaceous gland, is quiescent; the one on the right is growing. In Fig. 3, a group of four follicles from the scalp share one canal; the follicle on the left, much shorter than the others, and obscured by the sebaceous glands, is quiescent. The follicle at the right has no sebaceous gland, but this is not rare. In Fig. 4, a group of relatively short, quiescent follicles from the upper back, two follicles come together just above the entrance of their respective sebaceous glands and they share a common pilary canal. Several vellus hair follicles are found on each side of the principal follicle. In Fig. 5, the two growing follicles from the upper back of a child are much smaller than the follicles of adults, and the sebaceous glands are small. Fig. 6 shows the relatively enormous follicle of a beard hair. Several vellus hair follicles surround the main pilary unit. The pilary canal of beard follicles is divided into two distinct keratinous channels; the hair passes through one channel, and the sebum from the associated sebaceous gland passes through the other.

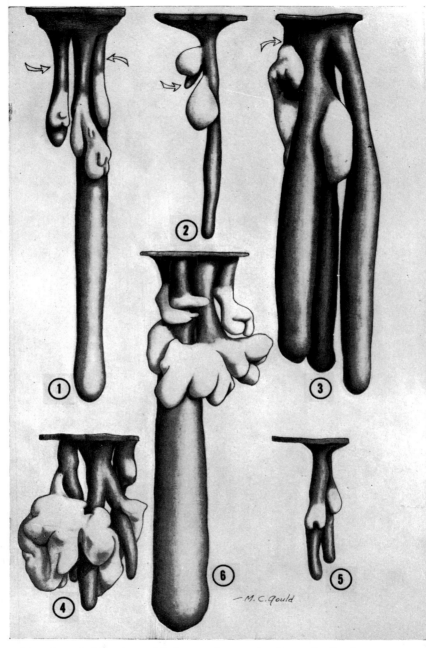

FIGS. 1 to 6. Drawings of balsa wood reconstructions of pilosebaceous systems from different regions of the body, by Dr. E. Van Scott. See text for explanations.

Development

Since Pinkus (1958) has described in detail the development of hair follicles in man, this brief account gives only a summary of these events.

The earliest primordia of hair follicles appear, at the end of the second and in the early part of the third fetal months, on the eyebrows, upper lip, and chin. Slightly later, primordia appear on the forehead and scalp almost simultaneously. Hair follicle anlagen do not begin to appear on the trunk and appendages until the fourth and fifth months. Thus, development begins on the head and spreads in a cephalocaudal progression. When in the fourth and fifth months, the follicles of the head are fully developed and form a hair, the few follicles on the back, abdomen, and the appendages are still developing. Follicles appear dyschronously even within the same body regions. As the skin grows, new follicles appear between those already there, and later still, two secondary follicles develop, one on each side, very near the follicles already present, establishing a grouping of hair follicles.

Hair follicles are the first cutaneous appendages to be formed from the relatively undifferentiated epidermis. The first sign of development is a crowding of cells at spaced focal spots in the basal layer of the epidermis, causing a slight bulging of the epidermis on its underside (Fig. 7) (Pinkus, 1958). The spacing of these primordia is characteristic of the various body regions. The nuclei of the cells in these *primitive hair germs* become smaller and stain darker than those around them. The basal cells and their nuclei then become elongated perpendicular to the epidermis and the hair germ begins to bulge conspicuously into the dermis. Fibroblasts from the dermis now form a cap around the bulge of the hair germ. This cap, the *dermal papilla,* shows intense reaction for alkaline phosphatase (Achten, 1959). The anterior face of the hillock of cells of the hair germ is at right angles to the basal layer of the epidermis, but the posterior face slopes gradually. As the hair germ elongates into the dermis it forms a *peg* of cells slanted anterioposteriorly. The large columnar cells at the periphery of the peg are arranged radially to the center, whereas the cells in the center are aligned longitudinally. The free end of the peg becomes clavate; as it plows its way downward, the middle of the bulbous free end becomes indented, the dermal papilla occupying the concavity. As the follicles grow still longer, the distal end also enlarges and grows around the dermal papilla, which finally comes to rest largely inside the bulb. At this time, first the central cells of the follicle, then its peripheral cells

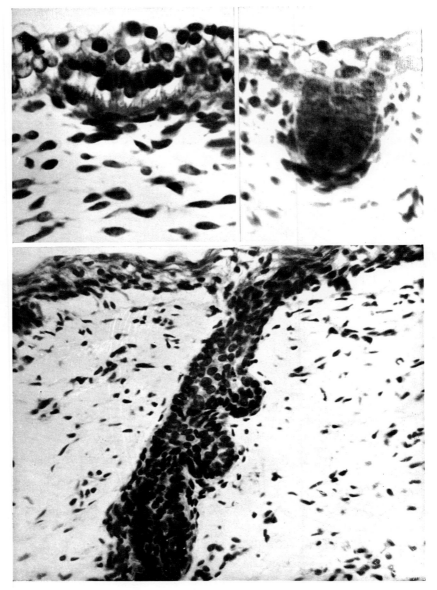

Fig. 7. Three early primordia of hair follicles in the scalp of a human embryo 3½ months old.

become laden with glycogen. The follicle then attains two swellings at its posterior side: the lower one, the "Wulst," or bulge of Pinkus, remains a solid hillock; the upper attains a spherical shape (Fig. 8). The cells in the center of the upper protuberance gradually accumulate lipid droplets and undergo sebaceous differentiation. Subsequent differentiation progresses centrifugally.

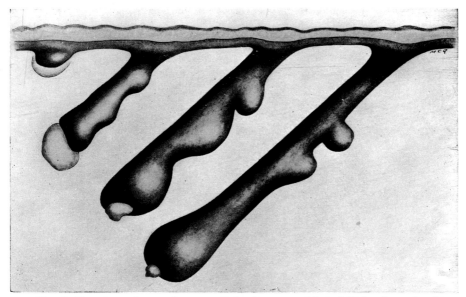

FIG. 8. Drawings of several stages of development of hair follicles from the skin of an embryo 4 months old. The two humps represent the sebaceous gland, above, and the bulge proper, below.

From the top of the follicle a cord of elongated cells extends into the epidermis. The cells in the center of the cord show keratohyalin granules at the same time that sebaceous differentiation begins. Preparations colored with Sudan black show that some of the cells in the center of this cord also undergo sebaceous differentiation, establishing a keratinous sebaceous path which hollows out the cord to form the pilosebaceous canal before the follicle begins to give rise to a hair. Although continuous with the epidermis, and relatively similar to it in structure, the pilary canal has some individuality and may have a profound effect upon the growth and differentiation of the follicle in postnatal life.

The expanded distal part of the follicle differentiates into a bulb that grows around the dermal papilla. The papilla remains attached to a *basal plate* of dermal cells by a narrow stalk (Fig. 9). Pigment cells, which before this phase of development are found throughout the bulb, retreat into the upper part, leaving the lower part of the bulb non-pigmented. The cells below the line of pigment form the *matrix* of the follicle. The cells of the bulb around the dermal papilla then align themselves longitudinally. Granules of *trichohyalin* appear in the cells in the center of the upper part of the bulb, a small distance above the apex of

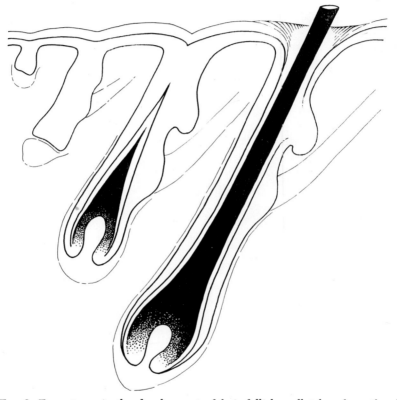

FIG. 9. Four stages in the development of hair follicles, all taken from the skin of a 5-month-old human embryo. On the left is the primordium growing from the epidermis. In the next diagram, the cord of cells has become longer and has developed an upper and lower swelling which will differentiate, respectively, into sebaceous glands and hair bulge. The condensation of mesenchymal cells at the base of the cord is the dermal papilla. In the third diagram the lower portion of the follicle has grown around the dermal papilla. A cone of inner sheath, formed above the bulb, is pushing its way through the cord. Behind the inner sheath is the tip of the growing hair (drawn solid black). The follicle on the extreme right is fully formed.

the dermal papilla. Other cells above them also develop trichohyalin granules, and a path is established in the center of the follicle all the way to the bottom of the pilary canal. The cells of this path later become keratinized and somewhat shriveled; this is the first inner root sheath. The follicle is now a tube, the outer root sheath, around a keratin cord, the inner root sheath. The differentiation of the tip of the *first* hair takes place in the upper part of the bulb above the dermal papilla. Parallel rows of cells from the proliferative *matrix* advance upward, forming a keratin cylinder in the center, the hair, and a tube of *different* keratin around it, the inner root sheath. Differentiation of the inner root sheath takes place as in postnatal life. The outer one-cell-deep *Henle's layer* attains trichohyalin precociously in the upper part of the bulb, forming a bell-shaped tube through which the still unkeratinized cells are funneled on their way upward. The slightly thicker *Huxley's layer* inside Henle's layer attains keratohyalin farther up in the bulb, and the *cuticle of the inner root sheath* on the inside keratinizes last. The hair keratinizes above the constriction of the bulb. The tip of the hair is always free of pigment, and the first hairs formed have no medulla. A glassy membrane is formed around the lower half of the follicle, below the *bulge,* when the first hairs begin to form. Two connective tissue envelopes also differentiate around the follicle. Lastly, the cells in the connective tissue between the bulge and the surface become elongated, increase in size, and differentiate in a band of smooth muscle, the *arrectores pilorum muscles.*

After a period of activity fetal hair follicles become quiescent and form a hair club above the level of the bulb; much of the follicle below the bulge is dissipated. Hair growth cycles, then, are established in the skin of the embryo as early as $4\frac{1}{2}$ months. All of the sequences that take place in the formation of the first follicle, the production of its first hair, and the reduction of active follicles to quiescent ones are the templates of operation of the follicle in postnatal life. Even the details remain the same. Thus, the various changes that take place subsequently during the hair growth cycles in postnatal individuals are actually a repetition of morphogenetic events.

The Hair

The morphologic characteristics of hairs vary from one species to another, and even the hairs of the same animal may differ markedly in various regions of the body. Hairs may be spiny, stiff, soft, long, short, thick, thin, woolly, colored, or white. Even in a single region there may be hairs of different length, texture, or color. The longer and coarser ones are the terminal hairs; the very short, soft, colorless ones are the vellus hairs. Other mammals also have a woolly underfur of medium length and color. A sharp general classification of hairs into precise types cannot be made on the basis of length alone. For example, the hairs of the scalp are characteristically longer than those of the back, but terminal and vellus hairs are present in both regions, and the length of terminal hairs on the back may approximate that of vellus hairs of the scalp.

During its life cycle the same hair follicle may give rise to more than one type of hair. In the skin of man, many of the follicles that in preadolescent years produce vellus-like hairs metamorphose at puberty into large follicles that produce coarse hairs. Conversely, in baldness the large follicles of the human male scalp may revert to produce lanugo. The hair follicles of the costovertebral melanotic spot of castrated female hamsters produce fine black hairs. After the animals have been treated with androgens, these follicles produce very large, coarse hairs (Hamilton and Montagna, 1950). The follicles of bristles in the merino lamb become the follicles of wool in the adult sheep.

The hair follicles in the axillae of infants and children are relatively large and apparently in an arrested active stage. Yet, they form only a broken cord of keratinous debris and not a hair. These hair follicles are rarely found in the telogen, or quiescent state.

Hairs show great variations in diameter and shape. Most hairs are oval or round, but others are so flattened that they resemble ribbons. Twisting of such ribbon-like hairs along the longitudinal axis may give the impression that the hair varies widely in diameter, although this is not the case, except in certain pathological conditions.

Hairs may be straight, wavy, or crimped. Although the factors responsible for the curling of hairs are not known, the observations of Mercer (1953) and others on the crimping of wool fibers are pertinent. Crimping in wool fibers seems to be brought about by the deflection of the hair bulb, the eccentric disposition of the fiber in the follicle, and asymmetric keratinization of the fiber. In fibers located eccentrically in the follicle, keratinization begins on the thin side of the inner sheath, proceeds across the fiber and is completed on the thick side (Auber, 1952). These differences in time sequence of keratinization of the two halves of crimped fibers are reflected by differences in their staining properties. The disposition of these two elements in each crimp is always the same; one is always on the inside of it and the other on the outside (Fraser and Rogers, 1953).

Hairs are composed of a cuticle on the outside, usually a medulla in the center, and a cortex between the two. The cuticle is a single layer of imbricated scales, with the free margins directed toward the tip of the hair. Although there is only one layer of cuticle cells, these are so elongated that many of them overlap at any one place, making the cuticle actually a multilayered structure. The scales are translucent and free of pigment. Inside the follicle, the cells of the cuticle of the hair are interlocked with those of the inner root sheath. This arrangement firmly anchors the hair in the follicle. The cuticle of the hair binds the cortex, which without its protection becomes frayed and falls apart. A thin layer of lipid and carbohydrate surrounds the cuticle, and may protect the hair from the effect of physical and chemical agents. Cuticles are classified as coronal, when each cell completely surrounds the hair and as imbricate when they do not. The free edge of the cuticle cells may be simple, dentate, or serrate. According to their size and shape, the cuticle cells can be further subdivided as elongate, acuminate, ovate, and flattened. In coarse hairs the free margins of the cuticle cells are not raised very high. These hairs do not interlock with each other, make poor textiles, and have a high luster, since the reflection of the light on the hair surface is relatively unbroken. The free margin of the cuticle cells of fine hairs such as wool are raised so high that the hairs interlock, making good textiles, and they are dull, since the reflected light is broken.

The bulk of the hair is the cortex, which is composed of elongated (fusiform), keratinized cells cemented together. In pigmented hairs, melanin granules are aligned longitudinally in the cells of the cortex. In the absence of pigment, hair appears translucent. Between the cells of the cortex are found variable numbers of fusi, delicate air spaces, which in the living portion of the hair root are filled with fluid (Hausman, 1932, 1944). As the hair grows and dries out, air replaces the fluid, and fusi are formed. Fusi, which are more numerous and larger in coarser hairs, are large at the base of the hair and disappear near the tip.

In the center of a hair is usually a medulla, which may be continuous, discontinuous, or fragmental. In the finest hairs, the medulla is usually absent. In coarse hairs it is continuous or fragmental. The type of medulla present can vary even within the same hair. The medulla is composed of large, loosely connected keratinized cells. Large intra- and intercellular air spaces in the medulla determine to a large extent the sheen and color tones of the hair by influencing the reflection of light. In many mammals the medulla forms a small part of the hair, but in the rodents, some carnivores, early primates, etc., the hair is composed mostly of large medulla cells held together by a thin tube of cortex.

The diameter of the hairs of the scalp increases rapidly and uniformly during the first 3 or 4 years after birth; it increases less rapidly and less uniformly during the next 6 years, and after that it increases slowly or not at all (Duggins and Trotter, 1950, 1951; Trotter, 1930, 1932; Trotter and Dawson, 1931, 1932, 1934; Trotter and Duggins, 1948, 1950).

Very few of the hairs have a medulla at birth. The percentage of medullated hairs increases rapidly during the first 7 months. From 7 months to the second year, the percentage of medullated hairs decreases. A period of great irregularity follows and then the percentage tends to rise slightly at 5 years. From birth to 2 years of age, the percentage of hairs with a medulla is slightly higher in girls than in boys. From the ages of 2 to 6, the percentages are similar, and from the ages of 6 to 14 the percentage is much higher in boys. Boys exhibit a higher percentage of scalp hairs with broken or continuous medullas than girls. Negro children have a higher percentage of medullated hairs than do white children. Usually, the number of cuticular scales per unit area drops slightly during the first year, but later there is no specific trend. Although adult human scalp hairs are believed to be rarely medullated, all hairs, with the exception of the very fine ones, show a fragmental or discontinuous medulla when viewed under polarized light. The medulla may be only one or two cells in diameter, but it is present nonetheless. Such hairs would appear nonmedullated when observed under the ordinary light microscope.

The Hair Follicle

Hair follicles are continuous with the surface epidermis by way of the pilary canal. They are slanted, their roots growing down to the panniculus adiposus. The follicles attain their greatest diameter at their base where they are dilated into an onion-shaped *bulb* (Fig. 10). An obovate "cavity" inside the bulb is completely filled with the loose connective tissue of the *dermal papilla*. The upper part of the follicle, that extends from the entrance of the duct of the sebaceous glands to the surface, is the pilary canal. Bundles of smooth muscle fibers, the *arrectores pilorum muscles*, extend at an acute angle from the surface of the dermis to the bulge, a swelling on the side of the hair follicle, just below the level of the sebaceous glands. These muscles, innervated largely by adrenergic nerves, contract under stress, pull the hair to a vertical position and draw the skin around the follicles giving rise to the elevations of "goose flesh" or *cutis anserina*. Vellus hair follicles have no arrectores pilorum muscles. In the cat and dog the arrectores pilorum

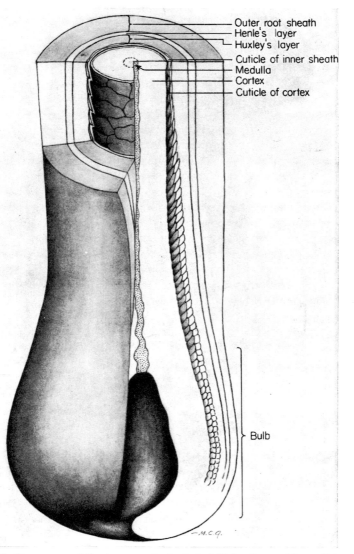

Fig. 10. Stereogram of the lower part of a hair follicle of man. The cellular details have been omitted, but the proportions and the relationships of the layers have been maintained.

muscles are well developed and are responsible for the raising of the fur in fear and anger. The muscles are particularly well developed in the follicles on the tail of most mammals.

Hair follicles are composed of an outer root sheath, an inner root sheath, and the hair in the center (Fig. 10). The thickness of the outer sheath is proportional to the size of the hair follicle and is thick in the follicles of large hairs. The inner root sheath is composed of three concentric layers: Henle's layer on the outside is one cell thick and rests against the outer sheath. Huxley's layer in the middle is two or more cells thick, and the single-layered cuticle of the inner sheath on the inside rests against the hair. The cuticle of the inner sheath is a layer of imbricated, scale-like keratinized cells, the free borders of which are directed downward and interlock with the cuticle cells of the hair. Hair follicles are surrounded by a connective tissue sheath in which the fiber of the inner layer are arranged circularly and those of the outer layer are disposed longitudinally. The outer root sheath is separated from the connective tissue sheath by a hyalin, noncellular glassy, or vitreous membrane. The connective tissue sheath is continuous above with the papillary body of the dermis and with the dermal papilla at the base of the follicle. Since these three connective tissue structures are continuous, they can be considered as a united connective tissue system. The hair follicle, then, is not in contact with the fibrous reticular layer of the dermis.

With the exception of man, all mammals possess large, stiff hairs around the face, the vibrissae, also referred to as sensory hairs, tactile hairs, sinus hairs, feelers, whiskers, etc. The follicles of these hairs are richly supplied with sensory nerves, and blood vessels form a system of cavernous sinuses around them which resemble erectile tissue. The nerves, mostly from the mandibular branch of the trigeminus, form compact networks around the follicle. Some tactile hairs are surrounded by skeletal muscle fibers. Other hair follicles, not surrounded by blood sinuses, also have rich and complex nerves around them. In man and in other mammals many hair follicles are associated with a plate of thickened epidermis, the Haarscheibe of Pinkus (1905), which is richly innervated and vascularized. The nerves of the Haarscheibe have been extensively studied by Tamponi (1939). Actually, all hair follicles are well supplied with nerves, and although they are not surrounded by cavernous tissue, their sensory function is acute.

The periods of activity and quiescence are different in different parts of the body, in different individuals, at different ages, and in the two sexes. In the scalp of the young, the growing period is very long and

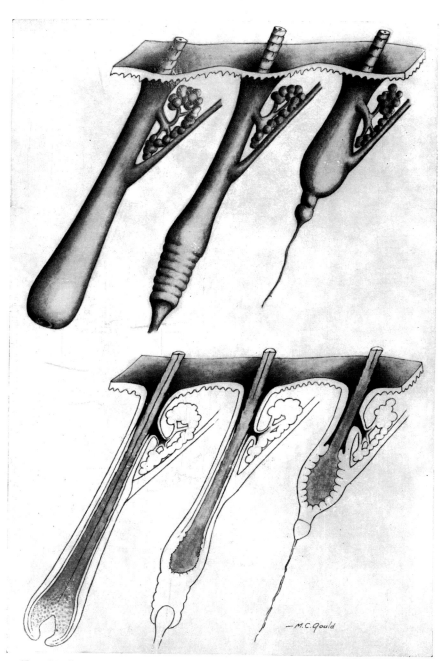

Fig. 11. Representation of three stages of the hair growth cycle, each seen in three dimension, above, and cut longitudinally, below. On the left is an active, *anagen* follicle; in the middle is a follicle in *catagen*; and on the right is a quiescent, or *telogen* follicle.

the period of rest is short. In the other parts of the body the periods of rest are usually longer than those of growth.

The resting, or quiescent, hair follicle is one half to one third the length of the active follicle and has no bulb. The deepest extension of the resting follicle lies entirely within the dermis rather than in the panniculus adiposus. The follicle contains a hair that is clavate at the base, called a club. Resting follicles consist of an epidermal sac that follows the outline of the club hair, and a cord of small cells growing downward from the sac to the dermal papilla; the point of contact is flattened at the base (Fig. 11). This stalk of cells, the "hair germ," will be described in greater detail later.

Numerous delicate keratinized fibers from the club extend laterally to the epithelial sac. A partially keratinized *capsule*, one or two cells in thickness is interposed between the cells of the epithelial sac and the club. Above the club, just below the entrance of the sebaceous gland at the base of the pilary canal, a horizontal wrinkle in the capsule forms a moat around the hair. In longitudinal sections, the moat appears as a fold on each side of the epithelial sac. Above the moat, in the pilosebaceous canal, the capsule, which corresponds to the inner sheath of the active follicle, blends with the stratum corneum. The epithelial sac proper consists of cells left behind by the outer sheath. The pedicle or hair germ, at the base of the epithelial sac, is also derived largely from the outer sheath, below the level of the bulge.

The transition from an active to an inactive follicle, catagen (Dry, 1926), occurs rapidly in the hair follicles of rodents, but relatively slowly in man. When follicles cease to produce a hair, they shrivel up and the lower part, below the bulge, including the bulb, largely disappears (Fig. 11).

The Cuticle of the Hair

The cells of the cuticle of the hair can be recognized in the upper part of the bulb as they sweep upward in a single row from the matrix (Fig. 10). About midway in the bulb the cells are cuboidal, the cytoplasm is strongly basophil and is stippled with basophil granules; in contrast to the cells of the cortex of the hair, these cells contain no melanin. In the upper region of the bulb, the cells become columnar, with the long axis oriented radially (Fig. 12). The cells remain oriented like this for a short distance above the bulb, and then their outer edges begin to be tipped upward as though the cells of the inner sheath lateral to them were expanding more rapidly than those of the cuticle of the hair, and swept their edges upward. The tipping upward of columnar cells, that are at

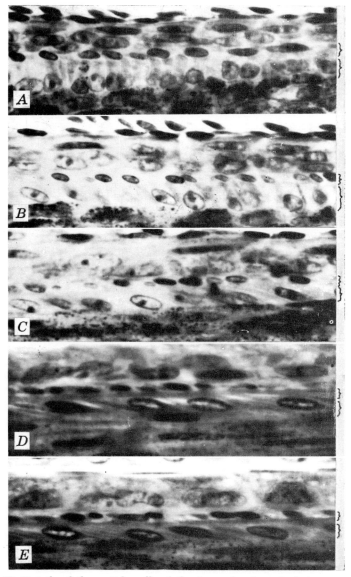

FIG. 12. Details of the cuticle cells of the inner sheath and of the cortex in the lower half of the same follicle. From top to bottom this series represents a progression from the bulb upward. In (A) and (B), observe the disparity between the size of the cuticle cells of the cortex and the size of the cuticle cells of the inner sheath. In (C), (D), and (E) these cells become gradually elongated, tipped, and imbricated. In (E), which is about midway up the follicle, the cells of the cuticle of the cortex are long and scale-like.

least twice as broad as they are high, causes them to become imbricated automatically. As their orientation shifts from a horizontal plane to a vertical one, the cuticle cells become flattened, and in vertical sections they appear as pointed scales (Figs. 10 and 12). This reorientation is completed below the midway mark of the follicle. In the upper half of the follicle, cuticle cells become hyalinized, their nuclei disappear, and adhere to the cells of the cortex. The development of the imbricated pattern must be achieved as a result of a series of morphogenetic movements. The cuticle cells arise from the matrix, move up into the upper bulb, increase in volume, and expand horizontally. They seem to be more firmly attached to the cortex, on the axial side, than they are to each other or to the cuticle cells of the inner sheath. The inner sheath must grow at least at the same rate as the hair, but its cells may increase in volume at a faster rate than those of the hair. If the cuticle cells of the inner sheath moved upward faster than those of the hair, they could pull the lateral borders of the cuticle cells of the cortex in an upward position and reorient them. Inherent morphogenetic potentials within the cells, however, could bring about these movements without the aid of such physical factors.

The staining properties of the cuticle cells suggest that the keratin they contain is different from that in the surrounding structures. Unlike the cells of the inner sheath, the cuticle cells of the cortex do not elaborate trichohyalin. With Altmann's acid fuchsin-methyl green, the cuticle cells of the cortex stain with methyl green after they have become reoriented and attenuated. Above the level of the bulb, these cells stain a brilliant green, and their nuclei are stained red. Farther up, the nuclei disappear, but the cells stain green up to the level of the sebaceous ducts, above which they become gradually fuchsinophil. In these same preparations the cortex stains with methyl green only in the region just above the bulb. The keratinized cortex is fuchsinophil. The medulla cells stain with methyl green until they become keratinized, in the upper half of the follicle. This staining reaction seems to indicate that the cuticle is not fully keratinized until it reaches the upper third of the follicle. The cells of the inner sheath are brilliantly fuchsinophil as soon as they acquire trichohyalin. The selective stainability with acid fuchsin and methyl green could denote chemical differences in the keratins.

The Inner Root Sheath

Progressing in a centripetal direction, the inner root sheath consists of Henle's layer, Huxley's layer, and the cuticle (Figs. 10 and 13). None of these layers contains pigment, even in follicles which produce heavily pigmented hairs. The inner sheath arises from the peripheral and central mass of cells of the matrix (Figs. 39 and 40). The cells, which move practically directly upward from the matrix, are arranged in concentric layers in the upper bulb. In the follicles of most mammals each of the three layers is one cell in thickness, but in the larger follicles of man, Huxley's layer is two cells thick. The cells in all three layers of the inner root sheath contain "trichohyalin" granules, first distinguished from keratohyalin granules by Vörner (1903). The staining properties of trichohyalin are slightly different from those of keratohyalin. Trichohya-

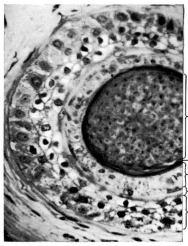

Keratogenous zone of cortex

Cuticles of inner sheath and cortex
Huxley's layer
Henle's layer

Outer root sheath

FIG. 13. Transverse section through the keratogenous zone of the active follicle from the scalp, stained with toluidine blue buffered to pH 5.0.

lin stains more readily with basic dyes than with acid dyes (Gavazzeni, 1908), and it is more strongly fuchsinophil. After mordanting, tricho-hyalin can be demonstrated with Heidenhain's or Regaud's hematoxylin.

The cells of Henle's layer acquire trichohyalin granules immediately after they have arisen from the matrix. The cells are first roughly cuboidal but become elongated vertically in the upper bulb. Tricho-hyalin granules are at first very small, but coalesce into large homogenous globules and parallel rods farther up in the follicle. Concomitant with these changes, the cells become hyalinized, and their nuclei become indistinct and then disappear. Unlike the cells in other keratinizing tissues, those of the inner sheath do not decrease appreciably in volume, and remain turgid, perhaps as a result of imbibition of fluid by tricho-hyalin (Auber, 1952).

The cells of Huxley's layer differentiate more slowly than those in Henle's layer (Figs. 13 and 14). In Huxley's layer trichohyalin granules first appear in the cells at the summit of the bulb, at which point the cells of Henle's layer are completely hyalinized. The granules are at first small, spherical, and evenly distributed in the cytoplasm. Higher up they coalesce and are larger and irregular. Some cells without trichohyalin granules send lateral cytoplasmic processes across Henle's layer; these may penetrate as far as the axial layer of the outer sheath. These *Flügelzellen* (Hoepke, 1927) represent living bridges of cytoplasm across the dead Henle's layer. Nutrients or energy sources from the outer sheath to the still-living cells of Huxley's layer may come across these bridges. The cells of Huxley's layer are hyalinized about midway up in the follicle.

The cells of the cuticle of the inner sheath do not acquire trichohyalin granules until they are about halfway up in the follicle. They are the smallest cells in the follicle and can be recognized even in the lower bulb. Above the bulb, the nuclei of the cuticle cells become elongated vertically. The cuticle cells remain small and compressed up to nearly halfway in the follicle, where they begin to show a few small, irregularly scattered trichohyalin granules. At this level the cells are somewhat flattened, and the proximal edges become slightly dislocated axially so that they overlap the distal ends of the preceding cells. Shortly after they acquire trichohyalin granules, the cuticle cells become hyalinized and their nuclei fade away. Above the middle of the follicle, the cuticle cells and Huxley's and Henle's layers all become fused into a solid hyalin layer. This layer stains with both acid and basic dyes and is intensely fuchsinophil.

In the follicles of the mouse, rat, sheep, and other animals, the inner sheath is thrown into horizontal folds or corrugations at the bottom of the pilary canal near the entrance of the sebaceous glands, as though its

---

Fig. 14. Sections through different levels of the same follicle from the scalp. (A) Section from just below the entrance of the sebaceous duct. The fused layers of the inner sheath form an incomplete basophilic band around the hair shaft. (B) Section from midway in the follicle. The layers of the inner sheath are all fused and stained intensely with toluidine blue. (C) Section just below the middle of the follicle. Henle's layer is fully keratinized and stains darkly, but Huxley's layer is still cellular and remains largely unstained. (D) Section through the keratogenous zone. The inner sheath is essentially like that in (C). (E) Section through the upper bulb of the follicle. Nearly all the inner sheath is cellular. (F) Section across the widest portion of the bulb, at the transition between the upper and lower regions of the bulb. In the center is the dermal papilla. Observe the relative thickness of the layers at the different levels of the follicle.

path had been barred or dammed. Corrugations do not occur in human follicles.

The inner sheath is eliminated in the pilosebaceous canal. In the sheep, the rat, and the mouse, Henle's and Huxley's layers fuse together,

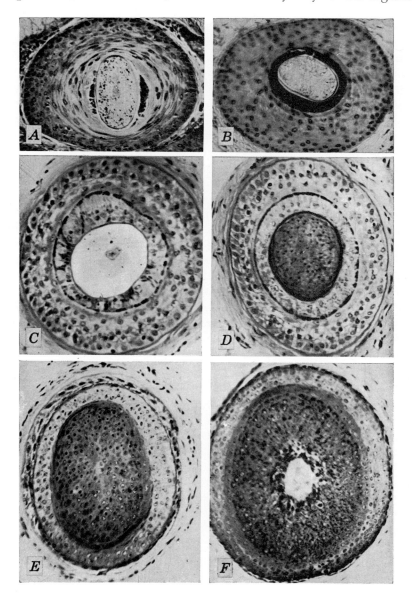

taper distally, and finally disappear (Auber, 1952). The disappearance could be due to chemical changes which culminate in a reabsorption or dissipation of the inner sheath. This could be brought about by enzymatic action. Perhaps a keratinase in the pilary canal digests selectively the inner sheath; hair, being slightly more acidic and covered by the epicuticle, a film of lipids and carbohydrates, might be protected from such enzymatic action. The enzymes could also be present in a quantity just sufficient for the elimination of the inner sheath only. This, however, is pure speculation.

In human follicles, the inner sheath forms a loose, horizontal, reticulated collar around the emerging hair in the widened portion of the pilosebaceous canal. This collar is more hyalin than the surrounding stratum corneum of the pilosebaceous canal. At the surface of the epidermis, the inner sheath is frayed and lost along with the surrounding stratum corneum. If a keratinase is present, it might also aid in the fragmentation and dispersal of the inner sheath in these follicles.

Since the inner sheath is interlocked with the hair, the two must grow and travel outward at approximately the same rate. The outer side of Henle's layer slides over the axial border of the outer sheath, which is stationary. These two layers have smooth surfaces at the interphase, which facilitates the movement of the inner sheath. The cells of Henle's layer are keratinized immediately after they rise from the matrix and slide easily against the partially keratinized axial cells of the outer sheath.

Chemical analyses of the inner root sheath have yielded interesting results (Rogers, 1958, 1959). Two-dimensional chromatograms of hydrolyzates of the inner root sheath of the rat vibrissae show the presence of all the amino acids found in hair, but in different proportions. The chromatograms also show spots not present in hydrolyzates of hair. The inner root sheath has greater amounts of glutamic and aspartic acids, histidine, and lysine than hair does. The inner sheath also contains very little tyrosine and phenylalanine. It contains little cysteic acid and no cystine, but appreciable amounts of methionine, perhaps in greater amounts than is found in hair. A surprising finding is the presence of citrulline in the inner root sheath; citrulline has not been demonstrated before on paper chromatograms of protein hydrolyzates. Since the protein in the inner root sheath differs considerably in its amino acid content from that of hair Rogers (1958) suggests that it is not a keratin. Trichohyalin and the fibrous protein in the cells of the inner root sheath have striking dissimilarities. Trichohyalin, for example, is labile in the presence of strong urea solutions, and to mild acid conditions, and citrulline is nearly absent from it. Other than this, the amino composition of the two substances is qualitatively similar. Rogers (1958) speculates that a conversion might take place from the amorphous trichohyalin to the fibrous protein.

The Outer Root Sheath

The thickness of the outer sheath of large follicles is usually uneven, causing the hair to be eccentrically located in the follicle (Fig. 14). Most of the follicles in the skin of man have some degree of swelling of the outer sheath on the side of the bulge. In the follicles of sheep both inner and outer sheaths have pronounced lateral swellings (Auber, 1952). When the bulb is bent or curved, as in the scalp of Negroes, the outer sheath is thicker on the convex than on the concave side. At the level of the sebaceous glands, the wall of the pilary canal, the outer sheath is indistinguishable from the surface epidermis. Below the level of the sebaceous glands the cells of the outer sheath store large amounts of glycogen and appear vacuolated and distorted in histological preparations. The cells in the middle third of the follicle, which contain more glycogen than those elsewhere, are reduced to flimsy, spongy sacs.

The outer sheath extends to the tip of the bulb, around which it is composed of two layers. The cells on the outside are slightly elongated and those of the inner surface are greatly flattened. Just above the bulb the sheath has three layers. It becomes gradually pluristratified and attains its greatest thickness a third of the way up the follicle. At this point nearly all of its cells are riddled with vacuoles, with the exception of those on the axial surface. The tall, columnar peripheral cells are oriented perpendicular to the axis of the follicle. In the upper third of the follicle, where the cells are not highly vacuolated, those at the outer periphery are cuboidal.

The peripheral columnar cells in the lower part of the follicle have minute basal cytoplasmic processes that push laterally through the thick vitreous membrane. These are best developed in the region just above the bulb. In the upper third of the follicle the peripheral cells have a fairly smooth base, or at least the cytoplasmic processes cannot be seen easily.

Over the entire length of the outer sheath, the cells at the periphery have more vacuoles than the cells on the axial surface which have a relatively intact cytoplasm. Intercellular bridges, desmosomes, and tonofibrils are particularly well developed in the more axially located cells. The cells which rest against Henle's layer are rich in tonofibrils; about halfway up the follicle their cytoplasm becomes hyalinized and under-goes partial keratinization (Gibbs, 1938).

In the outer sheath of human hair follicles both necrotic cells and mitotic figures are occasionally found, and cell death and cell division may bear a direct relation to each other. Mitotic activity is relatively common in the upper part of the follicle, where the outer sheath blends with the surface epidermis. This part of the outer sheath forms a kera-tinized surface layer which is sloughed off into the pilary canal, and the need for greater replacement of cells is obvious.

The upper and lower halves of active hair follicles have different fates (Fig. 42). The lower half, below the bulge, is a relatively transient structure which comes and goes with each hair growth cycle of the follicle. During catagen much of the outer sheath perishes; the remain-ing part forms the hair germ and the epithelial sac around the club hair. The upper part of the outer sheath is the stable element of the follicle.

The Vitreous or Glassy Membrane

This is a hyalin, noncellular, two-layered barrier between the outer root sheath and the connective tissue sheath. It is hardly visible around the upper part of the follicle, but it is thick around the middle part, and thickest around the widest part of the bulb (Schaffer, 1933). The vitreous membrane is very thin around the matrix, and nearly impossible to demonstrate in the papilla cavity. The thickness of the vitreous membrane in the various regions of the follicle is proportional to the size of the hair follicle.

The vitreous membrane has been interpreted as a concentrically stratified structure traversed by radial septa (Spuler, 1899), as a porous structure (Merkel, 1919), or as a homogeneous membrane (Patzelt, 1926). Some believe that it is formed from a condensation of a secretion from the cells of the outer sheath (Spuler, 1899; Stöhr, 1903; Cooper, 1930). Some, however, believe that the membrane originates from the connective tissue sheath (Hoepke, 1927; Merkel, 1919). We shall see that the vitreous membrane seems to have a dual origin.

The vitreous membrane is single-layered around the upper part of the follicles and two-layered where it is thickest, around the lower third or half of the follicle. Only the outer layer, which is continuous with the basement membrane of the epidermis, is visible around the entire follicle. It is a hyalin structure composed principally of delicate collagenous fibrils. With Masson's triacid method, it stains like the collagenous fibers. It remains unstained with toluidine blue. Unlike collagenous fibers, it reduces ammoniacal silver nitrate. With the PAS technique, it stains a pale pink.

In the lower half of the follicle, the basal cells of the outer sheath are tall columnar and very large, and their cytoplasm is riddled with large vacuoles. The outer borders of these cells terminate in delicate cytoplasmic processes which seem to push through the inner layer of the vitreous membrane. The inner layer, in histologic preparations, appears as a tangled skein of fibrils wound between the basal cytoplasmic processes. The mixture of fibrils and the cytoplasmic processes gives rise to an irregular, heterogeneous lamina. The fibrils are brilliantly PAS-positive. They are not stained by Van Gieson's stain, and with toluidine blue they stain metachromatically. The inner lamina of the membrane is thicker around that part of the outer sheath in which the basal cells are particularly rich in granules that stain metachromatically. The apparent relation between the metachromatic granules of the cells of the outer sheath and the fibrillar lamina suggests, probably erroneously, that the fibrils may be derived from the granules (Cooper, 1930). However, although both the granules and the fibrils stain metachromatically, only the fibrils are Schiff-reactive. Similarly, the fibrils are argyrophil, but the granules are not. If the fibrils are formed from the granules, chemical changes must occur during their formation. The substances in the granules might become depolymerized as they give rise to the fibrils. Polymerized glycoproteins of the ground substance, for instance, are either weakly PAS-reactive or nonreactive, but they become strongly reactive when depolymerized (Gersh and Catchpole, 1949).

During early catagen, the fibrillar inner lamina becomes very thick (Fig. 15), but the outer lamina remains unchanged. The conspicuously hypertrophied, PAS-positive inner lamina forms a wrinkled sac around the waning lower part of the follicle throughout catagen; at telogen it becomes fragmented and is resorbed. Resting hair follicles are surrounded by a thin, hyalin membrane, composed of one visible layer that corresponds to the outer lamina of the membrane around active follicles.

Rogers' (1957) studies of the vitreous membrane of the follicles of the mouse and the guinea pig with the electron microscope largely support the observations with the light microscope. The vitreous membrane of these animals consists of two layers of collagen fibrils with an axial periodicity of 500 Å and a diameter of 500 Å. The fibrils of the inner lamina are oriented parallel to the long axis of the follicle and those of the outer lamina are oriented perpendicular to it. At least in the mouse and the guinea pig, both layers of the vitreous membrane must be derived from the fibroblasts of the surrounding connective tissue sheath, being composed of collagen fibrils. In the developing follicles of mice 1 to 3 days old, Rogers found an electronoptically homogeneous layer about 200 Å thick, that corresponds to a true basement membrane adhering to the basal border of the outer sheath. This structure seems

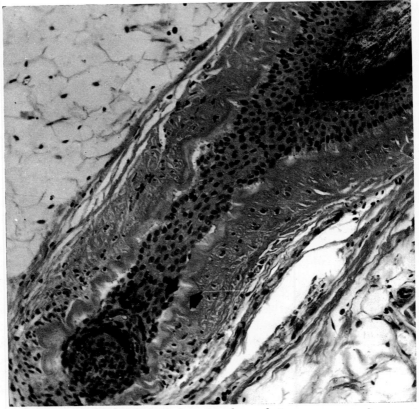

FIG. 15. Enormously thickened glassy membrane, between arrows, and connective tissue sheath around the waning lower part of a follicle from the scalp in the last stages of catagen. In the upper right corner is the well-formed club hair. (Courtesy of Dr. A. M. Kligman.)

to correspond to the inner layer of the vitreous membrane of the follicles of man. The two layers that Rogers describes are probably not distinguishable with the light microscope. No one has studied with the electron microscope the hair follicles during catagen, at which time the inner layer becomes enormously thickened.

The Dermal Papilla

The term "dermal papilla" should be used only to designate the connective tissue element that is enclosed by the bulb of the follicle during anagen, and which forms a compact ball of cells underneath the "hair germ" during telogen. In active follicles, the dermal papilla is attached to the connective tissue sheath by a narrow basal stalk. The vascularity of the dermal papilla depends upon the size of the follicles: the papilla of small follicles may have no vascular supply, whereas those of larger ones have varying numbers of blood vessels in them (Durward and Rudall, 1949).

The shape of the dermal papilla varies with the shape of the bulb. In the follicles of hairs that have more than one medulla, the papilla is split distally and terminates in as many apices as there are medullae. In the pig the papilla is shaped like an onion, terminating in a long central prong surrounded by rows of lesser prongs (Kränzle, 1912). All degrees of splitting may occur, ranging from one papilla with two apices to two or more completely separated papillae.

The dermal papilla exhibits striking morphologic changes during the cycle of hair growth. In the resting follicle, it is a compact ball of cells with dense, round nuclei and barely visible cytoplasm. Some pigment granules may be scattered between the cells. In a growing follicle, the papilla is more voluminous and the cells are farther apart. The nuclei are large and ovoid and stain a pale color with basic dyes. Between the cells is a hyalin ground substance and a basic argyrophil framework. It is generally believed that during catagen there is a reduction in the number of papilla cells, and that in early anagen the cells divide and increase in number (Wolbach, 1951). However, degeneration of papilla cells is not appreciable, and many of the mitotic figures found in the papillae of human hair follicles prove to be in the nuclei of endothelial cells. The number of papilla cells, then, remains fairly constant, and the changes that appear are due largely to fluctuations in the number of endothelial cells. Changes in the size of the papilla are mostly the result of changes in the size of its cells, of the increase and decrease in the size of the capillary plexus, and of the changes in the intercellular substances. Van Scott and Ekel (1958) in a meticulous study of the matrix of the bulb and the dermal papilla in the follicles of the scalp find that the volume of the matrix is approximately ten times that of the dermal papilla. They also find that the ratio of the number of cells in the papilla and the number of cells *dividing* in the matrix is about nine to one. During the early phases of male pattern baldness, a proportionate reduction occurs in the size of both the matrix and the papilla, and the geometric relationships between the two structures remains unaltered from the normal state. This phenomenon results in a progressive diminution in the size of the hair formed. In contrast, in lesions of alopecia areata both the volume of the matrix and the papilla are small, but the degree of reduction of the matrix is greater than that of the papilla. Successful therapy of alopecia areata is followed by an enlargement of the matrix to a normal size with no concurrent increase in the size of the papilla. It must, then, be concluded that there is a very close geometric relationship between the volume of the two structures and the number of cells in each.

The Blood Vessels of Hair Follicles

The blood vessels around the hair follicles in several species of animals have usually been demonstrated by injecting the vessels with India ink or other opaque substances (Ryder, 1958; Durward and Rudall, 1958). There is always a question, howewer, in such preparations, as to whether or not all of the capillaries have been injected. Since the endothelium of the cutaneous capillaries and end arterioles in the skin of man react specifically for alkaline phosphatase (Montagna and Ellis, 1957b; Klingmüller, 1957), this histochemical technique (Gomori, 1952) when applied to thick frozen sections, reveals the vascular beds around the hair follicles very clearly. Naturally, the illustrations in this chapter have been chosen for their photogenicity.

Hair follicles are surrounded by a dense and continuous plexus of capillaries, the pattern of which is different in active and quiescent follicles.

Parallel, longitudinally oriented vessels, which arise from deeper ones, extend from the papilla pore to the pilary canal of active follicles (Fig. 16). Horizontal cross-shunts and tortuous interconnecting shunts from the parallel vessels, outline a latticework around the lower part of the follicle (Fig. 17). The bore of the longitudinal vessels is larger than that of the cross-shunts, and they may be terminal arterioles. Most of the cross-shunts drop out just above the bulb and the middle third of the follicle is surrounded only by the palisade of parallel vessels. At the level of the sebaceous glands, cross-shunts again form a network that envelops both the glands and the pilary canal. Sebaceous glands are richly vascularized by baskets of capillaries that adhere to the acini following all of their contours. Above the entrance of the sebaceous gland, the parallel vessels branch out and form a loosely woven network

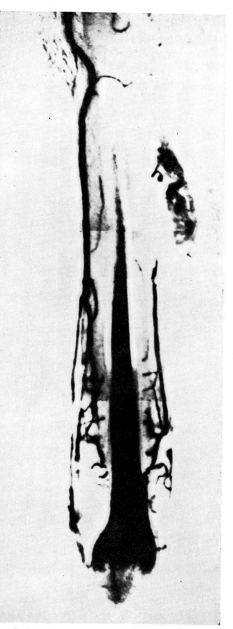

FIG. 16. The lower half of an active follicle from the scalp, showing the distributions of the major vessels. Frozen section treated with the method for alkaline phosphatase.

that extends to, and is continuous with, the loops of capillaries of the papillary plexus. These loops of capillaries form a vascular ring around the terminal part of the pilary canal. In the dermal papilla, capillaries from a central tuft of vessels extend to the walls of the inner surface of the follicle and come practically in contact with it (Fig. 18). The vascular system of each follicle, including the plexus around the sebaceous glands, is a continuous unit.

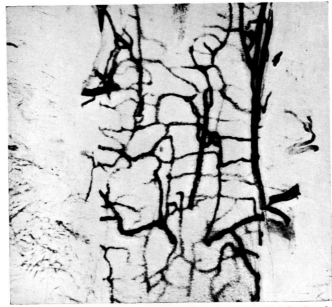

Fig. 17. Detail of the vascular plexus around the lower third of a follicle from the scalp.

Progressively smaller follicles are surrounded by progressively simpler vascular systems. The follicles of vellus hairs have only a few capillaries around the lower part and no vessels penetrate the dermal papilla. In contrast, the large sebaceous glands of these follicles are richly vascularized. There is also an inverse relation between the amount of phosphatase activity in a dermal papilla and the richness of its capillary plexus.

During the early changes of catagen, characteristic corrugations appear in the outer root sheath in the lower third of the follicle, and the vitreous membrane and connective tissue sheath become thicker and wrinkled (Figs. 19, 20, and 21). In spite of these and subsequent changes, the vascular system around the bulb and in the dermal papilla remains intact, with no signs of atrophy, and is similar to those of active follicles (Ellis and Moretti, 1959). Later in catagen, when the outer root sheath around the bulb is largely collapsed, the longitudinal palisade of vessels and the cross-shunts that form the lower plexus of the

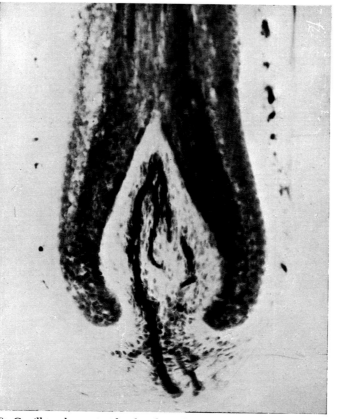

FIG. 18. Capillary loops inside the dermal papilla of a follicle from the scalp.

follicle are still intact. At this time the follicle is somewhat shortened, the dermal papilla is retreating upward, the vessels of the papilla lose their clear outlines, and a diffuse phosphatase reactivity seems to be spilled from the vessels into the surrounding connective tissue. Some of the capillary tufts within the dermal papilla become collapsed and show the first degenerative changes in the vascular system of the follicle. As catagen advances, the lower third of the follicle shrivels up and

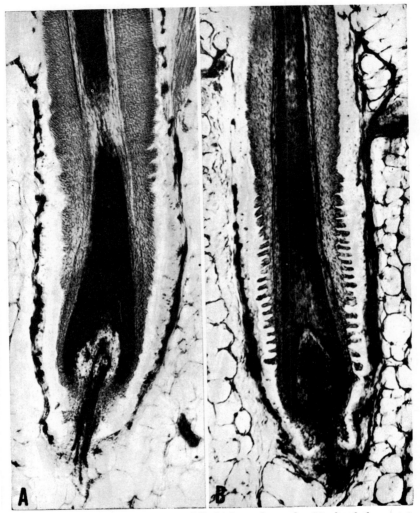

Fig. 19. (A) Early catagen in a follicle from the scalp. Much of the matrix is gone, the dermal papilla is partially released, and the outer root sheath is beginning to show transverse corrugations. The vessels are clearly outlined. (B) Slightly more advanced catagen, showing a spillage of alkaline phosphatase activity from the vessels into the surrounding tissue, and a greater corrugation of the outer root sheath. (Courtesy of Dr. R. A. Ellis.)

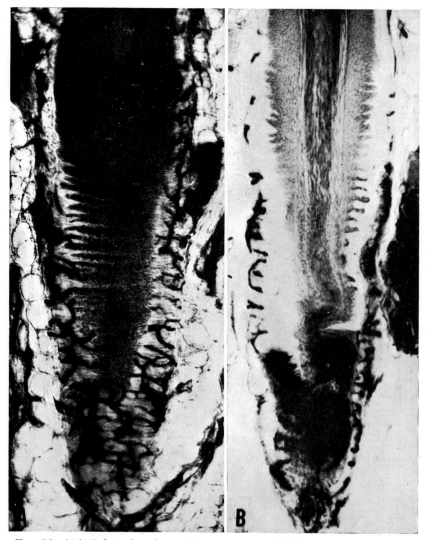

FIG. 20. (A) Relatively advanced catagen in a follicle of the scalp, showing the part of the follicle below the bulge. This is a fairly superficial cut, showing the cross-corrugation of the outer sheath, surrounded by a more or less intact vascular network. (B) More advanced catagen than in (A). Catagen here is not normal since a club is not forming. The lower part of the shrivelled bulb is bent. (Courtesy of Dr. R. A. Ellis.)

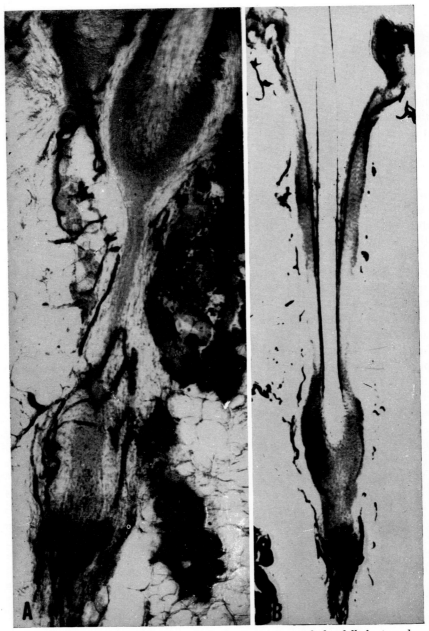

Fig. 21. (A) Late catagen, in which the lower part of the follicle is reduced to a cord of cells between the club and the dermal papilla. (B) Telogen. As in (A), the dermal papilla is free of blood vessels, which are bunched below it. (Courtesy of Dr. R. A. Ellis.)

retreats upward, leaving a trail or path of connective tissue behind; the dermal papilla, freed from the bulb, remains in contact with the retreating follicle. All of these changes take place inside of the lower vascular plexus of the follicle, which even in advanced changes remains relatively intact. When the lower third of the follicle is reduced to a thin, long strand of cells, some of the capillaries of the lower network degenerate, and there is a characteristic spillage of phosphatase reactivity from the blood vessels to the surrounding tissues. At the completion of catagen, most of the follicle below the bulge is reduced to a hair germ, at the base of which the dermal papilla is attached. Many of the capillary shunts in the lower follicular plexus and the palisade vessels are collapsed into a bundle that outlines the path of retreat of the follicle. The vessels in this bundle are still crisply reactive for alkaline phosphatase, and they are in the form of a bouquet just under the dermal papilla, which itself is free of vessels (Fig. 21). The vessels of the palisade flow around the epithelial capsule and continue up the upper part of the follicle, which has remained intact. Around the sebaceous gland and the infundibulum of the pilary canal, the upper follicular plexus remains intact, and is similar to that around active follicles. When the quiescent follicle becomes active again, the new bulb must advance through the collapsed bundle below the dermal papilla, growing inside it. Thus, the major vessels of the follicle remain intact during the catagenic changes, only some of the capillary cross-shunts and anastomoses degenerate. These vessels regenerate when a new follicle is formed.

Nearly the entire lower third of the follicle consists of the bulb; as the cells of the matrix proliferate and new cells move up to form the hair and the inner root sheath, in the upper part of the bulb, the cells grow many times their original volume and synthesize keratin. Farther up, in the keratogenous zone, the final phases of keratin formation take place. The cells of the outer root sheath around the keratogenous zone contain more glycogen than those in other levels (Montagna et al., 1952a) and more enzyme activity (Montagna, 1955, 1957). From the upper part of the bulb to the level of the keratogenous zone the follicle is surrounded by a glassy membrane that is thicker than at any other level. This region of the follicle is a very active tissue. Only 6 minutes after the injection of cystine labeled with S^{35}, a strong accumulation of radioactive particles can be recovered first around the general region of the keratogenous zone of the follicles of the sheep (Ryder, 1956b). This part of the follicle is also surrounded by the densest vascular networks, and must be an important site of exchange.

Exchange must also take place through the wall of the bulb that faces the dermal papilla (Fig. 22). Not all dermal papillae are equally supplied with vessels, and the amount of vascular tissue in a papilla is related to the size of the follicle; the wider the diameter of the follicle, the larger the capillary tufts it contains (Ryder, 1956a). The dermal

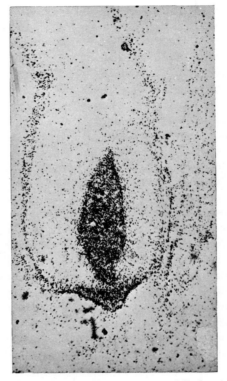

FIG. 22. Radioautograph of the bulb of an active follicle of a rat, 2 hours after the injection of S^{35}-sodium sulfate.

papillae of active, large human follicles are very wide and contain large numbers of capillaries. During periods of quiescence, the tissue of the papilla disengages itself from the capillary tuft by flowing away from it, and many of the capillaries atrophy.

These vicissitudes of the capillaries in the dermal papilla strengthen the belief that the number of papilla cells remains relatively the same during periods of activity and quiescence, and that the changes in the size of the papilla are largely due to the increases and decreases in the amount of capillary tissue and to the increase and decrease in the size of the papilla cells.

Innervation of Hair Follicles

All hair follicles are surrounded by some nerves. The arrangement of these nerves around the follicle is essentially similar to that of the dermal nerve networks, and the two of them together form nearly all of the sensory nerves of the hairy skin (Winkelmann, 1959, 1960).

Human hair follicles are surrounded by a collar of nerves the fibers of which converge toward 5 to 12 nerves that run along the sides of hair follicles before proceeding to the deep cutaneous tissues (Winkelmann, 1959; Weddell, 1941, 1945; Woollard et al., 1940). These nerves come practically in contact with the follicle in the region between the bulge and the duct of the sebaceous glands (Figs. 23, 24, and 25). The part of the follicle below the bulge always seems to be relatively free of them. Even though most diagrams show them there no one seems to have demonstrated successfully nerves around this part of the follicle, even with methylene blue (Miller et al., 1960). The collar of nerves is denser in its upper than in its lower limits (Figs. 26 and 27). Fibers extend from this plexus to the upper part of the pilary canal where they form a sparser network around the infundibulum of the follicle (Fig. 25); a few scattered fibers bear a casual relationship to the sebaceous glands. Very thin fibers from the higher follicle plexus rise to the base of the epidermis, divide into barely visible branches, and some are seen penetrating the epidermis. Fibers from the follicle network may also join the nerves to the arrectores pilorum muscles and those around the eccrine sweat glands. The major nerve collar is a double network of nonmyelinated fibers consisting of an outer layer of circularly arranged fibers, and an inner one in which the fibers are oriented longitudinally. The fibers of the inner layer end freely around the inner root sheath, and in very large hairs they may terminate in small terminal end buttons. All of these nerves contain specific cholinesterase, demonstrable with the acetylthiocholine iodide method (Montagna and Ellis, 1957a; Montagna, 1960). Histochemical preparations for acetylthiocholinesterase give such excellent demonstration of the nerves that they can be used for morphological observations as well (Figs. 26 and 27). Quiescent follicles are shorter than active ones, and the nerve collar around them is closer to their base than it is in active follicles. Some quiescent follicles are so short that their base partially slips out of the nerve plexus, which collapses or shrinks at their base

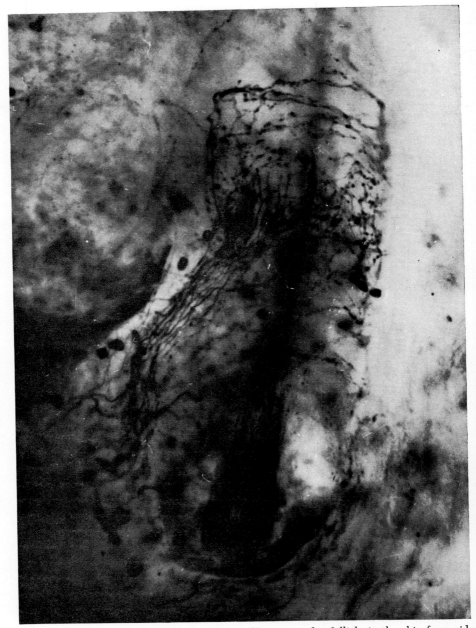

FIG. 23. Both circular and palisade nerve fibers around a follicle in the skin from side of the face near level of the eye of a 59-year-old woman. The nerves are stained supravitally with methylene blue. (Courtesy of Dr. M. R. Miller.)

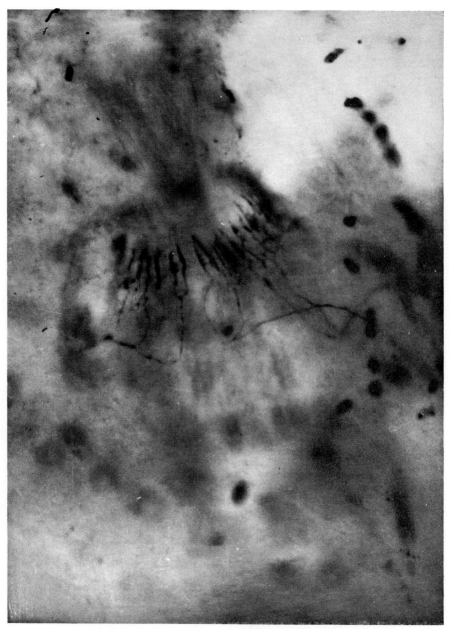

FIG. 24. This photograph, taken at a slight angle, shows part of the ring of palisade nerve fibers in focus, around a hair follicle from the skin of the same subject as in Fig. 23. The nerves are stained supravitally with methylene blue. (Courtesy of Dr. M. R. Miller.)

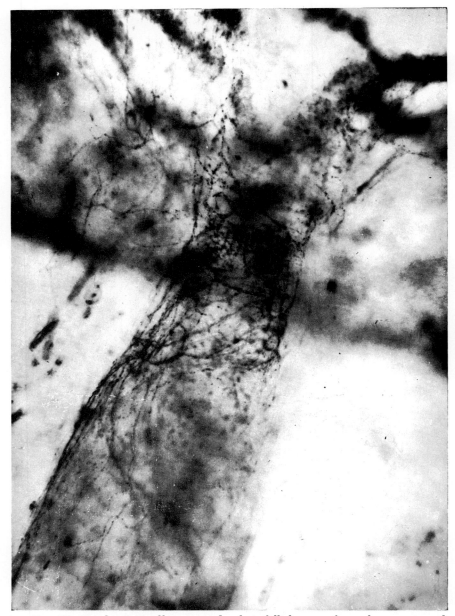

Fig. 25. Circular nerve fibers around a hair follicle, seen from above, over and below the palisade fibers. Free fiber endings are also seen in the dermis near the hair follicle opening. The nerves are stained supravitally with methylene blue. (Courtesy of Dr. M. R. Miller.)

together with the blood vessels (Fig. 27). The nerves however, seem to remain intact, and rich in cholinesterase (Montagna and Ellis, 1957a; Winkelmann, 1959).

These nerves contain specific cholinesterase; they are reactive when incubated with acetylthiocholine iodide as a substrate and not with

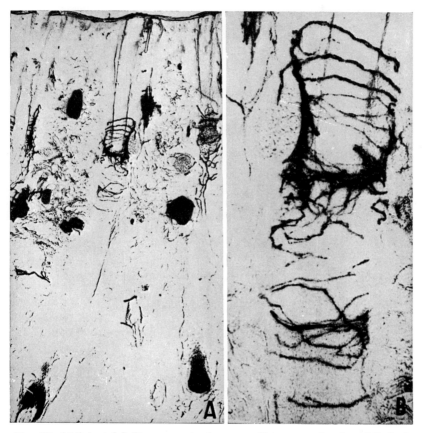

FIG. 26. (A) Acetylcholinesterase in the nerve fibers around a hair follicle from the scalp. (B) Detail of (A), showing only the horizontal fibers.

butyrylthiocholine iodide. The complete inhibition of the reaction by physostigmine also indicates that the enzyme is probably specific cholinesterase.

One of the functions of hairs, then, is to increase the perception of the surface to tactile stimuli (Winkelmann, 1959). The innervation of hair follicles is well adapted to tactile sensations, the hair shaft acting as a lever that increases the range of sensitivity to minute mechanical disturbances.

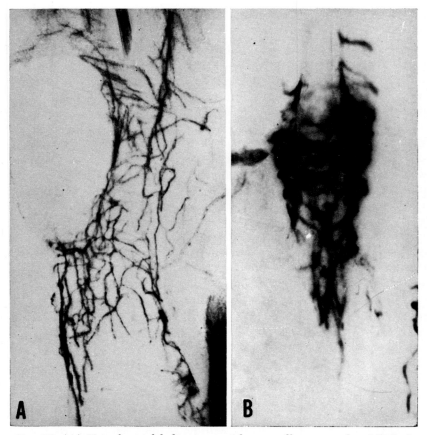

FIG. 27. (A) Net of acetylcholinesterase-rich nerve fibers around a follicle from the scalp; compare with Fig. 26(B). (B) Collapsed nerve network at base of a quiescent follicle in the scalp. Demonstrated with the technique for acetylcholinesterase.

Staining Properties of the Hair Follicle

The cells of the bulb have a strong affinity for basic dyes. They are colored an intense blue when stained with weak solutions of toluidine blue or methylene blue buffered from pH 3.0 to 5.0 (Figs. 32, 40, and 41). The cytoplasm remains unstained if the preparations are incubated in ribonuclease before they are stained with these dyes. The cytoplasmic basophilia is probably ribonucleic acid. When stained with basic dyes at the same concentration but at progressively higher pH values, all cells stain more intensely. Treatment with ribonuclease has no effect on the stainability of the cytoplasm of these and other cells when dyes buffered to pH 7.0 to 8.0 are used.

The cells of the matrix of active follicles have a high concentration of nucleic acid. In the upper bulb, the cells in each of the layers of the follicle are also rich in nucleic acids, although each layer has its own peculiarity. As the cells synthesize and accumulate keratin, they lose ribonucleic acid, suggesting that nucleoproteins are related to this synthesis. In the medulla, where keratinization is very slow, the cells remain moderately rich in ribonucleic acid a third of the way up the follicle. The cells of the cuticle of the cortex remain rich in ribonucleic acid until their outer borders begin to be tipped upward, when they lose most of their basophilic property. In the layers of the inner sheath, trichohyalin and ribonucleic acid are inversely proportional to each other. In the outer sheath, the scanty cytoplasm of the glycogen-rich cells has only a minimal amount of ribonucleic acid. The cells which abut against Henle's layer have a greater concentration of ribonucleic acid. The cells in the upper portion of the follicle are similar to those of the epidermis, with which the outer sheath is continuous.

The fibrils in the root of the hair are also stainable with basic dyes buffered from pH 4.0 to 8.0. The zone of keratinization of the hair root stains from pH 3.0 to 7.0, but not at lower pH values. With progressive maturation, keratin loses its ability to bind basic dyes at the lower pH values. Trichohyalin stains lightly at pH 5.0 and becomes progressively more strongly stained at higher pH values.

The fibrils in the cells just above the bulb stain with acid dyes equally intensely from pH 3.0 to 8.0. The smaller fibrils, seen first in the cells of the upper bulb, stain only with basic dyes. The numerous studies on the staining properties of keratin add little to the understanding of the formation of hair. Most staining procedures for keratin have no specificity. The pyridine-extraction test of Baker (1946) is excellent for the demonstration of delicate keratinous structures (Fig. 28). All of the fibrillar structures of the root of the hair as well as the keratinized hair and the inner sheath, including trichohyalin granules, are clearly stained with this method.

From their staining properties several things may be learned about hair follicles. Ribonucleic acid disappears from the cells of the bulb at the same rate that proteinous fibrils accumulate, suggesting that ribonucleic acid plays a role in the synthesis of proteinous material. The first stainable keratin fibrils are basophil, but as they mature the fibrils become both strongly basophil and acidophil. The fibrils in the fully formed keratin stain only with acid dyes. During maturation keratin may lose certain acid groups, or these groups may become so modified that they no longer bind basic dyes easily.

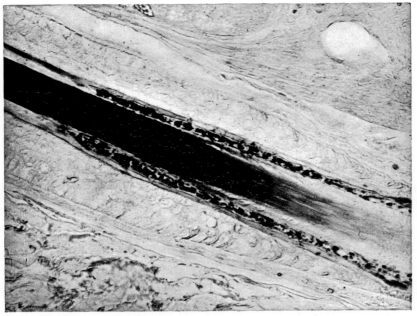

Fig. 28. Human hair follicle treated with the pyridine-extraction test of Baker and stained with acid hematein. The trichohyalin granules in the inner sheath, the keratin, and the fibrils below the keratogenous zone are all distinctly stained. (Courtesy of Dr. R. R. Suskind.)

The Feulgen Technique

In active hair follicles the staining of the nuclei is strongest in the cells of the matrix and fades gradually in the upper bulb (Fig. 29). In the matrix the intensely reactive nuclei are small, round, or oval and usually in mitosis. As the cells move into the different layers in the upper bulb their nuclei become larger, ovoid, and progressively less Feulgen-reactive. In Henle's layer, the nuclei lose their stainability above the middle of the bulb as the cells acquire trichohyalin granules.

The nuclei of the cells of Huxley's layer and those of the cuticle of the inner sheath and the cuticle of the cortex are Feulgen-reactive up to the middle of the follicle. In the cells of the hair root the nuclei remain strongly Feulgen-reactive up to the upper bulb. Above the bulb, as these nuclei become greatly elongated and aligned parallel to the axis of the hair, they stain a pale pink. The staining is barely visible in the keratinizing zone of the hair and becomes extinct above it. In the cells of the

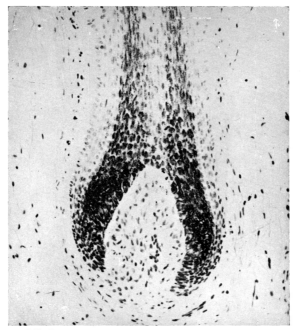

FIG. 29. Hair follicle from the scalp, stained with the Feulgen technique. The nuclei in the cells of the matrix, which are mostly in mitotic activity, are much more strongly reactive than those farther up in the follicle. The upper bulb contains pigment which masks the stainability of the nuclei.

medulla the nuclei remain round but weakly Feulgen-reactive up to the middle of the follicle, where they gradually disappear. In the lower half of the follicle the nuclei of the outer root sheath cells are large and round, are often misshapen, and mostly stain very lightly; only a few of them are strongly reactive. In the outer root sheath above the bulge the cells are less distorted, and their nuclei are strongly Feulgen-reactive.

The Mitochondria

It is difficult to demonstrate mitochondria in the cells of hair follicles, even in tissues prepared with care. Very small, thread-like mitochondria are seen around the nucleus of the cells of the matrix. Slightly more numerous, delicate filamentous ones are found in the cells of the upper bulb, which are larger than those in the matrix. Nowhere in the follicle are mitochondria as apparently numerous as they are in the cells of the surface epidermis. Rarely, a cell in Huxley's layer, or in the cuticle of the cortex, may abound in delicate filaments in its cytoplasm. Mitochondria and trichohyalin granules stain alike, and as soon as trichohyalin granules appear in cells it becomes impossible to separate them from the mitochondria. In the upper bulb, where the cells of the hair root become larger and elongated before keratinization, the cells are laden with pigment, which effectively masks the aggregates of mitochondria.

Mitochondria are not readily visible in the cells of the outer sheath. In the lower half of the follicle, where the cells of the outer sheath are engorged with glycogen, minute filaments may be seen in the scant cytoplasm around the nucleus. The larger, peripheral cells always have a larger assemblage of mitochondria than the more axial ones. Above the bulb, where the peripheral cells form a palisade of columnar cells, some of the smaller, less vacuolated cells contain numerous small filaments. This point is of interest, since some cells also contain more lipid than the surrounding ones. The peripheral cells contain mucopolysaccharide, which is presumably secreted laterally to form the inner layer of the vitreous membrane. The axial cells, however, which are slightly keratinized and comparable to cells in the upper part of the stratum spinosum of the epidermis, rarely have stainable mitochondria. In the upper half of the follicle, the cells of the outer sheath are smaller, and they contain more mitochondria than the cells farther down. The mitochondria of the cells of the pilary canal are similar to those of the epidermis.

There are very few visible mitochondria in the very small cells of the "hair germs" of resting hair follicles. The larger cells of the epidermal sac contain more of them. The partially keratinized axial cells, which anchor the keratinized rootlets of the club hair, are free of mitochondria.

It is surprising that an organ of such intense synthetic activity has so few demonstrable mitochondria. It is understandable that mitochondria should be scanty in the cells of the matrix, which are in a state of rapid proliferation. In the upper bulb, however, where the synthetic processes take place, one might expect more mitochondria. The greater number of mitochondria in the peripheral cells of the outer sheath is of particular interest. These cells not only store glycogen and secrete an acid polysaccharide to form the inner layer of the vitreous membrane, but they must also make these substances available to the growing part of the follicle. They seem to resemble glandular cells, and as such they contain numerous mitochondria.

The Golgi Apparatus

Only Parat (1928) seems to have studied the Golgi apparatus in hair follicles. He found that during the early development of the "hair germ" from the basal cells of the epidermis, the change in the orientation of the cells is reflected by a comparable shift in the orientation of the osmiophil bodies that he identified as the Golgi apparatus. In the cells at the sides of the "hair germ" the mass of osmiophil bodies is oriented perpendicular to the skin, and in those at the base of the "hair germ" it is parallel. When, later, the hair follicle forms the hair, the Golgi apparatus is found at the apical pole of the nucleus of the vertically elongated cells above the bulb. As the keratin fibrils are formed in these cells, the osmiophil bodies become less and less evident and finally disappear. In the inner sheath the Golgi apparatus is at the top of the cells, and it is lost when the trichohyalin granules are formed. In the cells of the outer sheath, where it is less well defined, the Golgi apparatus is oriented vertically. The orientation of the osmiophil bodies, then, reflects the vertical shift of the cells during the formation of the hair.

The Distribution of Lipids

The size, shape, and orientation of the Golgi bodies correspond to the clusters of intracellular sudanophil lipid bodies. Hair follicles contain only traces of sudanophil lipids (Nicolau, 1911), found as discrete granules of varying sizes, in nearly all of the nonkeratinized cells. The cells of the matrix have at their poles clusters of two or more lipid bodies, each with an eccentric sudanophobe vacuole, and the cytoplasm of these cells is delicately stippled with a sudanophil dust.

The thin, flattened cells of the outer root sheath around the lower bulb have more lipid bodies than all the other cells of the bulb. Farther up in the follicle, where the outer sheath is thickest, only the peripheral cells that rest upon the vitreous membrane still have visible sudanophil elements. The rest of the cells, distended and distorted by large amounts of glycogen, have only occasional lipid granules in the scanty cytoplasm left around the nucleus. Occasionally the well-developed desmosomes are very faintly sudanophilic. At the level of the duct of the sebaceous glands, the cells of the outer root sheath resemble those of the epidermis, and the sudanophil bodies they contain are identical to those of the epidermal cells (Montagna, 1950).

In the upper part of the bulb, the cells of the presumptive inner root sheath contain discrete lipid granules, but every trace of lipid disappears as soon as these cells acquire trichohyalin. The fragmenting inner sheath in the infundibulum of the pilosebaceous canal is strongly sudanophilic.

The cuticle cells of the inner root sheath and those of the hair lose the perinuclear sudanophil bodies almost as soon as they sweep upward from the matrix. In the hair root, the cells of the cortex and those of the medulla are relatively free of sudanophil lipids. Delicate, but clearly visible, granules are found in the apices of the cells of the dermal papilla.

In quiescent follicles, nearly all of the cells of the epithelial sac have lipid granules, but those in the partially keratinized capsule have none. The cells of the "hair germ" and those of the dermal papilla have no lipids.

During catagen the degenerating cells of the follicles often contain great quantities of lipids. The dermal papilla also shows an increase in lipids.

Glycogen

Active hair follicles are always rich in glycogen. In the connective tissue sheath some glycogen granules are found inside the cytoplasm of fibroblasts and extracellularly along the fibers. The inner layer of the vitreous membrane is PAS-reactive but diastase-resistant. The outer root sheath is laden with glycogen (Fig. 30); the cells in the middle third of the follicle contain so much glycogen that only a flimsy framework of cytoplasm is left. Glycogen is less abundant in the outer sheath in the upper and lower thirds of the follicle. None of the cells of the inner sheath have glycogen. The cuticle cells of the cortex in the region just above the bulb are rich in glycogen (Fig. 31), but they lose it as soon as they become cornified at about the middle third of the follicle. Just above the bulb, some cells of the cornifying cortex may have traces of glycogen, but the large medulla cells have glycogen from just above the dermal papilla to approximately half-way up in the follicle, when they become shrunken and cornified. The dermal papilla contains a PAS-reactive, saliva-resistant substance, but usually no glycogen.

In the cells of the outer root sheath glycogen granules form filamentous patterns that sweep through the cytoplasm and extend to the intercellular bridges. The outer peripheral cells above the bulb, although very large and vacuolated, contain very little glycogen. The cells are gradually depleted of glycogen as they become keratinized in their inner margins.

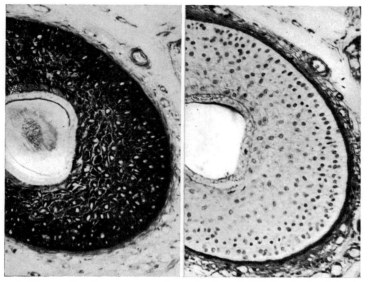

Fig. 30. Consecutive transverse sections of a beard follicle. At the left, the outer sheath is laden with glycogen. At the right, the glycogen has been removed, by digestion with saliva before staining with the PAS technique. The glassy membrane is strongly PAS-reactive saliva-resistant.

The quiescent hair follicles of most mammals contain no glycogen (Bollinger and McDonald, 1949; Johnson and Bevelander, 1946; Shipman *et al.*, 1955), but those of nearly all primates and man contain appreciable amounts of it in the cells of the epithelial sac (Brunner, 1907; Montagna and Ellis, 1959; Lombardo, 1934). Glycogen in these cells is arranged in a discrete fibrillar pattern in the cytoplasm. The keratinized capsule around the club hair has no glycogen. The cells of the dermal papilla, which nearly always contain glycogen during catagen, are free of it during telogen.

The distribution of glycogen in the different parts of hair follicles seems to bear some relationship to their rates of keratinization. The layers of the inner sheath, which are keratinized first, just above the bulb, never contain glycogen. The cuticle of the cortex and the medulla, which are keratinized slowly, contain glycogen in the lower third of the follicle. In the bulb, even some of the cells of the cortex have traces of glycogen. In all of these cases glycogen disappears as keratinization progresses.

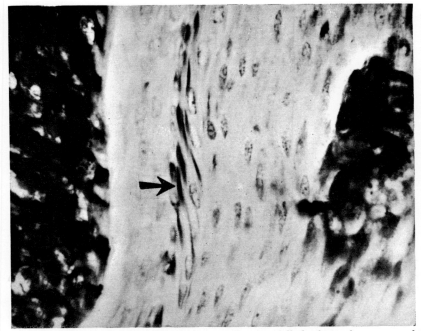

Fig. 31. Enlarged detail of the upper bulb of a follicle from the mons pubis, stained with the PAS technique. On the right are the cells of the outer sheath, rich in glycogen. The inner sheath contains no glycogen, but the cells of the cuticle of the cortex do (arrow). The medulla, on the extreme right, also contains glycogen.

Storage of glycogen bears an inverse relation to mitotic activity. The cells of the matrix of growing hair follicles have no glycogen; those of the outer sheath, which are laden with glycogen, are largely mitotically inert. Twenty-four hours after the scalp is exposed to epilating doses of X-rays, all the cells of the bulb accumulate glycogen, and they eventually perish (Montagna and Chase, 1956). Mitotically active cells, then, and the cells which are rapidly synthesizing keratin, do not contain demonstrable glycogen.

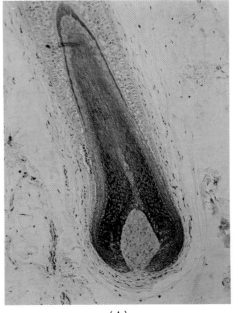

(A)

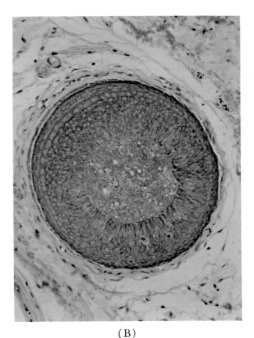

(B)

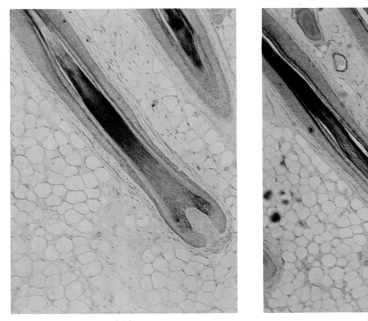

(C)   (D)

Fig. 32. (A) Longitudinal section through an active hair follicle from scalp, stained with toluidine blue buffered to pH 5.0. There is vivid metachromatic staining in the dermal papilla, and to a lesser degree, in the cells of the outer root sheath. (B) Transverse section through the bulb of a hair follicle from the mons pubis at a level just above the critical level, stained as above. The dermal papilla is brilliantly metachromatic. (C) —SH groups in a hair follicle from the scalp, prepared with the method of Barrnett and Seligman. (D) Another section through the follicle in (A) prepared to show the distribution of —S—S— groups.

Acid Mucopolysaccharides

Growing hair follicles contain a substance which stains metachromatically with thiazine dyes (Fig. 32). The ground substance of the dermal papilla of growing follicles stains intensely metachromatically (Montagna et al., 1951b). The cytoplasm of the papilla cells and of the endothelial cells of the capillaries stains orthochromatically. The stalk of tissue which connects the papilla to the connective tissue sheath is weakly metachromatic. The connective tissue sheath around the lower part of the bulb stains lightly metachromatically. That around the middle third of the follicle is strongly metachromatic; the area of metachromatic staining may extend to the level of the sebaceous glands and even encircle them. The metachromatic staining in this connective tissue is mostly found in the ground substance.

Around the base of the hair bulb, the cells of the attenuated outer sheath have a diffuse cytoplasmic metachromatic staining. Around the bulb, where the outer sheath is thicker, most of the cells, and particularly those in contact with the vitreous membrane, acquire numerous coarse granules which are stained metachromatically (Fig. 32). The intercellular substances in the vicinity of the bulge often stain intensely metachromatically. The cells of the bulb which line the papilla cavity stain slightly metachromatically, but the metachromasia is partially masked by the basophilia of these cells.

In quiescent hair follicles neither the epithelial nor the stromal elements contains substances which stain metachromatically. Occasionally the hair bulge of large follicles may contain kernels which stain strongly metachromatically.

Metachromatic staining usually indicates the presence of acid polysaccharides. The metachromasia described here is in Helly-fixed tissues stained with toluidine blue buffered to acid pH values; it resists alcoholic extraction and must be considered "true" metachromasia (Lison, 1935; Sylvén, 1941).

Normal skin contains appreciable amounts of hyaluronic acid and chondroitin sulfate B (Meyer and Chaffee, 1941; Meyer and Rapport, 1951; Pearce and Watson, 1949). Although some authors believe that both hyaluronic acid and chondroitin sulfate stain metachromatically with thiazine dyes (Bunting, 1950, Dempsey et al., 1947; Wislocki et al., 1947), hyaluronic acid and similar polysaccharides, which probably contain no sulfate, do not (Hale, 1946). Concentrations of hyaluronates weaker than 1% do not stain metachromatically (Meyer, 1947). Since the concentrations of hyaluronates in skin are probably not this high, the substances that stain metachromatically there may be only the chondroitin sulfates.

Hyaluronic acid can be digested with testicular or streptococcal hyaluronidase but chondroitin sulfate B cannot (Meyer and Rapport, 1951). Even if both substances were stained metachromatically, it should be possible to identify them by this selective enzyme hydrolysis. The metachromatically staining material in the dermal papilla, outer sheath, and mast cells resists digestion with testicular hyaluronidase, and probably contains chondroitin sulfate B.

In the hair follicles of the mouse, the rise and fall of metachromatically staining and of PAS-reactive, saliva-resistant substances can be followed during the periods of growth and rest (Montagna et al., 1952b). In the resting follicle, the rounded dermal papilla lies just beneath the "hair germ." The papilla cells are small, each having a dense nucleus and a narrow halo of cytoplasm. With toluidine blue, only the nuclei stain clearly, the cytoplasm remaining colorless. The cells of the dermal papilla are not PAS-positive.

In "anagen I," all of the cells of the "hair germ" are mitotically active and the follicle is becoming larger. The papilla cells are larger, and their nuclei less dense than in follicles in telogen. The cytoplasm of the papilla cells and the intercellular ground substance are still neither metachromatic nor PAS-reactive.

In "anagen II," the base of the proliferating cord of cells grows around the upper end of the papilla. The cup of cells thus formed is the beginning of the bulb. The papilla cells now have a large nucleus and a moderate amount of clear cytoplasm. They do not stain metachromatically with toluidine blue. The intercellular ground substance is PAS-reactive and appears as a delicate line around each papilla cell, the cytoplasm of which remains nonreactive. In "anagen IV," the hair bulb is fully formed and the inner sheath and the hair are growing. The tip of the newly formed hair shaft reaches the level of the sebaceous gland. At this time the dermal papilla is very large and is becoming elongated. The large papilla cells are riddled with colorless vacuoles but their cytoplasm is metachromatic and PAS-reactive. The intercellular ground substance is also richly metachromatic and PAS-reactive. The papilla becomes increasingly elongated and its cells more vacuolated. Both metachromatically staining and PAS-reactive substances become progressively abundant until the middle of "anagen VI." They remain in evidence until the end of "anagen VI" and the beginning of catagen, when they both disappear abruptly. Twenty-four days after the initiation of growth, the hair follicle is again in the resting phase, and a ball of small papilla cells which are neither metachromatic nor PAS-reactive lies under the "hair germ."

The metachromatic and PAS-reactive substances in the papilla appear to be superimposable, but they may be different substances. Some tissue elements, such as mast-cell granules, for example, stain strongly metachromatically but may be weakly PAS-reactive, and others, such as the basement membranes and cuticular borders are PAS-reactive but do not stain metachromatically. Also, since chondroitin sulfates are strongly metachromatic but only mildly oxidizable with periodic acid, the strongly PAS-reactive substance in the dermal papilla may represent something in addition to the acid polysaccharide (Meyer and Odier, 1946).

Sulfated acid polysaccharides, and substances belonging to the 1,2-glycol groups, then, are present together in the dermal papilla of the growing hair follicle, but not in that of the resting follicle. Whatever their exact nature, these substances in the dermal papilla of the hair follicle are present during the period of hair proliferation. They appear during anagen, at the stage of follicle development which immediately precedes hair proliferation. They disappear abruptly, just before catagen, when mitosis in the matrix cells has ceased. In animals injected with substances containing S^{35}, the S^{35} accumulates in large quantities in the dermal papilla a short time after the injection (Fig. 22) (Montagna and Hill, 1957). Sulfated mucopolysaccharides may also play a role in supplying sulfurous constituents for keratin synthesis and could be regarded as labile sulfur-bearing compounds (Sylvén, 1950).

Histochemistry of Enzymes

Since the histochemistry of the enzymes in hair follicles has been reviewed by Braun-Falco (1958), this chapter will deal mostly with details not covered by him.

Cytochrome oxidase, demonstrable with the method of Burstone (1959), is concentrated in the pilary canal of active follicles, and particularly in the cells of the matrix. The cells of the outer root sheath have a minimal reactivity, and those of the dermal papilla contain very small reactive granules similar to those in fibroblasts. In quiescent follicles some reaction is obtained in the cells of the pilary canal and those of the epithelial capsule, but practically none in those of the hair germ.

All of the living cells in hair follicles contain variable amounts of succinic dehydrogenase activity (Montagna and Formisano, 1955). In active follicles, the strongest enzyme activity is in the cells of the matrix and in those of the upper bulb. The coloration of the keratogenous zone proper is due to the reduction of the tetrazolium salts to monoformazans by the sulfhydryl groups there and not by the enzyme. All of the cells of the outer root sheath contain some enzyme, the brightest reaction being in the cells around the keratogenous zone. In the outer root sheath the cells at the periphery are always more reactive than the others. The cytoplasm of the cells of the dermal papilla is full of very small reactive granules. The cells of quiescent follicles all have less enzyme reactivity than those of active follicles. The cells of the dermal papilla of quiescent follicles have barely distinguishable enzyme reactivity in them.

Active and quiescent follicles contain surprisingly large amounts of monoamine oxidase (Yasuda and Montagna, 1960). The relative abundance and the distribution of this enzyme are very much like those of succinic dehydrogenase. In the outer root sheath of active follicles, strong enzyme activity is found around the keratogenous zone. The cells of quiescent follicles all contain moderate enzyme reaction.

Active or quiescent, hair follicles abound in amylophosphorylase activity (Braun-Falco, 1956a; Ellis and Montagna, 1958b), the enzyme being particularly concentrated in the outer root sheath of the upper half of active follicles. Around the lower half, the outer root sheath contains smaller amounts of enzymes. This is variable, however, and there are times when the lower half of active follicles may have large amounts of enzyme activity or none at all. The epithelial sac around the club of quiescent follicles contains moderate to large amounts of amylophosphorylase; the hair germ contains little activity. The presence of this enzyme in quiescent follicles, like the presence of glycogen in them, is singularly peculiar to the skin of man and that of other primates. In the skin of most nonprimates, quiescent follicles have neither glycogen nor phosphorylase.

There is abundant aminopeptidase in the outer root sheath around the keratogenous zone and around the bulb of active follicles (Adachi and Montagna, 1961). The matrix has much enzyme reaction, but the upper bulb does not. The dermal papilla has a greater concentration of enzyme than any other cutaneous structure. The endothelium of the capillaries around the follicles also shows appreciable amounts of enzyme activity. During catagen the entire bulb becomes very reactive, as does also the connective sheath around it. Quiescent follicles have a weak, generalized enzyme reaction, but the activity in their dermal papilla remains remarkably strong.

Hair follicles also contain β-glucuronidase (Braun-Falco, 1956b; Montagna, 1957). The matrix and the upper part of the bulb are reactive; the cells of the inner root sheath and those of the cortex lose their reactivity when they begin to undergo keratinization. The outer root sheath in the upper half of the follicle has moderate enzyme reaction; the reaction is strongest in the peripheral cells, and diminishes centripetally. The most intense reaction in the outer root sheath is around the level of the keratogenous zone. All of the cells of the dermal papilla of active follicles have strong β-glucuronidase activity. In quiescent follicles, the cells of the pilary canal, the epithelial sac, and the hair germ are all moderately reactive. The cells of the dermal papilla show practically no reaction.

Esterases are widely distributed in hair follicles (cf. Braun-Falco, 1958; Montagna and Ellis, 1958a). In active follicles the cells of the matrix and those of the upper hair bulb contain no tween esterases, but the differentiating cells in the region above the bulb and those in the keratogenous zone abound in it. The cells of the matrix and of the upper part of the bulb all contain small granules of nonspecific esterases. All of the cells of the outer root sheath, extending from the tip of the bulb to the wall of the pilary canal, contain tween esterases, and nonspecific esterases that can be demonstrated with a variety of substrates. Nonspecific esterase activity, indicated by the presence of granules, is concentrated in the outer layer of the outer root sheath around the lower one third of the follicle, and particularly around the keratogenous zone. Fine granules of all of these enzymes are present in the inner root sheath all along its length from the upper part of the bulb to the base of the pilary canal; the reaction is most intense where the inner sheath begins to be fragmented at the base of the pilary canal (Fig. 33) (Yun, 1958).

Quiescent hair follicles have moderate quantities of tween esterases evenly distributed throughout the epithelial sac; the hair germ has none. All of the cells of quiescent follicles have a stippling of very fine reactive granules of nonspecific esterases, very numerous in the cells at the base of the hair club. Clusters of cells in the epithelial capsule beneath the hair club are laden with nonspecific esterases (Montagna, 1955). As in active follicles, the inner root sheath at the bottom of the pilary canal, just below the entrance of the sebaceous glands, has a very strong reaction. The cells of the dermal papilla have no tween esterases, but they have varying small amounts of nonspecific esterases. The arrectores pilorum muscles abound in all esterases, including pseudo-cholinesterases and some specific cholinesterase.

When sections are treated with techniques that demonstrate specific cholinesterases, nerves surrounding some of the hair follicles are demonstrated (Montagna and Ellis, 1957a; Montagna, 1960; Winkelmann, 1960). These nerves are described elsewhere in this chapter.

Only the dermal papilla and the endothelium of the blood vessels that surround the hair follicles contain alkaline phosphatase. Regardless

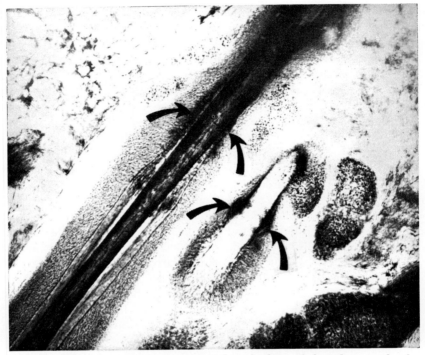

FIG. 33. AS esterase activity concentrated at the base of the pilary canal, where the inner root sheath is becoming fragmented (arrows).

of their state of activity, the dermal papilla of the smallest hair follicles is always strongly reactive for alkaline phosphatase. In progressively larger follicles, the papilla becomes less reactive. The papilla of the smallest follicles is avascular; that of progressively larger ones becomes gradually vascularized and its vascularity is the most dense in the largest follicles. In the best vascularized papillae, only the endothelium of the capillaries contains alkaline phosphatase; the surrounding connective tissue is weakly reactive. There is, then, an inverse relation between the size of the papilla and the amount of vascularity, and the amount of vascularity and the strength of the reaction for alkaline phosphatase in the dermal papilla (Montagna and Ellis, 1957b).

These observations focus attention upon the lower third of active follicles. In the bulb the cells of the matrix proliferate, ascend to higher levels, become larger and synthesize keratins, and they flow upward to the keratogeneous zone, where they die. The lower third of the follicles, then, is metabolically the most important part. The outer root sheath around this region contains more glycogen than it does at other levels (Montagna, 1956); it also contains greater concentrations of the enzymes described here. The follicle is surrounded at this level by a much richer bed of blood vessels than it is at the other levels.

Sulfhydryl Groups

Alcohol- and water-insoluble, protein-bound sulfhydryl groups can be demonstrated in hair follicles (Barrnett and Seligman, 1952), The outer sheath of active follicles is moderately and uniformly reactive throughout its length. Even the intercellular bridges and desmosomes show a moderate reaction. In the inner sheath, Henle's layer is more strongly reactive than Huxley's layer. The cells of Henle's layer are more strongly reactive in the region of the bulb than farther up in the follicle, where they become keratinized; the trichohyalin granules remain unstained (Figs. 32 and 34). The cuticle of the inner root sheath is moderately reactive, but that of the cortex is strongly reactive from the bulb to the surface of the skin. The cells of the matrix are only mildly reactive. The upper bulb is rich in sulfhydryl groups and the reaction becomes most intense just above this level (Goldblum et al., 1954; Montagna et al., 1954; Odland, 1953), in the keratogenous zone, which is composed of closely packed, parallel fibrils (Fig. 34). The keratinized hair shaft above this region is unreactive. The cells of the medulla contain only a moderate reaction; the glassy membrane and the connective tissue sheath show none. The fibroblasts and mast cells in the connective tissue sheath and the dermal papilla are lightly reactive. The arrectores pilorum muscles are strongly reactive.

The thick epithelial sac of resting hair follicles and the hair germ are weakly reactive. The club itself, except for some strongly reactive streaks which run parallel to the long axis of the hair, is unreactive. The capsule, which is made up of the brush-like processes of the club and the partially keratinized inner cells of the epithelial sac, is intensely reactive (Fig. 35). The distribution of sulfhydryl groups in the hair follicles of other animals is essentially similar to that in human follicles

(Eisen *et al.*, 1953). In the mouse, during early anagen, when follicles become elongated and form a bulb, both the follicle and the epidermis are rich in sulfhydryl activity. When in later anagen the follicles begin to produce a hair, the epidermis becomes thinner and its concentration of sulfhydryl groups becomes slight. During late anagen, only the keratogenous zone of hair follicles has a great concentration of sulfhydryl

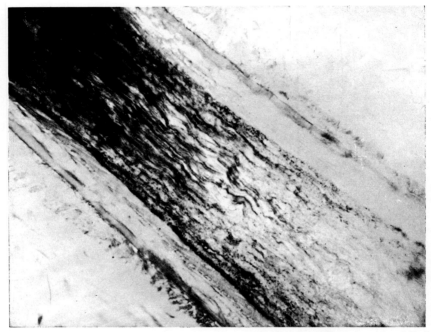

Fig. 34. Enlargement of the lower portion of the keratogenous zone of a follicle from the scalp showing that the cortex is formed by the accumulation of sulfhydryl-rich fibrils. The spaces in the inner sheath on either side of the cortex represent the unreactive trichohyalin granules. Stained with the technique of Barnett and Seligman for sulfhydryl groups.

groups. In catagen, a very intense reaction is found around the developing club hair, and the outer sheath shows a stronger reaction than during anagen.

On the basis of staining reactions with nitroprusside, two types of keratinization, soft and hard, have been identified in the skin (Giroud and Bulliard, 1935; Giroud *et al.*, 1934). Soft keratinization occurs in the surface epidermis; hard keratinization occurs in the hair cortex, horns, hoofs, and claws. The designation of soft and hard keratinization on the basis of histochemical reactions for —SH groups is unfortunate (Barrnett, 1953; Gavazzeni, 1908; Hardy, 152; Lapière, 1947; Mescon and Flesch, 1952; Van Scott and Flesch, 1954), since regions rich in sulfhydryl groups may be found in the epithelium of the tongue and esophagus, or in epidermis where the corneal layer is not fully keratinized. This is discussed more fully in the chapter on the epidermis.

FIG. 35. Quiescent follicle from the face, showing a concentration of —SH groups in the capsule around the hair club. The curved arrows point to the moat around the base of the pilary canal; the straight arrow indicates the area of contact between the hair germ and the dermal papilla.

Disulfide Groups

The cells of the hair bulb and those of the outer root sheath contain a moderate amount of disulfide groups. In the inner root sheath, Henle's layer is more strongly reactive than Huxley's layer. The trichohyalin granules contain no disulfide groups in either layer. The cells of the cuticle of the inner sheath show no appreciable reaction. The keratinized cortex of the hair is intensely reactive (Fig. 32). The dermal papilla stains moderately.

In resting hair follicles the club is only moderately reactive. The reaction is strong in the capsule around the club but mild in the epithelial sac.

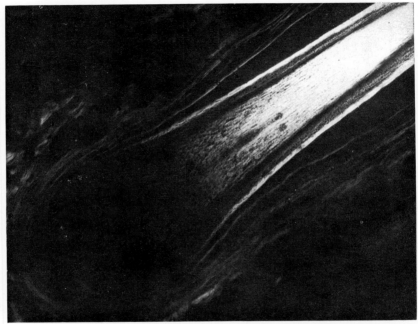

Fig. 36. Birefringence in the bulb of an active hair follicle from the scalp. The pre-keratogenous and keratogenous zones, Henle's layer of the inner sheath, and the glassy membrane are all birefringent.

Anisotropy

Those parts of hair follicles that synthesize keratin are anisotropic (Hoepke, 1927; Mercer, 1949; Odland, 1953). Thus, with the exception of the matrix, every part of hair follicles has a certain amount of birefringence (Figs. 35, 36, and 37).

Beginning with the bulb, the cells of Henle's layer are the first to become birefringent (Fig. 36). Huxley's layer, however, is birefringent some distance above the bulb, and the birefringence increases on up to the middle of the follicle. The cuticle cells of the inner sheath, which are very small and difficult to see, become anisotropic above the middle of the follicle. The layers of the inner sheath are fused together and very strongly anisotropic midway up the follicle. In the pilosebaceous canal the inner sheath forms a loosely meshed birefringent collar around the hair. Birefringence in the layers of the inner sheath develops con-

FIG. 37. Birefringence in: (*left*) an active follicle; and (*right*) a quiescent follicle containing a club hair.

comitantly with the acquisition of trichohyalin granules, although the granules themselves are isotropic.

In the hair, the cuticle is anisotropic only in the upper half of the follicle. The cortex becomes birefringent above the bulb, the anisotropy increases in the keratogenous zone, and attains its fullest brilliance above this level. The medulla cells are mostly isotropic (Figs. 37 and 38); they attain a granular anisotropy in the hair that has emerged above the surface of the skin, but this is seldom bright. The contrast between the anisotropy of the medulla and the cortex make possible the detection of the medulla under polarized light even when it is very small and fragmentary.

There are delicate birefringent fibrils even in the cells of the outer sheath. In the lower half of the follicle, the peripheral cells have radially arranged anisotropic fibrils, but in the middle segment fibrils are found in most of the cells. In the walls of the pilosebaceous canal the birefringent fibrils are arranged at an angle acute to the axis of the

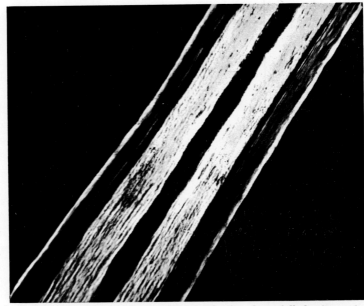

FIG. 38. Birefringence in the middle third of a hair follicle from the scalp. Birefringent fibrils can be seen in the cortex; the medulla is not birefringent. Henle's and Huxley's layers are fused and are almost equally birefringent.

follicle. The most axial cells in this region, which are partially keratinized, have the strongest birefringence.

In longitudinal sections of hair follicles, the outer layer of the vitreous membrane is anisotropic from above the bulb to the level of the pilosebaceous canal (Fig. 36). In transverse sections this structure is isotropic. The inner layer of the vitreous membrane is always isotropic, even during catagen, when it is very thick.

The inner layer of the connective tissue sheath is isotropic in longitudinal sections but anisotropic in transverse sections. The outer layer is birefringent in longitudinal sections but isotropic in transverse sections.

In quiescent follicles the club of the hair and the numerous keratinized rootlets which anchor it to the epithelial sac are completely birefringent [Fig. 37 (right)]. The cells of the capsule and of the epithelial sac are oriented radially around the club, and each has delicate birefringent fibrils. Above the level of the club the cells in the outer root sheath have delicate birefringent fibrils like those in the epidermis.

Hair Keratin and Keratinization

Hairs are part of a homologous series of epidermal derivatives which have a remarkably constant amino acid composition. These *keratins,* from the Greek *keras,* horn, are resistant to pepsin digestion and are insoluble in water, organic solvents, and dilute acids and alkalis. On acid hydrolysis, hair, horn, and nails yield histidine, lysine, and arginine in a molecular ratio of approximately 1:4:12 (Block, 1951). The protein of hair consists of polypeptide chains which are apparently held together by disulfide bonds, and which give X-ray diffraction patterns with a periodicity of 5.1 Å; this protein is α-keratin (Astbury and Woods, 1934). For a review of the physicochemical properties of keratins, see Bear and Rugo (1951).

In dividing keratins into hard and soft it is customary to assume that sulfhydryl groups are abundant only in sites where hard keratin is being formed (Giroud and Bulliard, 1935; Giroud *et al.,* 1934; Giroud and Leblond, 1951). This, as has been pointed out earlier, is erroneous (Eisen *et al.,* 1953; Van Scott and Flesch, 1954). Furthermore, the inner sheath of hair follicles, the medulla of hairs, and the stratum corneum of the epidermis, all of which have been designated soft keratin, are probably different substances. Assuming that cystine provides the cross links between the polypeptide chains of keratin, Bekker and King (1931) suggest that the term *keratinization* be used synonymously with *cystinization,* and that *cornification,* long used as a synonym for keratinization, be used to denote only a general hardening of protein without the intervention of cystinization.

Some keratinous substances contain more sulfur than others and may represent "different" keratins. Hot sodium plumbite applied to hairs or hoofs turns them black, whereas it turns the keratin of the stratum corneum brown (Giroud and Leblond, 1951). Chemical analyses also show more sulfur in some keratins than in others (Giroud *et al.,* 1929). Bekker and King (1931), studying the sulfur content of wool fibers and porcupine quills by chemical and histochemical methods, concluded that the keratinization of the cuticle, the cortex, and the medulla must all be different. The cuticle undergoes true keratinization, or cystinization. In the cortex, keratinization involves the incorporation of both cystine and tyrosine. In the medulla, however, they found tyrosine but no sulfur, and the author assumed that its cells dry up by a process of cornification, perhaps associated with a "keratinizing" agent other than cystine; this is not in agreement with most other authors, who have found at least some sulfhydryl groups in the medulla.

All of the substances casually called keratins in a growing hair follicle may be slightly different compounds. For example, the medulla and the inner root sheath are called soft keratins because they "are desquamated before the hair reaches the surface of the epidermis" (Leblond, 1951). Actually, neither of these substances is desquamated in the usual sense. The cells of the inner sheath contain trichohyalin, but we know little about trichohyalin. It contains no demonstrable sulfhydryl or disulfide groups, it is isotropic, although keratin fibrils are birefringent. It is strongly fuchsinophil, but many unrelated substances share this property. The hair cortex stains intensely with methyl green in the keratogenous zone. Above the keratogenous zone it becomes progressively more fuchsinophil. The cells of the cuticle of the cortex stain with methyl green in the upper bulb and retain this property up to the infundibulum, where they gradually become fuchsinophil. This similarity between the cuticle cells and the keratogenous zone of the cortex suggests that the cuticle keratinizes very slowly. Also, the cortex is rich in sulfhydryl groups only in the keratogenous zone, but the cuticle cells show it practically up to the surface of the skin. The medulla cells also undergo real but slow keratinization, since some sulfhydryl groups can be demonstrated in them all the way to the upper part of the follicle. The axial cells of the outer sheath in contact with Henle's layer, particularly those around the keratogenous zone and up, undergo some keratinization or cornification (Montagna *et al.*, 1951a, 1952a). Thus, some keratinization, or cornification, is found in all the layers of the hair follicle.

When a growing human hair is plucked, the upper bulb and nearly all of the outer sheath in the lower half of the follicle come out with it. When viewed under polarized light, the fully keratinized hair is strongly birefringent; the keratogenous zone is less birefringent, and in its lower part birefringence can be seen in the individual fibrils. The inner sheath is less brilliantly birefringent; the bulb is isotropic (Mercer, 1949). The physical properties of keratins can be followed by the course of action of certain substances on these plucked hairs. The consolidation of keratin can be followed at different levels of the follicle by determining the increase in resistance to temperature, enzymes and dilute acids and alkalis, and solutions of urea. Hair proper, which is birefringent and gives a typical α X-ray diffraction pattern, is stable in boiling water, but when exposed to 130°C it contracts, shows a marked reduction in birefringence and gives a β X-ray pattern. In general, substances not capable of attacking disulfide linkages have little effect on hair. X-Ray diffraction patterns of the bulb, which is isotropic or very scantily birefringent in the upper part, show an absence of oriented crystalline material. The bulb is the region where the cells are formed and the synthesis of keratin protein takes place. The rise of birefringent fibrils can be traced in the upper part of the bulb (Odland, 1953). X-Ray diffraction patterns of the strongly birefringent keratogenous zone are of the α type and are similar to those of the fully keratinized hair. The keratogenous zone, however, is easily dissociated and yields β-keratin. Keratin hardens immediately above the keratogenous zone in the consolidation zone (Mercer, 1949).

The protein in the cells of the hair root form fibrils (Mercer, 1949). When the fibrils are first formed in the upper bulb, they are held together by low energy bonds; they are easily digested by enzymes and yield β-keratin at moderate temperatures. When a plucked hair is dipped in urea, the part below the keratogenous zone is dissolved but the part above it only becomes swollen. If exposed to 90°C the part below the keratogenous zone becomes disoriented but not contracted; a much higher temperature is required to disorient the part above, but the disorientation is accompanied by contraction (Mercer, 1949).

Wool fibers have an inherent continuous bilaterality that runs the length of the fiber from the root to the tip (Horio and Kondo, 1953b). When cross sections of fibers, or defatted whole fibers are stained with Janus green or other basic dyes, approximately half of the fibers is stained, and the other half remains practically unstained. The stained, or basophil, segment has been referred to as DA (for dye-accessible), and that which remains unstained, non-DA (for non-dye-accessible). The DA is resistant to strong acid but the non-DA is not; however, the non-DA is resistant to strong alkali. The stainability of the two segments may be reversed when appropriate acid dyes such as orange G or ponceau 2R are used. The fiber, then, is composed of a basophil segment which is resistant to acid and an acidophil segment which is resistant to alkali.

The acidophil segment always faces the inside of the curvature of the crimp and the basophil portion faces the outside. Since this relation of the segments is always maintained in a crimp, there is diagonal twist or crossover in the region between successive crimps. When cross sections of fibers taken through any one point on a lock of wool forming coincident waves are stained, the acidophil segment of each fiber is oriented toward the direction of the bending. Single wool fibers tend to coil rather than to crimp or wave; the crimping is brought about by extrinsic conditions. When many fibers are placed together, the individual fibers cannot coil, and the resultant force available in the group produces the crimp. The greater the coiling action of the mass of fibers, the finer are the waves produced. The crimping phenomenon is not peculiar to wool fibers and has been observed even in rayon fibers (Horio and Kondo, 1953a). Mercer (1953), whose findings are in essential agreement with those mentioned above, calls the basophil part of the fiber *orthocortex* and the acidophil part *paracortex*. To add to the confusion, Fraser and Rogers (1953) call these segments S and H, respectively. Thus, the less stable, basophil segment is the DA, S, or orthocortex, and the more stable, acidophil element is the non-DA, H, or paracortex.

The follicles of crimped wool fibers have a deflected bulb, the position of the fiber in them is eccentric, and keratinization of the fiber is asymmetrical (Auber, 1952). Keratinization begins on the side of the keratogenous zone that faces the thin side of the inner sheath and progresses across to the opposite side. Thus, keratinization is dyschronous in the two segments; the basophil segment becomes keratinized after the acidophil segment (Fraser and Rogers, 1954).

When fibers are oxidized with peracetic acid and then stained with toluidine blue, the previously acidophil segments become basophil (Fraser *et al.*, 1954). The acidophil segments are relatively resistant to the action of potassium thioglycollate at pH 12.2, but the basophil segments become swollen. The basophil segment on the outside of the crimp, then, is the less keratinized segment. This specific asymmetry has not been found in human hairs (Mercer, 1953). The development of waves, curls, and kinks in human hairs, however, may result from such mechanisms as described here. The follicles of the kinky hairs of the Negroes are relatively straight, but their bulbs are deflected and the hairs are somewhat eccentrically located in the follicles. These two factors, at least, are comparable to those in the follicles of the sheep.

Electron Microscopy

Under the electron microscope the cells of the matrix, the presumptive cells of the hair and the inner root sheath, have typical but small mitochondria with cristae mitochondriales, agranular vesicles, and many small dense particles of ribonucleic acid. The cells contain no keratin filaments, pigment granules, or endoplasmic reticulum (Birbeck and Mercer, 1957a, b, c). Adjacent cells have no points of adhesions and there are gaps between them.

In the upper limits of the matrix, midway in the bulb, in small localized areas, adjacent cells of the presumptive cortex show some adhesions, but there are still gaps between the cell surfaces. The processes of the melanocytes are visible in the gaps. The cells seem to phagocytose the pigment-bearing tips of the melanocytic processes and become pigment-bearing cells. Fibrous keratin is first seen in these cells as loose, parallel strands of fine filaments about 60 Å in diameter. The filaments, the mitochondria, and the nucleus become oriented parallel to the long axis of the follicle. In the region immediately above the constriction of the bulb, a dense, amorphous intracellular substance forms between the fine filaments and cements them into bundles of fibrils. At progressively higher levels in the follicle, more filaments and interfilamentous cement are formed until the entire cell is packed with fibrils. As a final step in keratinization, more interfilamentous cement substance is added and the fibrils are consolidated. Hair keratin, then, is a complex of fine filaments (α-filaments) embedded in an amorphous substance (γ-keratin). The amorphous substance has a higher content of cystine than the fibrils.

As soon as they begin to differentiate just above the level of the matrix, the presumptive cells of the cuticle of the cortex show greater density than the cells of the cortex; their cell membrane becomes very smooth, and a layer of cement firmly attaches them to one another. There are no gaps between them; the processes of the melanocytes do not penetrate between them, and the cells of the cuticle remain unpigmented. These particular changes take place precociously, but keratinization takes place late in the cuticle cells. The keratin formed is amorphous, like the γ fraction found between the fibrils in the cells of the cortex. In the final stage of keratinization the cells have parallel laminae surrounded by an outer keratinized layer. The inner part of the fully keratinized cell is insoluble in solvents that normally hydrolyze keratin.

The three concentric cylinders of cells of the inner root sheath arise from the peripheral portion of the matrix. These cells, like those of the hair cuticle, are held together by an adhesive cement that first appears at about the middle of the bulb. The characteristic intracellular product in all three layers is trichohyalin. Unlike the cortical hair keratin, which originates as filaments, trichohyalin begins as amorphous droplets, first in the cells of Henle's layer midway up in the bulb. Synthesis of trichohyalin in the cells of Huxley's layer and in those of the cuticle of the inner sheath begins at higher levels, above the constriction of the bulb. Farther up in the follicle, the amorphous trichohyalin droplets *seem* to be transformed to fibrous plates, or corrugated sheaths, about 100 Å in width. An electron-dense cement substance, similar to that found between the cells of the hair cuticle, is formed in the spaces between the cell membranes in the inner root sheath.

Development of the Bulb, and Growth and Replacement of Hair

Hair follicles originate from thickenings at the base of the embryonic epidermis (Figs. 8 and 9), proliferate into solid cords, and grow into the subjacent dermis, pushing ahead of them an aggregate of dermal cells. The enlarged base of each cord then grows around the cluster of dermal cells forming the bulb. During the early stages of development, all of the cells of the epidermal cord are mitotically active. When the follicle has attained its full length, mitotic activity becomes restricted largely to the matrix. New cells from the matrix move up and become differentiated into hair and inner root sheath (Fig. 40). In man one rarely finds mitotic divisions in the cells of the outer sheath, but in the follicles of rodents, mitotic activity in the outer root sheath continues at a rapid rate throughout the period of activity.

If an imaginary line were drawn across the widest diameter of the dermal papilla (Figs. 39 and 40), the line would separate the bulb into two regions at the "critical level" (Auber, 1952). The lower part, the matrix, consists of rapidly dividing undifferentiated cells, and the upper part consists of cells that are differentiating into the inner root sheath and the hair (Fig. 39). In mice injected with Colcemid, every cell of the matrix probably undergoes division once in approximately 13 hours (Bullough and Laurence, 1958). Although some mitotic activity can be found in the upper part of the bulb of the follicles of man and other mammals, it is too scant to account for much of the growth of the hair. Even the medulla arises at least in part from the matrix. Kligman (1959) believes that mitotic activity in the follicles of the scalp of man may be found throughout the bulb. The "mitotic" cells that he finds in the

---

FIG. 39. The bulb of a hair follicle from the scalp. The cells in the lower half of the figure, the matrix, are moving upward to form the layers of the inner sheath and the cortex. The outer sheath cannot be seen clearly: (A) cortex; (B) cuticle of cortex; (C) cuticle of inner sheath; (D) Huxley's layer; (E) Henle's layer; (F) outer sheath.

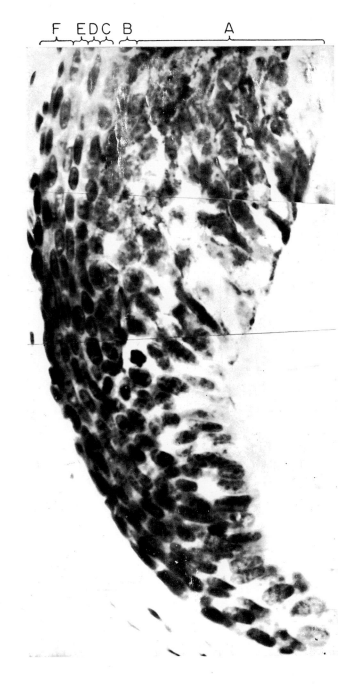

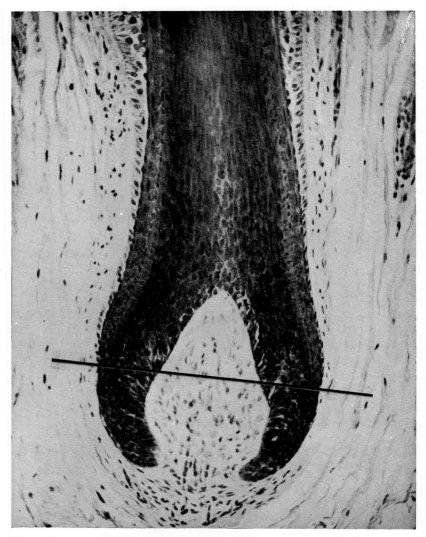

Fig. 40. Longitudinal section through an active hair follicle from the scalp, stained with toluidine blue buffered to pH 5.0. The black line indicates the critical level, which separates the upper from the lower bulb. The section is slightly parasagittal and the medulla is not visible. Cells can be seen sweeping upward from the matrix. The cells of the outer sheath are vacuolated and have very little cytoplasm left.

upper bulb after the local injection of colchicine, however, appear to be dead cells that have moved up in mass from the matrix. The cells from the matrix move upward in rows to the upper part of the bulb, where they increase in volume and become elongated vertically. Cells move across the critical level, into the *pre-elongation region,* where they become slightly larger and align themselves vertically (Auber, 1952). Above this, where the bulb is constricted, the region of *cellular elongation* consists of conspicuously elongated cells with very sharp boundaries due to delicate, acidophil fibrils piled against them. Farther up, in the cortical *pre-keratinization region,* the fibrils are coarser and more numerous and stain with basic dyes. Immediately above this region, in the *keratogenous zone,* the cells become hyalinized, and distinct fibrils can be seen only with certain techniques and under polarized light. Depending upon the length of the follicle, the keratogenous zone terminates at a level one third to one half of the way between the tip of the papilla and the surface of the skin. The mature hair above the keratogenous zone has a smaller diameter. The four regions just described have been given other names (Mercer, 1949), but they seem less appropriate.

Melanin is precisely distributed in hair follicles. The matrix is usually free of it, and the separation of upper and lower regions of the bulb at the critical level is clear. In man the outer and inner root sheaths are free of melanin regardless of the degree of melanization of the hair. Traces of pigment may occasionally spill into the inner root sheath, and very small dendritic cells may be found there, but the dividing line is very sharp between the cells of the hair proper, which are pigmented, and those of the sheaths, which are not. In some primates, in the seal (Montagna and Harrison, 1957) and others, the outer root sheath contains a large population of dendritic, melanin-producing melanocytes. It is also likely that the outer root sheath of the hair follicles of man may contain nonmelanotic melanocytes, which become active under certain conditions (Montagna and Chase, 1956).

Many of the large cells that line the cupola of the dermal papilla are dendritic melanocytes, carried there from the epidermis by the original primary hair germ (Chase *et al.,* 1951). Dendrites radiating from these cells are insinuated between the undifferentiated cells of the cortex and the medulla as they glide up from the matrix, but not between the cells of cuticle, which have no spaces between them. These melanocytes are larger than, but otherwise similar to, those found in the epidermis.

The upper part of the bulb is comparable to the spinous layer of the epidermis. In both places, undifferentiated epidermal cells become larger, acquire pigment, synthesize fibrous proteins, are reoriented, and undergo final keratinization.

Growth of hair is the result of cell proliferation in the matrix, and the increase in volume of these cells as they move up from the upper part of the bulb. The architecture of the follicle may also play some role in the dynamics of growth. The disproportionate swelling of the bulb cannot be explained entirely by the enclosure of the dermal papilla. A large mass of cells, then, is funneled through a relatively narrow neck, maintaining the rate of growth of the hair with greater ease than if the matrix and upper bulb were of the same diameter as the hair. Perhaps the cells are under pressure as they pass through the neck of the bulb, and a constraining mechanism could funnel them upward and keep the follicle from expanding laterally. Henle's layer of the inner sheath establishes the skeletal framework of the funnel by becoming keratinized precociously just above the critical level. The cells of the outer sheath, being engorged with glycogen, form a firm but resilient girdle, outside of which the vitreous membrane and the connective tissue sheath give rigidity to the whole structure. The cells outline patterns of shearing lines as they move up from the matrix, but emphasis on pressure and other such physical factors, may be ill-advised since cells could possess inherent powers of orientation and perform the proper morphogenetic movements without the need of extrinsic factors.

Sometimes a single follicle may form more than one hair. This must not be confused with the condition in which several hair follicles share a common orifice to the outside. In the follicles of bristles with a flanged medulla, the dermal papilla is lobed and the number of lobes corresponds to the number of medullae (Kränzle, 1912; Moebius, 1892; and Toldt, 1912). Beard follicles occasionally produce a variety of anomalies that range from single hairs with a doubled medulla to conjoined or completely separate hairs, known as pili multigemini (Giovannini, 1907 and 1908, 1909, and 1910). When duplication of hair occurs in a single follicle, there is a corresponding duplication of the dermal papilla. Such close correspondence between the subdivisions of the papilla and the number of hairs formed in a single follicle focuses attention on the dermal papilla, each lobe of which must induce hair formation from a common matrix on its own accord. Each hair of pili multigemini is surrounded by its own inner sheath, but all the hairs in one follicle share the same outer sheath. This is logical since the matrix gives rise only to the hair and the inner sheath. The outer sheath is self-propagating and is, in fact, the major source from which the matrix itself is formed in each hair generation.

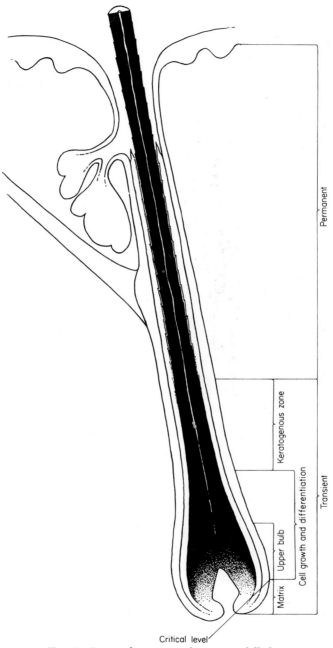

Fig. 41. Regional anatomy of an active follicle.

Three things herald the onset of catagen, even before visible changes in form and size occur: the glassy membrane around the bulb becomes very thick and corrugated (Figs. 15, 19, 20, and 41) the dendritic melanocytes contract, making the last segment of hair formed white, and mitotic activity in the matrix stops. In spite of the cessation of mitotic activity, the cells from the bulb continue to flow up toward the

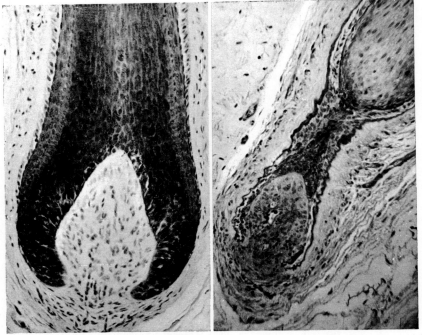

FIG. 42. Hair follicles from the scalp. On the left is the bulb of an active follicle. On the right is the lower part of a follicle during catagen; in the upper right hand corner of this figure, a club hair is being formed; the matrix is completely degenerated, and the dermal papilla is being released. The vitreous membrane around the degenerating bulb is very thick.

keratogenous zone where they become dammed and produce a club. Since the cells move up to be keratinized, the bulb becomes largely depleted of its cells, setting the dermal papilla free. As the bulb gradually decreases in volume, it loses its turgidity and the outer root sheath around it begins to collapse. The follicle remains clavate at the keratogenous zone (Fig. 42); below this the outer root sheath forms a cord of cells that remains in contact with the dermal papilla. Around the club the outer root sheath forms a sac of cells several layers thick;

the cells in contact with the club become partially keratinized into a hyalin capsule. The strand of cells below the epithelial sac becomes progressively thinner and shorter, as some of its cells degenerate or become keratinized. The definitive strand, which contains a few melanocytes scattered among the undifferentiated cells is the hair germ proper. The dermal papilla, now completely free, remains at the base of the hair germ (Figs. 21 and 41). At the beginning of catagen, the

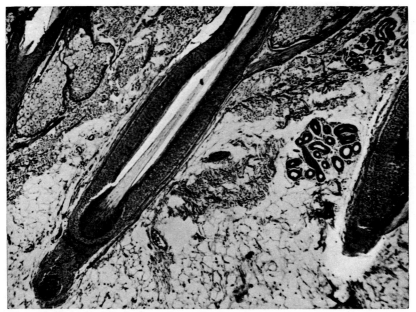

Fig. 43. Catagen follicle from the scalp showing the club forming in the keratogenous zone, and the shriveling of the bulb. (Courtesy of Dr. A. M. Kligman.)

connective tissue sheath around the lower part of the follicle, and the inner layer of the glassy membrane, become very thick (Schaffer, 1933). Suggestions that the wrinkling of the connective tissue sheath may squeeze the follicle upward (Wolbach, 1951), and that the cells in the strand divide and push the club upward (Segall, 1918) do not survive scrutiny. When the strand is formed, the greatly thickened and wrinkled connective tissue sheath and glassy membrane hang loosely around it (Fig. 43), and mitosis in its cells is of no consequence. The retreat of the follicle upward seems to be brought about, first, by the cessation of mitosis and the continued movement upward of the cells of the bulb, and then, by an orderly, progressive degeneration of some of the cells in the epidermal strand. Thus, the hair germ is formed largely from the cells of the outer sheath; the matrix plays a minor role in establishing it. The changes that take place in hair follicles after exposure of the scalp to irradiation support this (Montagna and Chase, 1956). Twenty-four hours after exposure to X-rays, most of the cells

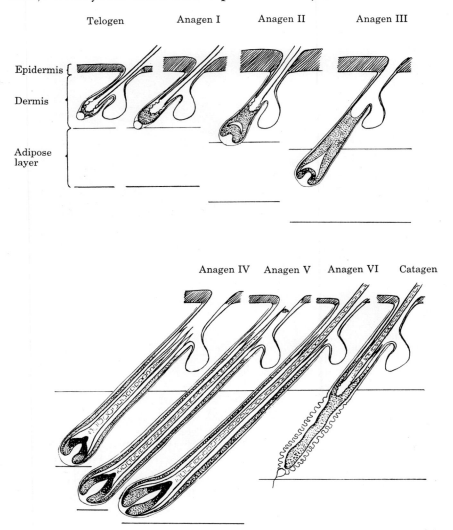

Fig. 44. The growth cycle of the hair follicles of the mouse (drawn to scale). The epidermis becomes increasingly thicker in the early stages of anagen. The dermis and adipose layer become thickened after anagen III. See Fig. 45.

of the matrix are destroyed; one week later the bulb is largely lost, and the lower part of the follicle is reduced to a thin cord of cells composed mostly of the collapsed outer root sheath. At this time, also, the dermal papilla is free. Since some of the cells perish and others become keratinized in disorderly clusters, the follicle becomes shorter. At the completion of these events the short cord of cells has a relatively brief quiescent period and then becomes active and rebuilds an entirely new follicle. Since after irradiation the matrix is destroyed, there are not

Fig. 45. Skin from the back of a mouse with quiescent follicles on the left, and active ones on the right. Contrast the total thickness of the skin on the left and on the right.

enough cells to form a club, and the hair becomes acuminate at its base and falls out. Thus, the hair germ is composed of cells that come mostly from the outer sheath. The seed, or the germinative source of each generation of hair follicles, must reside in the outer sheath and not in the bulb. Hair follicles in the scalps of atomic bomb victims showed approximately the same changes as those described here (Liebow et al., 1949). Radiation, then, or other agents which are injurious to dividing cells, precipitate and abbreviate catagen by destroying the matrix (Kligman, 1959).

The cycles of growth of the hair follicles of the mouse are depicted in Figs. 44 and 45. The principles found here apply in a general way also to the follicles of other animals. In early anagen, the hair germ forms the bulb (Bullough and Laurence, 1958; Chase, 1958). The cycles of growth of each follicle consist of the building up and tearing down of a complex structure. After a period of rest, the follicle is built anew from raw materials, and each hair follicle goes through the same process. During catagen, most of the cells of the bulb keratinize; there being not enough mitosis, the follicles undergo retrograde morphogenetic transformation, and become very small and undifferentiated with only a few cells left for the next hair generation. When a new hair is formed, it either dislodges the club hair in the epithelial sac or it grows alongside it.

The patterns of growth and rest, as well as the rate of growth of hair, vary in different species and in different regions of the body in the same animal. Animals which replace their coat annually shed the club hairs at a certain time of the year, more or less at once, when the new hairs grow out. In rats and mice, growth periods are frequent and in waves which sweep anteroposteriorly and ventrodorsally, and all of the follicles in a particular area of the growth wave are in the same growth phase (Butcher, 1934, 1951; Chase and Eaton, 1959). The total growing period of each follicle is about 19 days in the mouse and 21 to 26 days in the rat. In both animals, the hairs grow approximately 1 mm a day. In man, each follicle has its own cycles of growth, independent of neighboring ones. Information about hair growth in man is scanty; this tedious and unexciting work, though important, has failed to capture the fancy of investigators. Without accounting for differences attributable to environmental conditions, race, age, sex, and particular body region, human hair is said to grow approximately 0.3 mm per day (Myers and Hamilton, 1951). The quiescent periods of hair follicles may be very short, like those of the scalp, or long like those of the general body surface.

When the club hairs of the mouse or rat are plucked, their follicles become active at once, even if the clubs remain lodged in the epithelial sacs. There is a certain minimal number of hairs in a certain area that must be plucked to produce this response (Durward and Rudall, 1958). Clipping and shaving normally have no effect on growth, although more meticulous observation may prove this statement too dogmatic. Under normal conditions, when the club hair is plucked from a resting follicle, full regrowth of hair occurs in the mouse in 19 to 21 days regardless of age and sex. Replucking may be carried out in the same follicle many times and the hair regrows each time in the same way without fatiguing.

Substantial information about the time required for human follicles to regrow hairs after plucking is lacking; time seems to vary from 147 days for the hairs of the scalp to 61 days for those of the eyebrows (Myers and Hamilton, 1951). When a growing hair is plucked, most of the lower half of the follicle, including the matrix, is pulled out with it. The recovery of such follicles is necessarily very slow.

The Problem of Regeneration

Reports on the new formation of hair follicles during wound healing should be accepted with extreme caution and even skepticism. The formation of new hair follicles has been reported in the repaired wounds of mice (Lacassagne and Latarjet, 1946), rats (Taylor, 1949; Butcher, 1959), rabbits (Breedis, 1954; Billingham, 1958; Billingham and Russell, 1956) and man (Kligman and Strauss, 1956). From these reports it could be inferred that repaired hairless wounds could, in time, be partially repopulated with hairs.

The meticulous observations of Breedis (1954), and later Billingham and Russell (1956), on the differentiation of new hair follicles from the new epidermis of the wounds of rabbits cannot be dismissed lightly. Yet, Straile (1959), who repeated and re-examined these experiments, found the results equivocal, since he could not strike out the likelihood that follicles had moved into the wound tissue from the periphery. The only unequivocal proof of neoformation of hair follicles in adult animals is in the antlers of deer (Billingham, 1958; Billingham et al., 1959). Every year these animals form anew enormous amounts of skin and hair over the growing antlers. The observations of neoformation in human skin are burdened with grave misgivings. Let the reader be assured that by questioning the reports of hair neoformation in the literature he does not close his mind to the possibility that new formation of hair in the adult could occur. Neoformation is spoken of too glibly, even by those who know better, like myself (Montagna, 1956). By retaining an air of skepticism we will force those who wish to prove the occurrence of this phenomenon to give more convincing proof.

It is unfortunate that many of those interested in hair growth have looked covetously at baldness, with an eye toward "regrowing" or "restoring" hair, and have been guided by emotion or by commercialism. Locked within hair follicles in the haired or balding scalp, are the secrets of growth and differentiation. Search for the key to these secrets should transcend the eagerness to "regrow" hair on a bald scalp, an achievement which by itself would be of no great importance. To understand the phenomena that guide growth and differentiation of hair is to understand growth, which is the basis of all biological phenomena (Montagna, 1959).

General Conclusions

Hair follicles produce a hair in a pattern that can be followed linearly over a short distance from the undifferentiated cells to the fully keratinized ones. Cells that arise from the matrix do a variety of similar, but subtly different things in the formation of the hair and the inner root sheath. There is still much to be learned and we are still ignorant about the agents that guide the precise periods of growth and rest. The formation of different keratins in cells that are in contact with each other, the precise distribution of pigment in follicles, the energy requirements for growth and differentiation, and the effects of physical and chemical factors on the growth of hair are now better understood than they have ever been before (see Montagna and Ellis, 1958b).

Hair follicles develop from proliferations at the base of the embryonic epidermis. These primitive pilary complexes soon become associated with mesodermal elements, and the follicles perish if this association is disturbed. In the hair follicles of the fetus, functioning melanocytes are distributed throughout the bulb, the inner root sheath, and the outer root sheath; yet, in the adult follicle, visible pigment cells are found only in the upper part of the bulb, above the matrix. The distribution of melanocytes in the fetal hair follicles, then, is similar to that found in the adult follicles of many primates. It is likely that melanocytes, though not active, still reside within the outer root sheath of the adult follicles of man. They can be activated by certain agents, such as X-rays (Montagna and Chase, 1956). The first keratinized structure in the embryonic follicle is the tip of the inner root sheath. The follicle gradually adds more inner root sheath from behind, and the hair is formed inside the inner sheath. When the follicle has attained its definitive length, the inner root sheath and the hair move up to the surface; the inner sheath becomes fragmented in the pilary canal, and the hair emerges to the surface free of it. None of the early fetal hair follicles has an intrinsic vascular pattern. Blood vessels form around the follicles and in the dermal papillae as the follicles become thicker and produce larger hairs. Hair follicles undergo at least one catagen phase during fetal life.

Fetal skin has a denser population of hair follicles per surface area than the skin of the adult. Hair follicles are distributed evenly over the body of the early fetus, but the head has a greater population of them than other regions of the body. The subsequent growth and re-shaping of the body causes the hair follicles in the trunk and the extremities to be spaced farther apart than they are in the head. In the adult, the head has about three times as many hair follicles as the trunk has; the arms and legs have the least. In spite of differences in the quality of hairs produced, there is no significant difference in the number of hair follicles in the skin of men and women (Szabó, 1958).

Three-dimensional models of hair follicles from serial sections by Van Scott (1958), show that the follicles from the various regions of the body have minor but characteristic modifications. In the adult scalp the large hair follicles grow singly or in groups; those in groups remain separate units up to just below the epidermis, at which point they become joined in a common pilary canal. The hair follicles of the beard occur singly, and their pilary canals are characteristically divided into two channels: the hair passes through one of these; the other is a continuation of the excretory duct of the sebaceous gland. Approximately one half of the hair follicles in the upper back are in groups of two that come together at the pilary canal.

The matrix in the lower part of the bulb is the proliferative element of hair follicles. Proliferative growth that occurs in the upper part of the bulb is of small importance (cf. Kligman, 1959). The cells of the matrix divide, move up the bulb in rows, and differentiate into a hair and inner root sheath. The outer root sheath, formed in the early stages of the growth cycle, remains fairly static. In the rodents, in which the growth period of a follicle is very brief and rapid, mitotic activity continues in the cells of the outer root sheath, up to the onset of catagen. Undifferentiated cells from the matrix move into the upper part of the bulb, and become larger as they undergo gradual differentiation. Since the cuticle of the hair and that of the inner sheath are interlocked, hair and inner sheath must grow at the same rate.

Dendritic melanocytes in the upper part of the bulb feed out melanin to the passing presumptive cells of the cortex and medulla of the hair, but not to those of the cuticle of the hair and the inner root sheath. When a follicle is nearing the end of its growth cycle, melanin formation stops, as does also the formation of a medulla, if the hair is medullated. The hair that grows during this last period, therefore, is white. After these initial changes, a club hair is formed above the bulb in the region of the keratogenous zone. The bulb, then, is largely depleted by a flow of cells from the matrix; the outer root sheath around it collapses, forming a cord of cells in which is the seed for the next generation of hair.

When activity is set off again, the hair germ rebuilds an entirely new follicle which again manufactures hair and inner root sheath.

Active hair follicles are rich sources of chemical substances, many of which have been studied with histochemical methods. In spite of lack of refinements, histochemical findings are interesting. The catalogue of substances, principal among them the enzymes, is steadily attaining significance. These enzymes all have a precise distribution in growing and in quiescent follicles.

Under the electron microscope, the fibrous keratins in the presumptive cortical cells first appear as bundles of fine filaments; the filaments rapidly aggregate and form larger fibrils aligned parallel to the long axis of the cells. The bundles grow longer and thicker, and above the constriction of the bulb, a cement substance is formed between them. Fibrous keratin appears to consist of a system of fine parallel filaments about 60 Å in diameter, held together by a nonfibrous cement substance high in cystine. Trichohyalin granules in the inner root sheath seem to be nonfibrous at first, but later *apparently* transform into fibrils different from those that form in the cortex of the hair. If these are similar to the keratohyalin granules, the likelihood is that they are nonfibrous. The keratin of the inner root sheath has different properties from those of the hair cortex.

The formation of keratin is preceded by the synthesis of a nonfibrous macromolecular precursor, which is then transformed into fibrous protofibrils, arranged into more organized structures, and finally the product is hardened into keratin. All cells that form fibroprotein have dense ribonucleoprotein particles arranged in clusters in their cytoplasm (Mercer, 1958). The nonfibrous precursors are first transformed into protofibrils spontaneously by the formation of linear or helical aggregates in which the original structure of the macromolecule is preserved (Mercer, 1958). The protofibrils may owe their orientation to a slight initial flow in the deformed cells; this controls the direction of the fibrils which are added subsequently.

The formation of cytoplasmic fibrils is a basic mechanism that later becomes associated with the decomposition and the elimination of certain cytoplasmic and nuclear elements. In the differentiating cells of the hair cortex, the cytoplasmic fibrils gradually reach such a high concentration that the cells consist practically entirely of fibrils. When, finally, nuclear and cytoplasmic activities cease, the nonkeratin constituents are mostly eliminated.

The large, active follicles of man have dense networks of blood vessels around the bulb and keratogenous zone. The rest of the follicle is surrounded mostly by a few linearly arranged arterioles and capillaries. The dermal papilla of large active follicles is richly vascularized; that of progressively smaller ones is less vascularized and that of vellus follicles is avascular. Progressively smaller follicles have progressively poorer vascular beds around them; the very small follicles of vellus hairs have practically no vessels. During the transition from active state to quiescence, when the follicle becomes shorter, the bulb, which is largely dissipated, withdraws partially or entirely from the lower vascular plexus. The major part of the vessels remains collapsed at the base of the follicle in the connective tissue bed that marks the path followed by the withdrawal of the bulb (Ellis and Moretti, 1959). The dermal papilla also largely withdraws from its vessels.

Hair follicles are surrounded by a plexus of nerves just below the entrance of the sebaceous glands into the pilary canal. If nerves are also found around the lower part of the follicle, they are not demonstrable with the methods available. These nerves, like those that surround the sinus hair follicles of other mammals, contain specific cholinesterase and are probably sensory nerves.

Although we know nothing about the energy requirements for mitosis in the cells of the matrix of the follicles of man, Bullough and Laurence (1958) have found some interesting facts in the skin of mice. The cells of the matrix have no diurnal rhythms, and forced exercise does not depress mitosis. Even in starved mice, mitotic activity is not depressed in the matrix until after the animals are in a state of collapse. Only full shock affects mitotic activity in the matrix; partial shock does not. When bits of skin from fully shocked mice are incubated with glucose, mitotic activity in the matrix returns to a normal state.

Mitosis in the hair bulb of mice requires adequate supplies of oxygen and of some suitable carbohydrate substrate; in the absence of either, mitotic activity is inhibited. Glucose, fructose, and pyruvate are ideal substrates for the support of mitotic activity. Any substance that inhibits glycolysis, the Krebs cycle, the cytochrome system, or energy transfer, inhibits mitotic activity. High mitotic activity can only be maintained by a high level of energy produced in the cells, and it must be expected that the bulb must normally have available large quantities of glucose and oxygen.

The only valid information we have on the nutritional requirements for the growth of hair is that of Ryder (1958) on the growth of the wool of sheep. The weight of wool that a sheep produces is controlled by the amount and quality of the food available. A poor diet reduces the breaking strength, and the length and diameter of wool fibers; a reinforcement of the diet with both protein and carbohydrate corrects these defects and increases wool production. Carbohydrate is needed to provide energy for protein utilization, for the release of protein for wool formation, and for mitotic activity in the matrix. Cystine or methionine, while essential for hair growth in many animals, are not needed by the sheep, which can synthesize cystine from sulfate. B vitamins are necessary agents for the growth of hair, and pantothenic acid seems to be associated with the utilization of copper. Deficiency of copper causes a loss of pigment in hair, and in wool, a loss of the crimp. Copper is believed to catalyze the oxidation of SH— to —S—S— groups, although it has not been possible to detect copper in the follicles either with histochemical methods or with the use of Cu^{64}.

Within a few minutes after the injection of S^{35}-labeled cystine, radioactive particles appear first in the outer root sheath above the bulb (Ryder, 1958) which it must enter from the surrounding capillary net directly, and not through the vessels of the papilla. Soon after an injection of C^{14}-labeled glucose, radioactive particles are recovered in the bulb and not above it, showing that they have entered largely by way of the capillaries in the papilla and those around the bulb.

An investigator must have a thorough knowledge of the normal cycles of growth of the follicles of the *particular species* of animal studies to interpret the effects of those hormones said to "accelerate" or "retard" the growth of hair. Different species sometimes respond differently to the same hormone; for example, cortisone compounds, which initiate hair growth in certain alopecic diseases in the scalp of man, suppress hair growth in the rat (see Mohn, 1958, for complete details on the effects of hormones on hair growth in the rat).

Male rats have coarser hair than females do. Spontaneous growth waves in females lag behind those of males, but the cycle of growth in each follicle is the same in both sexes. Sex differences disappear after gonadectomy. Daily treatment with estrogen retards the initiation and the rate of both spontaneous and induced hair growth in animals that have been gonadectomized, adrenalectomized, hypophysectomized, or rendered deficient in thyroid hormone. Estrogen induces the growth of fine, sparse hair in all animals except those that have been hypophysectomized. Daily treatment with androgen has no apparent effect on hair growth, except that it promotes a coarse pelage in all except hypophysectomized rats.

Spontaneous replacement of hair is noticeably retarded during pregnancy and lactation; although induced growth by plucking is normal, hair growth is transiently accelerated when the young are removed from the mother. These effects are not duplicated by treating intact females with progesterone, but are partially simulated when nursing females are treated with luteotropic hormone.

Adrenalectomy accelerates the initiation and the spread of growth waves in rats but has no effect on the rate of growth of the individual follicles. Adrenalectomy has no effect on induced growth, and the pelage regrown is unaffected. Daily treatment with small doses of cortisone inhibits the spontaneous initiation of hair growth in intact, gonadectomized, or adrenalectomized rats, but has no effect on follicles already growing. Large doses of cortisone completely inhibit hair growth in intact rats, but have no effect on follicles already growing. All hair growth is inhibited when propylthioracil-treated or hypophysectomized animals are injected with small doses of cortisone. In all of these cases growth commences as soon as the cortisone is discontinued. Daily treatment with deoxycorticosterone has no effect on hair growth in intact or adrenalectomized rats.

Continuous treatment with adrenaline inhibits spontaneous hair growth in intact rats and delays the response to plucking, but growth proceeds normally once it has started. Prolonged treatment with adrenaline produces a local inhibition of spontaneous or induced growth. These effects are neither mediated nor potentiated by the thyroid. They are, however, partially linked to adrenocortical activity. Adrenaline inhibits hair growth more in cortisone-treated, adrenalectomized rats than in adrenalectomized animals not receiving cortisone; the effects are not due to the cortisone.

Spontaneous growth is markedly retarded in alloxan-diabetic animals, but after an initial delay, induced growth is normal. Treatment with phlorhizin does not affect hair growth despite a continued glycosuria and hypoglycemia. Insulin restores spontaneous replacement to normal in alloxan-diabetic animals, and enhances growth in intact animals despite the low level of glucose it produces in the blood. Glucose-treated intact animals, on the other hand, have normal regrowth after plucking, but their spontaneous growth is often retarded. Insulin, then, seems to be more directly involved in hair growth than glucose, perhaps by regulating the utilization of glucose from the blood during the early stages of follicle growth.

An intake of propylthiouracil that produces a deficiency in thyroid hormone inhibits the spontaneous waves of hair growth. Induced growth, however, is practically normal. Injections of thyroxine accelerate spontaneous replacement of hair in propylthiouracil-treated rats and in normal rats; the cycle of growth, however, remains normal regardless of how activity is initiated. Thyroxine and cortisone have antagonistic effects on hair growth, and one hormone can be used to offset the effects of the other. Such a relationship does not exist between thyroxine and gonadal hormones.

Hypophysectomy, which accelerates the initiation and spread of spontaneous growth waves, has no effect on the rate of growth; the cycle of growth is normal after plucking, but the pelage is infantile. The administration of ACTH inhibits hair growth in intact, gonadectomized, and hypophysectomized rats, but has no effect on that of adrenalectomized animals. This inhibition is obviously mediated through the adrenal cortex. The pituitary also exerts a restraint on hair growth by means of the adrenal cortex. Hypophysectomy removes this restraint.

Implants of pituitary tissue or injections of growth hormone restore the pelage of hypophysectomized rats to an adult texture. Hair remains infantile in hypophysectomized rats even after treatment with gonadal hormones. Sex hormones, then, modify the type of hair produced only if growth hormone is present.

Clinical observations indicate that during the postpartum period, women experience a diffuse loss of scalp hair. An examination of the hairs from the scalp of a large number of women shows some interesting results. About 15% of the follicles of nonpregnant women are quiescent (Lynfield, 1960). In pregnant women the percentage of quiescent follicles is appreciably reduced, and in variable periods after partum it becomes variably higher.

The beard in Caucasian men grows faster than that of Japanese (Hamilton, 1958). In contrast to the high incidence in Caucasian women, Japanese women show no facial hirsutism. Men of both ethnic groups have similar values for the mean diameter of coarse hairs and for the percentage of gray hairs with advancing age. Growth of axillary hair is more pronounced in Caucasian than in Japanese men and women. Caucasian men also have a greater tendency to develop coarse hairs on the external ears and to become bald than do Japanese men.

While growing, a follicle produces hair at its fullest capacity. Increased hair production, then, can only be achieved by initiating activity in quiescent follicles. Mildly irritating agents often initiate the growth of quiescent follicles. In the human scalp, doses of X-ray high enough to cause severe damage to growing follicles actually initiate growth in quiescent ones (Montagna and Chase, 1956). In the mouse and rabbit, a dose of X-ray of about 1500 r stimulates resting follicles, while damaging growing ones (Chase, 1958). After epilating doses of X-ray, the bulb of active follicles in the human scalp largely degenerates. X-Rays accelerate all the changes of catagen in active follicles, except that a club hair is not formed and the hair falls out. When the degenerative changes have ceased, the follicles remain in telogen for a time, and then grow normally again. The effects of ionizing radiation of hair follicles can be studied by examining unstained hairs plucked from the irradiated scalp under the low power of the microscope (Van Scott, 1958, 1959). Changes, seen clearly 2 days after irradiation, progress until 10 to 14 days. The changes begin in the matrix and continue to the rest of the bulb until it is completely atrophied. After 10 to 14 days, when the bulb has completely disintegrated, the ends of the hairs are tapered, and they fall out at the end of 3 weeks. A few follicles, probably not fully hit by the radiation, recover during the first week and continue to produce a hair. The hair that these follicles form has a smaller diameter which can be identified from its distance from the bulb as that portion of the hair that was produced during the time that the follicle suffered from the effects of the irradiation. The percentage of growing hairs that show such morphological defects from the irradiation may be calculated by examining one hundred or more hairs pulled from the areas of the scalp exposed to X-rays. During the week after the irradiation, the percentage of damaged hairs increases linearly in relation to time and dose of irradiation.

Therapeutic doses of amethopterin in man cause a transient but reversible injury to the hair bulb (Van Scott, 1958, 1959). The hair formed while the drug is administered has a smaller diameter but it returns to normal after the cessation of the therapy. The hairs from such patients have zones of constrictions, the degree of constriction corresponding to the dose of the drugs.

The population of hair follicles in adult animals is apparently fixed. Observations on the healing of skin wounds in mice, rats, guinea pigs, rabbits, and man suggest that new hair follicles may form from the adult epidermis (Breedis, 1954; Billingham, 1958; Billingham *et al.*, 1959; Kligman and Strauss, 1956; Kligman, 1959). Most of these observations, however, do not survive critical appraisal (Montagna, 1959; Straile, 1959).

Indisputable evidence that follicles can be formed in adult skin is obtained only in the antlers of deers (Billingham, 1958; Billingham *et al.*, 1959). The antlers are deciduous and shed annually. When they regrow, they are first completely covered by "velvet," a layer of typical hair-bearing skin. Later, when fully grown, the skin dries out and peels off, leaving the bony core exposed. Thus the deer regenerates each year a relatively large area of skin, complete with hair follicles.

Although many follicles do perish and the bald scalp may seem to be glabrous, it is, nonetheless, hairy. The hair follicles there have undergone a gradual regressive transformation that culminates in vellous-type follicles. The hair produced by these follicles is short, fine, and colorless (Ellis, 1958). Together with this transformation there is also a reduction in the superficial vascular plexuses of the scalp and an increase in the size of the sebaceous glands. The typical arrangement of hair follicles in groups found in the scalps of children and young men gradually becomes diffuse, and in old men, hair groups are no longer recognized. Thus, the study of male baldness is the study of specific aging changes in the scalp and not that of a diseased condition. Let us hope that future studies of baldness will be guided by these initial details, and that they will be motivated by a desire to find the truth.

REFERENCES

Achten, G. 1959. Recherches sur la kératinisation de la Cellule épidermique chez l'Homme et le Rat. *Ext. Arch. biol. (Liège)* **70**: 1-119.

Adachi, K. and W. Montagna. 1961. Histology and cytochemistry of human skin. XXII. Sites of leucine aminopeptidase (LAP). *J. Invest. Dermatol.* (In press.)

Astbury, W. T. and H. J. Woods. 1934. X-ray studies of the structure of hair, wool, and related fibres. II. The molecular structure and elastic properties of hair keratin. *Phil. Trans. Roy. Soc.* **A232**: 333-394.

Auber, L., 1952. The anatomy of follicles producing wool-fibres, with special reference to keratinization. *Trans. Roy. Soc. Edinburgh* **62**: 191-254.

Baker, J. R. 1946. The histochemical recognition of lipine. *Quart. J. Microscop. Sci.* **87**: 441-470.

Barrnett, R. J. 1953. The histochemical distribution of protein-bound sulfhydryl groups. *J. Natl. Cancer Inst.* **13**: 905-925.

Barrnett, R. J. and A. M. Seligman. 1952. Histochemical demonstration of protein-bound sulfhydryl groups. *Science* **116**: 323-327.

Bear, R. S. and H. J. Rugo. 1951. The results of X-ray diffraction studies on keratin fibers. *Ann. N.Y. Acad. Sci.* **53**: 627-648.

Bekker, J. G. and A. T. King. 1931. Sulphur distribution in the component structures of wool and porcupine quills. *Biochem. J.* **25**: 1077-1080.

Billingham, R. E. 1958. A reconsideration of the phenomenon of hair neogenesis with particular reference to healing of cutaneous wounds in adult mammals. *In* "The Biology of Hair Growth" (W. Montagna and R. A. Ellis, eds.), pp. 451-466. Academic Press, New York.

Billingham, R. E. and P. S. Russell. 1956. Incomplete wound contracture and the phenomenon of hair neogenesis in rabbits' skin. *Nature* **177**: 791-792.

Billingham, R. E., R. Mangold and W. K. Silvers. 1959. Part IV. Neogenesis of hair follicles in adult skin. The neogenesis of skin in the antlers of deer. *Ann. N.Y. Acad. Sci.* **83**: 491-498.

Birbeck, M. S. C. and E. H. Mercer. 1957a. The electron microscopy of the human hair follicle. 1. Introduction and the hair cortex. *J. Biophys. Biochem. Cytol.* **3**: 203-214.

Birbeck, M. S. C. and E. H. Mercer. 1957b. The electron microscopy of the human hair follicle. 2. The hair cuticle. *J. Biophys. Biochem. Cytol.* **3**: 215-222.

Birbeck, M. S. C. and E. H. Mercer. 1957c. The electron microscopy of the human hair follicle. 3. The inner root sheath and trichohyaline. *J. Biophys. Biochem. Cytol.* **3**: 223-230.

Block, R. J. 1951. Chemical classification of keratins. *Ann. N.Y. Acad. Sci.* **53**: 608-612.

Bollinger, A. and M. D. McDonald. 1949. Histological investigation of glycogen in skin and hair. *Australian J. Exptl. Biol. Med. Sci.* **27**: 223-228.

Bonnet, R. 1892. Ueber Hypotrichosis congenita universalis. *Anat. Hefte* **1**: 233-273.

Braun-Falco, O. 1956a. Über die Fähigkeit der menschlichen Haut zur Polysaccharidsynthese, ein Beitrag zur Histotopochemie der Phosphorylase. *Arch. klin. exptl. Dermatol.* **202**: 163-170.

Braun-Falco, O. 1956b. Zur Histopographie der β-Glucuronidase in normaler menschlicher Haut. *Arch. klin. exptl. Dermatol.* **203**: 61-67.

Braun-Falco, O. 1958. The histochemistry of the hair follicle. In "The Biology of Hair Growth" (W. Montagna and R. A. Ellis, eds.), pp. 65-87. Academic Press, New York.

Breedis, C. 1954. Regeneration of hair follicles and sebaceous glands from the epithelium of scars in the rabbit. *Cancer Research* **14**: 575-579.

Brunner, H. 1907. Über Glykogen in der gesunden und kranken Haut. *Kongr. Deutsch. Dermatol. Ges. Jena* pp. 521-579.

Bullough, W. S. and E. B. Laurence. 1958. The mitotic activity of the follicle. In "The Biology of Hair Growth" (W. Montagna and R. A. Ellis, eds.), pp. 171-186. Academic Press, New York.

Bunting, H. 1950. The distribution of acid mucopolysaccharides in mammalian tissues as revealed by histochemical methods. *Ann. N.Y. Acad. Sci.* **52**: 977-982.

Burstone, M. S. 1959. New histochemical techniques for the demonstration of tissue oxidase (cytochrome oxidase). *J. Histochem. and Cytochem.* **7**: 112-122.

Butcher, E. O. 1934. The hair cycles in the albino rat. *Anat. Record* **61**: 5-19.

Butcher, E. O. 1951. Development of the pilary system and the replacement of hair in mammals. *Ann. N.Y. Acad. Sci.* **53**: 508-516.

Butcher, E. O. 1959. Restitutive growth in the hair follicle of the rat. *Ann. N.Y. Acad. Sci.* **83**: 369-377.

Chase, H. B. 1958. Physical factors which influence the growth of hair. In "The Biology of Hair Growth" (W. Montagna and R. A. Ellis, eds.), pp. 435-439. Academic Press, New York.

Chase, H. B. and G. Eaton. 1959. The growth of hair follicles in waves. *Ann. N.Y. Sci.* **83**: 365-368.

Chase, H. B., H. Rauch and V. W. Smith. 1951. Critical stages of hair development and pigmentation in the mouse. *Physiol. Zool.* **24**: 1-8.

Cooper, Z. K. 1930. A histological study of the integument of the armadillo, *Tatusia novemcincta. Am. J. Anat.* **45**: 1-37.

deMeijere, J. C. H. 1894. Über die Haare der Säugetiere, besonders über ihre Anordnung. *Gegenbaur's morphol. Jahrb.* **21**: 312-424.

Dempsey, E. W., H. Bunting and G. B. Wislocki. 1947. Observations on the chemical cytology of the mammary gland. *Am. J. Anat.* **81**: 309-341.

Dry, F. W. 1926. The coat of the mouse (*Mus musculus*) *J. Genet.* **16**: 287-340.

Duggins, O. H. and M. Trotter. 1950. Age changes in head hair from birth to maturity. II. Medullation in hair of children. *Am. J. Phys. Anthropol.* **8**: 399-416.

Duggins, O. H. and M. Trotter. 1951. Changes in morphology of hair during child-hood. *Ann. N.Y. Acad. Sci.* **53**: 569-575.

Durward, A. and K. M. Rudall. 1949. Studies on hair growth in the rat. *J. Anat.* **83**: 325-335.

Durward, A. and K. M. Rudall. 1958. The vascularity and patterns of growth of hair follicles. *In* "The Biology of Hair Growth" (W. Montagna and R. A. Ellis, eds.), pp. 189-217. Academic Press, New York.

Eisen, A. Z., W. Montagna and H. B. Chase. 1953. Sulfhydryl groups in the skin of the mouse and guinea pig. *J. Natl. Cancer Inst.* **14**: 341-353.

Ellis, R. A. 1958. Ageing of the human male scalp. *In* "The Biology of Hair Growth" (W. Montagna and R. A. Ellis, eds.), pp. 469-485. Academic Press, New York.

Ellis, R. A. and W. Montagna. 1958b. Histology and cytochemistry of human skin. XV. Sites of phosphorylase and amylo-1,6-glucosidase activity. *J. Histochem. and Cytochem.* **6**: 201-207.

Ellis, R. A. and G. Moretti. 1959. Vascular patterns associated with catagen hair follicles in the human scalp. *Ann. N.Y. Acad. Sci.* **83**: 448-457.

Fraser, R. D. B. and G. E. Rogers. 1953. Microscopic observations of the alkaline-thioglycollate extraction of wool. *Biochim. et Biophys. Acta* **12**: 484-485.

Fraser, R. D. B. and G. E. Rogers. 1954. The origin of segmentation in wool cortex. *Biochim. et Biophys. Acta* **13**: 297-298.

Fraser, R. D. B., H. Lindley and G. E. Rogers. 1954. Chemical heterogeneity and cortical segmentation in wool. *Biochim. et Biophys. Acta.* **13**: 295-297.

Gavazzeni, G. A. 1908. Trichohyalin. *Monatsh. prakt. Dermatol.* **47**: 229-242.

Gersh, I. and H. R. Catchpole. 1949. The organization of ground substance and basement membrane and its significance in tissue injury, disease and growth. *Am. J. Anat.* **85**: 457-521.

Gibbs, H. F. 1938. A study of the development of the skin and hair of the Australian opossum, *Trichosurus vulpecula. Proc. Zool. Soc. London* **B108**: 611-648.

Giovannini, S. 1907. Sopra tre peli bigemini fusi ciascuno in un fusto unico. *Anat. Anz.* **30**: 144-153.

Giovannini, S. 1908. Sull'esistenza nell'uomo di papille pilifere con più propagini terminali semplici (Papille pilifere composte). *Anat. Anz.* **32**: 206-215.

Giovannini, S. 1909. Papille pilifere con propagini terminali composte, con propagini avventizie e bigemine. *Anat. Anz.* **34**: 230-249.

Giovannini, S. 1910. I peli con papilla composta. Con una tavola. *Anat. Anz.* **37**: 39-55.

Giroud, A. and H. Bulliard. 1935. Les substances à fonction sulfhydryle dans l'épiderme. *Arch. anat. microscop.* **31**: 271-290.

Giroud, A. and C. P. Leblond. 1951. The keratinization of epidermis and its deriva-tives, especially the hair, as shown by X-ray diffraction and histochemical studies. *Ann. N.Y. Acad. Sci.* **53**: 613-626.

Giroud, A., H. Bulliard and A. Giberton. 1929. Y a-t-il une accumulation élective de soufre précédant la kératinisation? *Compt. rend. soc. biol.* **101**: 1024-1025.

Giroud, A., H. Bulliard and C. P. Leblond. 1934. Les deux types fondamentaux de kératinisation. *Bull. histol. appl. physiol. et pathol. et tech. microscop.* **11**: 129-144.

Goldblum, R. W., W. N. Piper and A. W. Campbell. 1954. A comparison of three histochemical stains for the demonstration of protein-bound sulfhydryl groups in normal human skin. *J. Invest. Dermatol.* **23**: 375-383.

Gomori, G. 1952. "Microscopic Histochemistry, Principles and Practice" Univ. of Chicago Press, Chicago, Illinois.

Hale, C. W. 1946. Histochemical demonstration of acid polysaccharides in animal tissues. *Nature* **157**: 802.

Hamilton, J. B. 1958. Age, sex, and genetic factors in the regulation of hair growth in man: A comparison of Caucasian and Japanese populations. *In* "The Biology of Hair Growth" (W. Montagna and R. A. Ellis, eds.), pp. 400-432. Academic Press, New York.

Hamilton, J. B. and W. Montagna. 1950. The sebaceous glands of the hamster. I. Morphological effects of androgens on integumentary structures. *Am. J. Anat.* **86**: 191-233.

Hardy, M. H. 1952. The histochemistry of hair follicles in the mouse. *Am. J. Anat.* **90**: 285-337.

Hausman, L. A. 1932. The cortical fusi of mammalian hair shafts. *Am. Naturalist* **66**: 461-470.

Hausman, L. A. 1944. Applied microscopy of hair. *Sci. Monthly* **59**: 195-202.

Hoepke. H. 1927. Die Haare. *In* "Handbuch der mikroskopischen Anatomie des Menschen" (W. von Möllendorff, ed.), Vol. 3, Part 1, pp. 66-68. Springer, Berlin.

Horio, M. and T. Kondo. 1953a. Theory and morphology of crimped rayon staples. *Textile Research J.* **23**: 137-157.

Horio, M. and T. Kondo. 1953b. Crimping of wool fibers. *Textile Research J.* **23**: 373-386.

Johnson, P. L. and G. Bevelander. 1946. Glycogen and phosphatase in the developing hair. *Anat. Record* **95**: 193-199.

Kligman, A. M. 1959. The human hair cycles. *J. Invest. Dermatol.* **33**: 307-316.

Kligman, A. M. and J. S. Strauss. 1956. The formation of vellus hair follicles from human adult epidermis. *J. Invest. Dermatol.* **27**: 19-23.

Klingmüller, G. 1957. Kapillardarstellungen mittels Phosphatasefärbungen in gefriergetrocknetem Hautgewebe. *Proc. 11th Intern. Congr. Dermatol., Acta Dermato-Venereol.* **3**: 433-436.

Kränzle, E. 1912. Untersuchungen über die Haut des Schweines. *Arch. mikroskop. Anat.* **79**: 525-559.

Lacassagne, A. and B. Latarjet. 1946. Action of methylcholanthrene on certain scars of the skin in mice. *Cancer Research* **6**: 183-188.

Lapière, M. S. 1947. Les substances à fonction sulfhydrile dans la peau normale et dans divers états pathologiques cutanés. *Arch. belges dermatol. syphilig.* **3**: 176-186.

Leblond, C. P. 1951. Histological structure of hair, with a brief comparison to other epidermal appendages and epidermis itself. *Ann. N.Y. Acad. Sci.* **53**: 464-475.

Liebow, A. A., S. Warren and E. DeCoursey. 1949. Pathology of atomic bomb casualties. *Am. J. Pathol.* **25**: 853-1027.

Lison, L. 1935. Études sur la métachromasie. Colorants métachromatiques et substances chromotropes. *Arch. biol. (Liège)* **46**: 599-668.

Lombardo, C. 1934. Il glicogeno in alcuni derivati epidermici della cute umana. *Giorn. ital. dermatol. e sifilol.* **75**: 185-186.

Lynfield, Y. L. 1960. Effect of pregnancy on the human hair cycle. *J. Invest. Dermatol.* **35**: 323-327.

Mercer, E. H. 1949. Some experiments on the orientation and hardening of keratin in the hair follicle. *Biochim. et Biophys. Acta* **3**: 161-169.

Mercer, E. H. 1953. The heterogeneity of the keratin fibers. *Textile Research J.* **23**: 388-397.

Mercer, E. H. 1958. Electron microscopy and biosynthesis of fibers. *In* "The Biology of Hair Growth" (W. Montagna and R. A. Ellis, eds.), pp. 113-131. Academic Press, New York.

Merkel, F. 1919. Beobachtungen über den Haarwechsel in der menschlichen Kopfhaut. *Anat. Hefte* **57**: 295-322.

Mescon, H. and P. Flesch. 1952. Modification of Bennett's method for the histochemical demonstration of free sulfhydryl groups in skin. *J. Invest. Dermatol.* **18**: 261-266.

Meyer, K. 1947. The biological significance of hyaluronic acid and hyaluronidase. *Physiol. Revs.* **27**: 335-359.

Meyer, K. and E. Chaffee. 1941. The mucopolysaccharides of skin. *J. Biol. Chem.* **138**: 491-499.

Meyer, K. and M. Odier. 1946. Contribution à l'étude de l'acide chondroitine-sulfurique. *Experientia* **2**: 311-312.

Meyer, K. and M. M. Rapport. 1951. The mucopolysaccharides of the ground substance of connective tissue. *Science* **113**: 596-599.

Miller, M. R., H. J. Ralston III and M. Kasahara. 1960. The pattern of cutaneous innervation of human hand, foot and breast. *In* "Advances in Biology of Skin," Vol. I. "Cutaneous Innervation" (W. Montagna, ed.), Pergamon Press, New York.

Moebius, K. 1892. Die Behaarung der Mammuths und der lebenden Elephanten, vergleichend untersucht. *Sitzber. preuss. Akad. Wiss.* **28**: 1-12.

Mohn, M. P. 1958. The effects of different hormonal states on the growth of hair in rats. *In* "The Biology of Hair Growth" (W. Montagna and R. A. Ellis, eds.), pp. 336-393. Academic Press, New York.

Montagna, W. 1950. Perinuclear sudanophil bodies in mammalian epidermis. *Quart. J. Microscop. Sci.* **91**: 205-208.

Montagna, W. 1955. Histology and cytochemistry of human skin. IX. The distribution of non-specific esterases. *J. Biophys. Biochem. Cytol.* **1**: 13-16.

Montagna, W. 1956. "The Structure and Function of Skin." Academic Press, New York.

Montagna, W. 1957. Histology and cytochemistry of human skin. XI. The distribution of β-glucuronidase. *J. Biophys. Biochem. Cytol.* **3**: 343-348.

Montagna, W. 1959. Introduction. *In* "Hair Growth and Hair Regeneration." *Ann. N.Y. Acad. Sci.* **83**: 302-304.

Montagna, W. 1960. Cholinesterases in the cutaneous nerves of man. *In* "Advances in Biology of Skin," Vol. I. "Cutaneous Innervation" (W. Montagna, ed.). Pergamon Press, New York.

Montagna, W. and H. B. Chase. 1956. Histology and cytochemistry of human skin. X. X-Irradiation of the scalp. *Am. J. Anat.* **99**: 415-446.

Montagna, W. and R. A. Ellis. 1957a. Histology and cytochemistry of human skin. XII. Cholinesterases in hair follicles of the scalp. *J. Invest. Dermatol.* **29**: 151-157.

Montagna, W. and R. A. Ellis. 1957b. Histology and cytochemistry of human skin. XIII. The blood supply of the hair follicles. *J. Natl. Cancer Inst.* **19**: 451-456.

Montagna, W. and R. A. Ellis. 1958a. L'histologie et la cytologie de la peau humaine. XVI. Répartition et concentration des estérases carboxyliques. *Ann. histochim.* **3**: 1-22.

Montagna, W. and R. A. Ellis (eds.), 1958b. "The Biology of Hair Growth." Academic Press, New York.

Montagna, W. and R. A. Ellis. 1959. The skin of the potto (*Perodicticus potto*). *Am. J. Phys. Anthropol.* **17**: 137-162.

Montagna, W. and V. R. Formisano. 1955. Histology and cytochemistry of human skin. VII. The distribution of succinic dehydrogenase activity. *Anat. Record* **122**: 65-77.

Montagna, W. and R. J. Harrison. 1957. Specialization in the skin of the seal (*Phoca vitulina*). *Am. J. Anat.* **100**: 81-114.

Montagna, W. and C. R. Hill. 1957. The localization of S^{35} in the skin of the rat. *Anat. Record* **127**: 163-172.

Montagna, W., H. B. Chase and J. B. Hamilton. 1951a. The distribution of glycogen and lipids in human skin. *J. Invest. Dermatol.* **17**: 147-157.

Montagna, W., H. B. Chase and H. P. Melaragno. 1951b. Histology and cytochemistry of human skin. I. Metachromasia in the mons pubis. *J. Natl. Cancer Inst.* **12**: 591-597.

Montagna, W., H. B. Chase and W. C. Lobitz, Jr. 1952a. Histology and cytochemistry of human skin. II. The distribution of glycogen in the epidermis, hair follicles, sebaceous glands and eccrine sweat glands. *Anat. Record* **114**: 231-248.

Montagna, W., H. B. Chase, J. D. Malone and H. P. Melaragno. 1952b. Cyclic changes in polysaccharides of the papilla of the hair follicle. *Quart. J. Microscop. Sci.* **93**: 241-245.

Montagna, W., A. Z. Eisen, A. H. Rademacher and H. B. Chase. 1954. Histology and cytochemistry of human skin. VI. The distribution of sulfhydryl and disulfide groups. *J. Invest. Dermatol.* **23**: 23-32.

Myers, R. J. and J. B. Hamilton. 1951. Regeneration and rate of growth of hairs in man. *Ann. N.Y. Acad. Sci.* **53**: 562-568.

New York Academy of Sciences, 1951. The Growth, Replacement, and Types of Hair. *Ann. N.Y. Acad. Sci.* **53**.

New York Academy of Sciences. 1959. Hair Growth and Hair Regeneration. *Ann. N.Y. Acad. Sci.* **83**.

Nicolau, S. 1911. Recherches histologiques sur la graisse cutanée. *Ann. dermatol. syphilig.* **2**: 641-658.

Odland, G. F. 1953. Some microscopic studies of the keratinization of human hair. *J. Invest. Dermatol.* **21**: 305-312.

Parat, M. 1928. Contribution à l'étude morphologique et physiologique du cytoplasme. Chondriome, vacuole (appareil de Golgi), enclaves, etc.; pH, oxidases, peroxydases, rH de la cellule animale. *Arch. anat. microscop.* **24**: 73-357.

Patzelt, V. 1926. Zum Bau der menschlichen Epidermis. *Z. mikroskop.-anat. Forsch.* **5**: 371-462.

Pearce, R. H. and E. M. Watson. 1949. The mucopolysaccharides of human skin. *Cancer J. Research* **E27**: 43-57.

Pinkus, F. 1905. Über Haut in Organen neben dem menschlichen Haar (haarscheiben) und ihre vergleichen de anatomische Bedeutung. *Arch. mikroskop. Anat.* **65**: 121-177.

Pinkus, F. 1927. Die normale Anatomie der Haut. *In* "Handbuch der Haut- und Geschlechtskrankheiten" (J. Jadassohn, ed.), Vol. 1, Part 1. Springer, Berlin.

Pinkus, H. 1958. Embryology of hair. *In* "The Biology of Hair Growth" (W. Montagna and R. A. Ellis, eds.), pp. 1-32. Academic Press, New York.

Rogers, G. E. 1957. Electron microscope observations on the glassy layer of hair follicle. *Exptl. Cell Research* **13**: 521-528.

Rogers, G. E. 1958. Some observations on the proteins of the inner root sheath cells of hair follicles. *Biochim. et Biophys. Acta* **29**: 33-43.

Rogers, G. E. 1959. Newer findings on the enzymes and proteins of hair follicles. *Ann. N.Y. Acad. Sci.* **83**: 408-428.

Ryder, M. L. 1956a. Blood supply of the wool follicle. *Wool Inds. Research Assoc. Bull.* **18**: 142-147.

Ryder, M. L. 1956b. Use of radioisotopes in the study of wool growth and fibre composition. *Nature* **178**: 1409-1410.

Ryder, M. L. 1958. Nutritional factors influencing hair and wool growth. *In* "The Biology of Hair Growth" (W. Montagna and R. A. Ellis, eds.), pp. 305-330. Academic Press, New York.

Schaffer, J. 1933. "Lehrbuch der Histologie und Histogenese." Engelmann, Leipzig.

Segall, A. 1918. Ueber die Entwicklung und den Wechsel der Haare beim Meerschweinchen (*Cavia cobaya* Schreb). *Arch. mikroskop. Anat.* **91**: 218-291.

Shipman, M., H. B. Chase and W. Montagna. 1955. Glycogen in skin of the mouse during cycles of hair growth. *Proc. Soc. Exptl. Biol. Med.* **88**: 449-451.

Spuler, A. 1899. Cited from Hoepke (1927).

Stöhr, P. 1903. Entwickelungsgeschichte des menschlichen Wollhaares. *Anat. Hefte* **23**: 1-66.

Straile, W. E. 1959. A study of the neoformation of mammalian hair follicles. *In* "Hair Growth and Hair Regeneration" (O.v.St. Whitelock, ed.). *Ann. N.Y. Acad. Sci.* **83**: 499-506.

Sylvén, B. 1941. Über das Vorkommen von hochmolekularen Esterschwefelsäuren im Granulationsgewebe und bei der Epithelregeneration. *Acta. Chir. Scand.* **86** Suppl. 66: 1-151.

Sylvén, B. 1950. The qualitative distribution of metachromatic polysaccharide material during hair growth. *Exptl. Cell Research* **1**: 582-589.

Szabó, G. 1958. The regional frequency and distribution of hair follicles in human skin. *In* "The Biology of Hair Growth" (W. Montagna and R. A. Ellis, eds.), pp. 33-38. Academic Press, New York.

Tamponi, M. 1939. Nuovo contributo alla conoscensz del "Disco del Pelo" (Haarscheibe di Pinkus), con particolare Riguardo alla sua iconografia macroscopica. *Arch. ital. dermatol., sifilog. e venereol.* **15**: 378-394.

Taylor, A. C. 1949. Survival of rat skin and changes in hair pigmentation following freezing. *J. Exptl. Zool.* **110**: 77-111.

Toldt, K., Jr. 1912. Beiträge zur Kenntnis der Behaarung der Säugetiere. *Zool. Jahrb.* **33**: 9-86.

Trotter, M. 1930. The form, size, and color of head hair in American whites. *Am. J. Phys. Anthropol.* **14**: 433-445.

Trotter, M. 1932. The hair. *In* "Special Cytology" (E. V. Cowdry, ed.), Vol. 1, pp. 41-65. Hoeber, New York.

Trotter, M., and H. L. Dawson. 1931. The direction of hair after rotation of skin in the guinea-pig: an experiment on hair slope. *Anat. Record* **50**: 193-196.

Trotter, M. and H. L. Dawson. 1932. The direction of hair after rotation of skin in the newborn albino rat: A second experiment on hair slope. *Anat. Record* **53**: 19-30.

Trotter, M. and H. L. Dawson. 1934. The hair of French Canadians. *Am. J. Physical Anthropol.* **18**: 443-456.

Trotter, M. and O. H. Duggins. 1948. Age changes in head hair from birth to maturity. I. Index and size of hair in children. *Am. J. Phys. Anthropol.* **6**: 489-506.

Trotter, M. and O. H. Duggins. 1950. Age changes in head hair from birth to maturity. III. Cuticular scale counts of hair of children. *Am. J. Phys. Anthropol.* **8**: 467-484.

Van Scott, E. J. 1958. Response of hair roots to chemical and physical influence. *In* "The Biology of Hair Growth" (W. Montagna and R. A. Ellis, eds.), pp. 441-449. Academic Press, New York.

Van Scott, E. J. 1959. Evaluation of disturbed hair growth in alopecia areata and other alopecias. *Ann. N.Y. Acad. Sci.* **83**: 480-489.

Van Scott, E. J. and T. M. Ekel. 1958. Geometric relationships between the matrix of the hair bulb and its dermal papilla in normal and alopecic scalp. *J. Invest. Dermatol.* **31**: 281-287.

Van Scott, E. J. and P. Flesch. 1954. Sulfhydryl and disulfide in keratinization. *Science* **119**: 70-71.

Vörner, H. 1903. Ueber Trichohyalin. Ein Beitrag zur Anatomie des Haares und der Wurzelscheiden. *Dermatol. Z.* **10**: 357-376.

Weddell, G. 1941. The pattern of cutaneous innervation in relation to cutaneous sensibility. *J. Anat.* **75**: 346-367.

Weddell, G. 1945. The anatomy of cutaneous sensibility. *Brit. Med. Bull.* **3**: 167-172.

Winkelmann, R. K. 1959. The innervation of a hair follicle. *Ann. N.Y. Acad. Sci.* **83**: 400-407.

Winkelmann, R. K. 1960. "Nerve Endings in Normal and Pathologic Skin." C. C Thomas, Springfield, Illinois.

Wislocki, G. B., H. Bunting and E. W. Dempsey. 1947. Metachromasia in mammalian tissues and its relationship to mucopolysaccharides. *Am. J. Anat.* **81**: 1-37.

Wolbach, S. B. 1951. The hair cycle of the mouse and its importance in the study of sequences of experimental carcinogenesis. *Ann. N.Y. Acad. Sci.* **53**: 517-536

Woollard, H. H., G. Weddell and J. A. Harpman. 1940. Observations on the neuro-histological basis of cutaneous pain. *J. Anat.* **74**: 413-440.

Yasuda, K. and W. Montagna. 1960. Histology and cytochemistry of human skin. XX. The distribution of monoamine oxidase. *J. Histochem. Cytochem.* **18**: 356-366.

Yun, J. 1958. Alkaline phosphatase and esterases in the skin of hairless mice. M.S. thesis, Brown University, Providence, R. I.

CHAPTER 5

The Sebaceous Glands

Introduction

Sebaceous glands, first described by Eichorn in 1826, are as characteristic of mammalian skin as hair follicles are. Let it be emphasized at the outset that although all sebaceous glands are structurally similar, the glands over the different parts of the human body often have different properties such as responses to trophic agents. They display remarkable species differences. In man, sebaceous glands are largest and most numerous in the scalp, forehead, cheeks, and chin, where 400 to 900 of them may be found in each square centimeter of skin surface. Over the rest of the body, sebaceous glands are fewer than 100 per square centimeter (Benfenati and Brillanti, 1939). These figures are relatively meaningless, since the number and size of the glands vary in individuals. In some regions, such as the anconal surface of the hand, the number varies from none to 50 per square centimeter of skin (Johnsen and Kirk, 1952). There are none on the palms and soles and on the dorsum of the foot. The glands are large and numerous on the midline of the back, and largest on the face and around the genitalia. In other mammals, sebaceous glands are widespread over the body; they are largest and particularly numerous in the external auditory meatus and in the perianal region. The whales and porpoises, which are nearly, or absolutely, free of cutaneous appendages, have no sebaceous glands.

Most sebaceous glands are appendages of hair follicles and open inside the pilosebaceous canal. The size of the glands often varies inversely with the size of the hair follicles with which they are associated, the largest glands being found where hair follicles are small or absent. These differences in size are often relative, and moderately large glands may appear to be very large when associated with small hair follicles. On the face very large glands, scattered among less spectacular ones, empty into the dilated pilary canals of vellus hair follicles (Fig. 1). Struck by their impressive size and function, and to distinguish them from the smaller ones, Kligman and Shelley (1958) called these glands "sebaceous follicles," a designation used first by Horner (1846). Some sebaceous glands open directly onto the surface of the skin. In man, such glands are found in the palpebrae (Meibomian glands), in the buccal mucosa and the vermilion surface of the lips (Miles, 1958a, b), on the nipples (Perkins and Miller, 1926), on the prepuce (Tyson's glands), occasionally on the glans penis, and on the labia minora (Machado de Sousa, 1931). In other mammals, aggregates of sebaceous glands, free of hair follicles, often attain gigantic sizes; the rat, mouse,

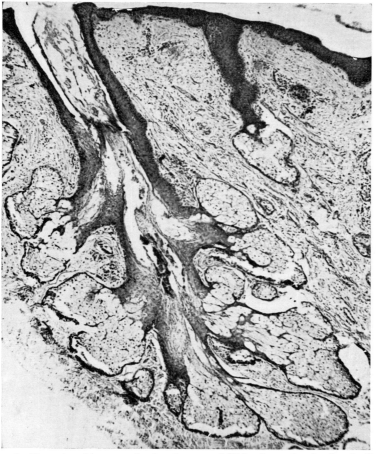

Fig. 1. Gigantic sebaceous gland, sebaceous follicle, from the forehead. Stained with hematoxylin and eosin. From Strauss and Kligman (1960). (Reprinted by permission of the authors and the *A.M.A. Arch. Dermatol.*)

and rabbit have preputial or inguinal glands; marmosets and shrews have large fields of abdominal sebaceous glands, and nearly all mammals have large aggregates of sebaceous glands in the anal and circumanal regions. The sebaceous glands of the general skin of the black lemur open directly onto the surface and not into the pilary canals (Montagna *et al.*, 1961).

Sebaceous glands are holocrine, usually multiple acinar glands (Figs. 2 and 3); their general configuration is often determined by their relative abundance in an area and by the nature of the dermis in

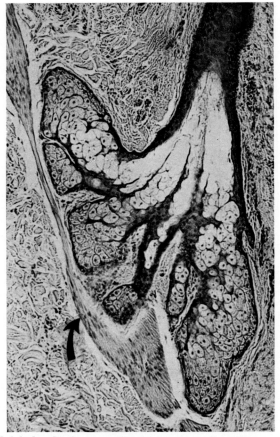

FIG. 2. Multilobulated sebaceous gland from the scalp. The arrow points to the arrectores pilorum muscle. Stained with hematoxylin and eosin.

which they grow (Clara, 1929). Regardless of their size, shape, or position, their cellular morphology is similar.

The acini of each gland are attached to a common excretory duct that consists of stratified squamous epithelium continuous with the wall of the pilary canal, or with the surface epidermis. In the glandular acini the cells show a centripetal enlargement, those in the center being large, often misshaped, and moribund; the cells at the outer periphery are undifferentiated and resemble those of the epidermis. The mature acini and the ducts contain *sebum,* a substance composed of lipids and cell debris. The various acini in one glandular unit are

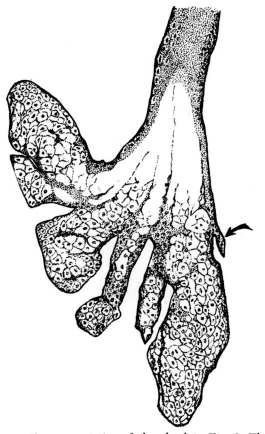

FIG. 3. Diagrammatic representation of the gland in Fig. 2. The stippled areas represent the regions of undifferentiated sebaceous cells. The arrow points to an undifferentiated acinus.

in different states of maturity; in some only the central cells are laden with lipid droplets; in others the cells may show lipid accumulation as far as the outer periphery of the acinus (Figs. 4 and 5B). Just as keratinization characterizes the end point in epidermal cells, lipid accumulation and fragmentation characterize that of sebaceous cells.

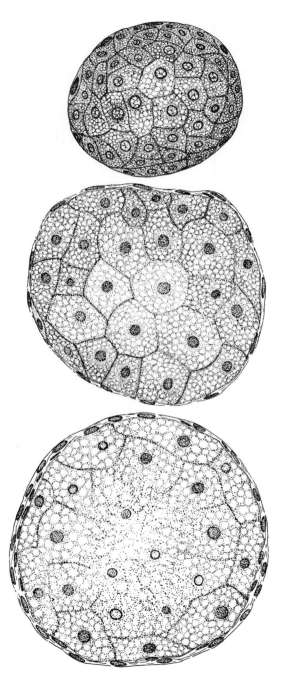

"Sebaceous differentiation" as used in this book denotes the orderly accumulation of lipid droplets in cells; at the completion of differentiation the cells become fragmented and form the sebum.

Development

The development of sebaceous glands is intimately associated with that of hair follicles. Thus, there is a dyschrony in development from region to region in most mammals. In man, the sebaceous glands in the scalp and face are well differentiated even in the fetus of $3\frac{1}{2}$ months, when those elsewhere have not yet made an appearance. Two bulges on the same side of hair follicles develop even before the follicles are fully differentiated. The lower hump is the "bulge" of the hair follicle, to which the muscle will be attached. The upper one is the anlage of the sebaceous gland; the cells in its center lose their glycogen and become larger as they accumulate discrete lipid droplets. Within any one cell all of the lipid droplets seem to appear more or less simultaneously, and the cells become gradually larger as the individual droplets increase in size. The largest cells in the center finally break down. Similar sebaceous differentiation and final decay also take place in the cells in the center of the solid cord, above the level of the sebaceous gland. This column of sebaceous cells extends for a distance through the epidermis, parallel to the surface, establishing the pilosebaceous canal and its opening to the surface (Fig. 5A). From their earliest differentiation around 3 months to term, the sebaceous glands are relatively large and functional. The vernix caseosa which incrusts the skin of the newborn is secreted in part by the sebaceous glands. Even in the newborn the glands are large, but they become small shortly after birth, remain small through infancy and childhood and develop fully in the prepuberal years. They are larger in men than in women.

In the mouse and the rat some of the hair follicles and the sebaceous glands associated with them develop during the first 3 or 4 postnatal days. The glands appear first as solid cellular buds along the side of the follicle, immediately above the bulge for the attachment of the arrector pili muscle. Sebaceous differentiation of the cells of the buds,

FIG. 4. Semi-schematic representation of sebaceous differentiation and maturation. Differentiation begins in the center of the acinus, as seen in the one at the top and spreads centrifugally. In the middle acinus differentiation is nearly complete, and in the acinus at the bottom, the mature cells in the center are beginning to break down.

however, does not begin until the inner sheath of the follicle has been formed.

Most sebaceous glands develop in association with hair follicles. The follicles, however, may be very small and subsequently drop out. In histologic sections of the labia minora of newborn, each of the

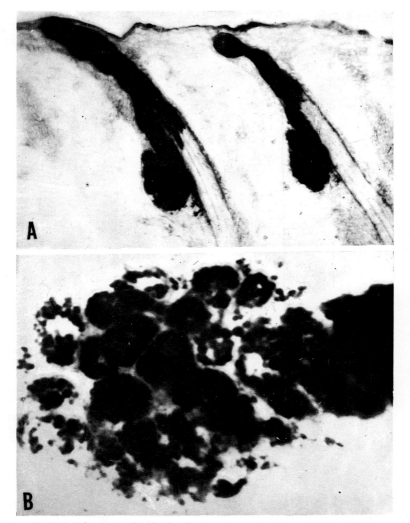

Fig. 5. (A) Sebaceous glands developing in association with hair follicles on the scalp of an embryo 3½ months old. Colored with Sudan black. (B) Detail of (A), showing the progression of lipoidal accumulation from the center to the periphery.

large nests of glands is arranged around a minute vellus hair follicle, which later disappears. Even in the labia minora of the adult, which have a glabrous surface, sebaceous glands are often arranged around abortive, or disoriented hair follicles. The preputial glands of the rat and the white inguinal gland of the rabbit sometimes have one or more hair follicles growing through the rich sebaceous fields. Obviously, the glands that develop postnatally on the vermilion border of the lip and on the buccal mucosa are not formed from follicles. Yet, even in the buccal mucosa, Dr. Miles (personal communication, 1959) found one relatively well-developed active hair follicle.

Basophilia

The cytoplasm of the undifferentiated, potential sebaceous cells is strongly basophilic (Fig. 6); the basophilia, which is abolished by ribonuclease, is apparently due to ribonucleoproteins. Young sebaceous acinar buds are intensely basophil throughout; in more mature acini the peripheral cells stain with basic dyes, but the more central ones do not.

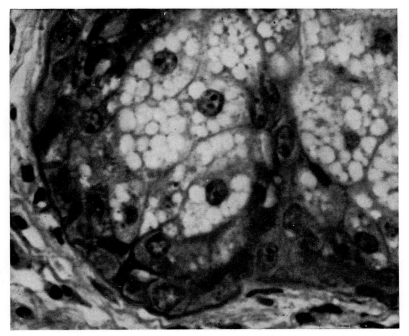

FIG. 6. Basophilic staining, showing ribonucleic acid, in the peripheral cells of a sebaceous gland from the human axilla.

There is a progressive centripetal loss of basic staining, and the spongy cytoplasm of the mature cells laden with lipid droplets is acidophil.

Under the electron microscope, the basophilic elements in the cytoplasm of undifferentiated cells appear as cisternae of ergastoplasm. Fine nucleoprotein granules are dispersed over the surface of the ergastoplasmic membranes and in clusters and rosettes throughout the cytoplasm (Palay, 1957), and seem to correspond to the cytoplasmic basophilia. The number of nucleoprotein granules remains unchanged even when the cells become more lipid-laden. Their concentration per unit area, therefore, decreases.

Mitochondria

Although mitochodria are numerous and not difficult to demonstrate, very few biologists have studied them in sebaceous cells. Nicolas *et al.* (1914), who described them briefly in human sebaceous glands, thought that lipid droplets develop at the expense of mitochondria. Thus, mitochondria would seem to decrease in numbers progressively as

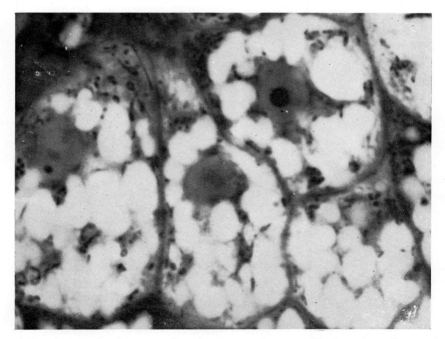

FIG. 7. Mitochondria in moderately mature sebaceous cells from the axilla. Each lipid globule is surrounded by discrete mitochondria.

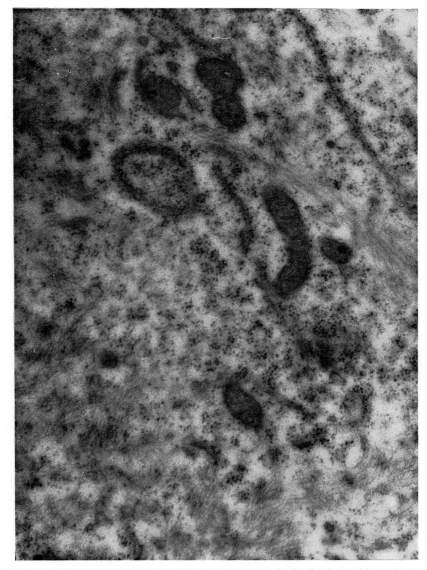

FIG. 8. Electron micrograph of the white inguinal gland of a rabbit which is sebaceous, showing the bimodality of predisposition of an undifferentiated cell. In the cytoplasm may be seen keratin tonofilaments, rough- and smooth-surfaced endoplasmic granules, and mitochondria. Fixed 2 hours in 2% osmic acid, and stained with lead oxide. (Courtesy of R. C. Henrikson.)

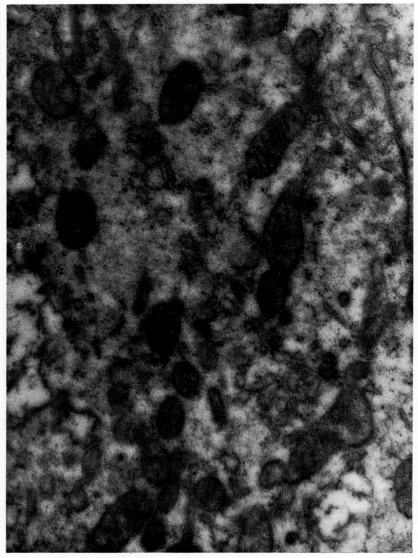

Fɪɢ. 9. Electron micrograph of a peripheral cell from the white inguinal gland of the rabbit which is undergoing sebaceous differentiation. Observe the mitochondria, the rough-surfaced and smooth-surfaced endoplasmic reticulum, and the numerous, small lipid vacuoles. Fixed 4 hours in 2% osmic acid and stained with lead oxide. (Courtesy of R. C. Henrikson.)

transformation continues; only scattered fragments are said to remain in mature cells between lipid droplets (Ludford, 1925).

The mitochondria in human sebaceous glands can be easily demonstrated with a number of staining methods. We prefer the aniline acid fuchsin-methyl green method applied to tissues that have been fixed in Regaud's mixture and postchromed for at least 1 week at 36°C (Montagna, 1955) (Fig. 7). The distribution, number, and general morphology of mitochondria in the cells of the sebaceous ducts, and in the indifferent cells at the periphery of the sebaceous acini, resemble those in the cells of the surface epidermis. In fact, these cells are practically indistinguishable from those of the epidermis. The numerous mitochondria are in the form of short and often wavy rodlets. At the beginning of sebaceous differentiation, mitochondria become crowded in the perinuclear cytoplasm around lipid granules, which develop near the mitochondria but not directly from them. Each lipid droplet is surrounded by mitochondria. With continued sebaceous transformation the volume of the sebaceous cell increases manyfold, but the population of mitochondria neither increases nor decreases. In mature sebaceous cells mitochondria are stranded in the flimsy network of cytoplasm between the lipid globules. They remain moderately normal in appearance and in number until the late stages of sebaceous decay, when they are no longer distinguishable. This may not be very informative concerning the role of mitochondria in lipid synthesis, but it is significant that their number does not decrease as sebaceous transformation progresses. They are not transformed into lipids, but may play a directive role in the synthesis of sebaceous lipids.

Studies of sebaceous glands with the electron microscope largely confirm these findings (Figs. 8 and 9) (Palay, 1957, on the Meibomian glands of the rat; Charles, 1960, on the sebaceous glands of man). Rogers (1957), however, finds, in the sebaceous glands of the mouse, dense granules within the mitochondria, which he interprets as the beginning of lipid droplet formation inside the mitochondria. Since mitochondria are numerous even in relatively mature sebaceous cells, Roger's interpretations are questionable.

The Golgi Apparatus

All evidence points to the Golgi apparatus as the locus of the cell that is most intimately associated with the synthesis of lipid droplets in sebaceous differentiation. The Golgi element has been studied principally in the glands of the mouse, in the white inguinal glands of the rabbit, and in human sebaceous glands (Bowen, 1926, 1929; Ludford, 1925; Melczer and Deme, 1942, 1943). The undifferentiated cells at the base of the acini and those in the excretory ducts, contain perinuclear Golgi bodies which reduce osmic acid. As sebaceous accumulation begins, these osmiophil rodlets and granules increase in number, and osmiophobe lipid droplets, probably corresponding to the Golgi internum, develop within each of these elements. As the lipid globules increase in size, the osmiophil bodies at their periphery become reduced to curved or crescentic rods or shells around them. When sebaceous cells attain maturity, the Golgi material is practically all gone. The lipid droplets which appear in the center of the Golgi bodies are at first osmiophobic, but become progressively osmiophilic as they become larger. Short treatment of osmicated sections with turpentine or potassium permanganate bleaches the lipid droplets but not the accompanying Golgi elements. In the sebaceous glands of the cat, the indifferent peripheral acinar cells have numerous perinuclear osmiophil ringlets with an osmiophobe center. In the mature sebaceous cells, the large lipid globules remain osmiophobic, but they are surrounded by a delicate osmiophil ring. In the degenerating sebaceous cells, there are minute osmiophil fragments among osmiophobe lipid masses (Montagna, 1949b). This sequence of events also takes place in the hamster (Montagna and Hamilton, 1949). The only difference between these results and those of other authors is that the lipid droplets in the sebaceous glands described here are nearly always osmiophobic. This discrepancy might be explained by the fact that the preparations described here were postosmicated for a shorter period of time. These results are constant, and they are similar to those obtained with Baker's acid hematein test for phospholipids. In the sebaceous glands of man, the hamster, and the dog, there are acid hematein-reactive elements the shape and distribution of which resemble those of the osmiophilic Golgi bodies (Montagna and Hamilton, 1949; Montagna et al., 1948; Montagna and Parks, 1948; Suskind, 1951).

FIG. 10. Frozen section, colored with Sudan black B, of tissues from mice treated with methylcholanthrene, to show regeneration of sebaceous glands from the cells of the outer sheath of a hair follicle. (A) Perinuclear sudanophil bodies in the cells of the outer sheath 4 days after the application of the carcinogen. (B) Five days after treatment the number of perinuclear sudanophil bodies increases. (C), (D), and (E) Progressive sebaceous differentiation of the cells of the outer sheath on the sixth day. (F) Part of a fully redifferentiated sebaceous gland. Compare the size of the cells on the upper right hand with those on the lower left.

When the skin of the mouse is painted with methylcholanthrene, its sebaceous glands become fragmented and disappear within 4 days. They will regrow within 1 week from the cells of the outer root sheath, if the follicles are actively growing. In frozen sections colored with

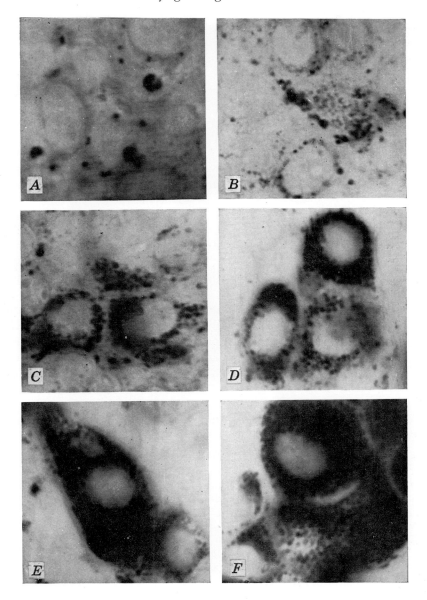

Sudan black, the cells of the external root sheath possess discrete perinuclear sudanophil bodies similar to those described in epidermal cells. An increase in the size and number of perinuclear sudanophil

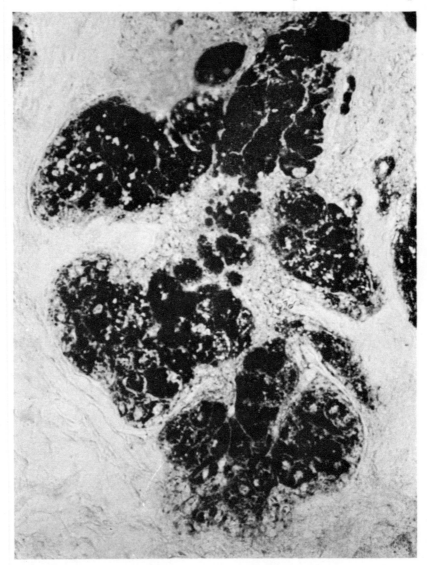

Fig. 11. Sebaceous gland colored with Sudan black. Observe the centripetal progression of maturation of sebaceous cells. Frozen section from the nose of a newborn. (Courtesy of Dr. R. R. Suskind.)

bodies in focal groups of cells in the outer root sheath indicates the first sebaceous transformation (Figs. 10 and 11). The perinuclear sudanophil bodies seem to be identical to the osmiophil granules and the acid hematein-positive elements, and one must assume that they are at least a part of the Golgi bodies of "lipochondria." These lipoidal bodies which we identify as the Golgi element, whatever they may be, are apparently implicated, perhaps by direct transformation, in the process of sebaceous transformation.

Under the electron microscope, during their early stages of development, the lipid or "secretion" droplets consist of a loosely arranged network of strands apparently suspended in a clear circular or elliptical space (Palay, 1957). The spaces are delimited from the rest of the cytoplasm by several tightly opposed membranes. Each layer of these membranes consists of a "bidimensional grid" composed of intercommunicating tubules laid more or less at right angles to one another in the plane of the layer. The secretory droplets apparently form in the cytoplasmic spaces enclosed by the sinuous curves of the agranular reticulum. As the cells mature, the cytoplasm becomes compressed into the interstices between the droplets, which become larger and more numerous until only thin plates of cytoplasm containing mitochondria, fine granules, and tubules separate the droplets (Figs. 8 and 9). The strands inside the droplets disappear and the "husks" around the droplets become thinner. These "husks" of agranular membranes around each droplet correspond to the osmiophil shells described above, and, therefore, to the Golgi elements. In contrast, Charles (1960), in human sebaceous glands, finds that lipid droplets do not arise within membrane structures, but his material is rather poor and of no consequence, as far as this issue is concerned. In conclusion, and in agreement with the findings of Palay (1957), sebaceous transformation occurs within the structures that correspond to the Golgi apparatus, either by chemical alterations of the substances of the membranes, or by a segregation of materials in the cytoplasm.

Lipids

Sebum is markedly different from tissue fats. Thus, a number of unusual substances not found anywhere else in the body must be synthesized within the sebaceous glands (Lederer and Mercier, 1948). It is not possible to generalize about the chemical nature of sebum since it differs widely from species to species. It is difficult to collect sebum uncontaminated by surface lipids, and this may account for the fact that cholesterol and free fatty acids are perhaps the only substances which occur constantly in it (Wheatley, 1952, 1953). For example, cyclic triterpene alcohols occur in the wool fat of sheep and goats, whereas the sebum of man and the horse contains the acyclic triterpene, squalene. In the dog and rabbit, triterpenes and their alcohols are probably absent. The origin of the free fatty acid in surface lipids is puzzling but it might be explained in terms of lipases which are known to be present in the sebaceous glands and the epidermis (Montagna, 1955; Nicolaides and Wells, 1957). These fatty acids could also be formed as a result of hydrolysis of sebum through rancidification. Surface lipids contain both saturated and unsaturated fatty acids with odd numbers of carbon atoms. This is unusual since in other tissues only the even-numbered acids occur. In the unsaturated fatty acids of skin surface lipids, the double bond is located in the 6:7 position, whereas in other cases it is more usual to find it in the 9:10 position. The presence of squalene is difficult to explain, and its origin and functions are unknown.

Although it is not possible to obtain pure sebum for chemical analysis, there is a large amount of information on the surface lipids of the skin. From these data may be deduced some of the contribution of sebaceous lipids. The amount of surface lipids on a particular area of skin could be dependent in part upon the number, the size, and the rate of secretion of sebaceous glands, the thickness of the stratum corneum and possibly also the wetness of the skin. Sweating may be a prime factor in the spread of sebum over the surface. In addition to sebaceous lipids, surface lipids contain unknown amounts of lipid products of keratinization. The age and sex of the individual and a variety of physiological and physical factors also play important roles in controlling the amount of surface lipids. Among the many papers on surface skin lipids, those of MacKenna et al. (1950, 1952), Wheatley (1952), and Kvorning (1949) are particularly informative; Nicolaides and Rothman (1953) have studied surface lipids by analyzing the composition of hair fat, and Schmidt-Nielsen et al. (1951) have made notable attempts to separate sebum from the corneal lipids by analyzing the contents of the sebaceous plugs from individual gland orifices. Human surface lipids contain on an average about one third free fatty acids and one third esterified fatty acids. These form a homologous series which ranges from short to long chains. The surface contains a mixture of unsaponifiable matter, normal-chain aliphatic alcohols, and some squalene. Vitamin A, β-carotene, vitamin K, or provitamins D_2 and D_3 have not been detected by chemical tests. Surface lipids contain small amounts of vitamin E and appreciable amounts of acidic or phenolic reducing compounds which may function as antioxidants. Sebum, or surface lipids, contain few glycerides and only traces of phospholipids. The entire complex mixture of surface lipids is extremely hydrophilic (Rothman, 1954).

It would be too much to expect histochemical methods to be particularly illuminating in separating specifically the individual lipids of such complex mixtures, when even chemical methods leave much to be desired. Yet the application of some tests can be useful in understanding the accumulation of lipids within the glandular tissue.

Using a series of tests of doubtful specificity, Melczer and Deme (1942) found the lipids in human sebaceous glands distributed in concentric layers, each layer supposedly consisting of different types of lipid. Other studies of human glands have failed to show this layering (Montagna *et al.*, 1948; Suskind, 1951).

Human sebaceous glands are strongly sudanophilic (Figs. 11 and 12). The cells of the duct system and the many undifferentiated cells at the periphery of the acini, or between adjacent acini, all have numerous, discrete perinuclear sudanophil bodies. Lipid accumulation in young sebaceous acini begins in the cells in the center and progresses centrifugally to the more peripheral cells (Montagna and Noback, 1946a, b, 1947). The outermost cells may contain only small perinuclear sudanophilic bodies, or, in fully mature acini, they may be inflated with large lipid spherules (Fig. 12). As the cells store lipids, their volume increases manyfold (Figs. 4, 10, and 12), and the total volume of the acini increases. In the cells which are moderately mature, the lipid droplets are spherical and of uniform size (Fig. 12C). Just before the breakdown, the lipid droplets coalesce, forming globules of different sizes. There is a species difference in the ultimate size which the mature lipid droplets attain. They are large in the glands of man and very small in those of the mouse (Figs. 10 and 12). The uniformity of the lipid droplets in mature sebaceous cells are good indices of the normality of the glands. When the lipid globules are of strikingly different sizes, the well-being of a gland has been disrupted. This holds true for the glands of man as well as those of all the animals studied. For an over-all study of lipids, Sudan black is excellent since it colors lipids indiscriminately, although Sudan III and IV, being less powerful lipid colorants, are occasionally more instructive. For example, in the sebaceous glands from the costovertebral pigmented spot of the hamster, Sudan IV shows a unique concentric stratification of lipids, but Sudan black does not (Montagna and Hamilton, 1949).

When frozen sections of the skin of man and of laboratory animals

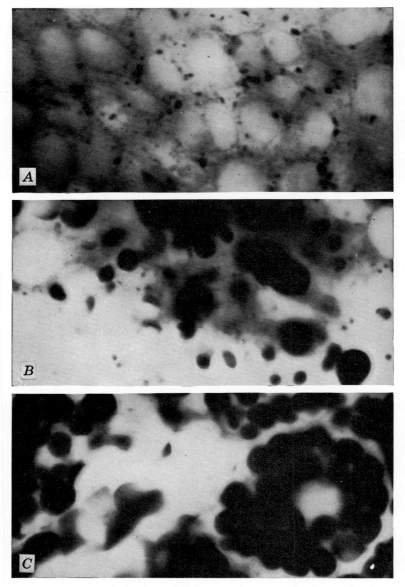

FIG. 12. Enlarged details from Fig. 4. Distribution of lipids in sebaceous cells. (A) Perinuclear lipid droplets in the cells of sebaceous duct. (B) Peripheral cells of a sebaceous acinus which are beginning to show lipid storage. (C) Mature sebaceous cells showing the relatively equal size of lipid droplets.

are subjected to secondary osmication, only the sebum in the excretory ducts of the sebaceous glands becomes blackened. The newly formed sebum in the center of the acini and the lipid droplets in sebaceous cells are osmiophobic. In the glands of the rabbit, the lipids in the peripheral acinar cells are weakly osmiophilic. Although we do not know specifically what this means, the old sebum, being osmiophilic, must differ chemically both from the sebum just formed and from the lipid droplets in the sebaceous cells, which are osmiophobic (Montagna, 1949b).

Nile blue sulfate colors the mature sebum pink or red; the newly-formed sebum is usually colored purple, and the sebaceous lipid droplets, pink. The peripheral cells contain purplish or blue lipid droplets. Although Nile blue is not a specific histochemical reagent, a rose color usually indicates the presence of neutral lipids. One might surmise, then, that sebum and sebaceous cells contain appreciable amounts of triglycerides.

In sebaceous glands the new sebum shows a positive reaction to the Fischler method for the alleged demonstration of fatty acids, while the old sebum in the excretory ducts does not (Montagna and Hamilton, 1949). When sections treated with these methods are subsequently colored with Nile blue, the previously uncolored sebum as well as the discrete lipid droplets in the sebaceous cells becomes pink. Although these tests are not specific for fatty acids, they demonstrate that changes take place in the lipids as the sebum becomes aged.

In the rat, phospholipids, demonstrated with the use of the Smith-Dietrich method and the more specific acid hematein test of Baker, are present in the spongy cytoplasm of the mature and degenerating sebaceous cells, and in the sebum, as well as in granules and rodlets in the cytoplasm of indifferent sebaceous cells, or cells in the process of sebaceous transformation. These elements are comparable to mitochondria and/or the Golgi element (Baker, 1946; Cain, 1947, 1950). The distribution of phospholipids in human sebaceous glands is similar to that just described for the rat. Larger masses of reactive materials are found in the sebum within the sebaceous ducts and hair follicles than within the gland itself. It is not surprising to find phospholipids in the sebum, since analyses of surface lipids show slightly more than 1% phospholipids (Engman and Kooyman, 1934).

In sebaceous glands an orderly progression of events leads to the formation of sebum. Sebum contains histologically demonstrable cholesterol esters, some phospholipids, and possibly triglycerides. The blocked sebum in comedones and in sebaceous cysts contains, in addition, free cholesterol. Demonstrable differences appear between the sebum in the excretory ducts and that just formed in the centers of the glands.

Histochemical demonstrations of cholesterol or cholesterol esters usually give a positive reaction in the sebum. Free cholesterol combines with digitonin to form acetone-insoluble birefringent crystals. After sebaceous glands are treated with digitonin, only the sebum in the excretory ducts of the preputial glands of the rat reveals digitonide crystals (Montagna and Noback, 1946b). Digitonide crystals are not found in the glands of the general skin in the rat or other animals studied. Normal human sebaceous glands contain no free cholesterol, but the stagnant sebum of comedones and of early acne cysts contains an abundance of it.

When viewed under polarized light, sebaceous glands reveal variable amounts of anisotropic lipids. With minor exceptions, the distribution of these lipids corresponds to the color reaction obtained with the Schultz test. In human sebaceous glands only the fully formed sebum consistently contains birefringent lipids. Suskind (1951) observed some birefringent lipids in the glands of 30 out of 45 samples of human skin. In most of the 45 specimens the sebum in the pilosebaceous exits and in the excretory ducts was anisotropic. Those sebaceous acini which exhibit marked anisotropy also give the most intense Schultz reation. In the preputial glands of the rat only the sebum is strongly birefringent. In the glands of the rat, dog, and cat, birefringence is more extensive, being present in the degenerating and mature sebaceous cells as well as in the sebum (Fig. 13). In these glands the sebum appears as a birefringent homogeneous mass; in sebaceous cells birefringent lipids are in the form of spherules and acicular crystals. In the glands of the rabbit the sebum is weakly birefringent, but the peripheral sebaceous cells contain abundant anisotropic spherules and acicular crystals. These birefringent lipids are not colored with Sudan IV, Nile blue sulfate, or Baker's acid hematein test. After short treatment with Sudan black, the spherocrystals are colored pink, but the acicular crystals remain colorless or are a light blue. With longer treatments in Sudan black the birefringent lipids become deeply colored and isotropic. After secondary osmications there is no birefringence in the peripheral lipids, but the blackened sebum shows increased anisotropy. The spherocrystals, but not the acicular crystals, are dissolved in 90% alcohol; 95% alcohol or acetone removes all birefringent lipids. Heating to 60°C destroys birefringence, but it reappears virtually unchanged as the sections are cooled to room temperature. Cooling to —2°C increases the anisotrophy of all sebaceous lipids, but the induced anisotropy is lost when the sections are rewarmed to room temperature (Montagna, 1949a, b; Montagna and Noback, 1947; Montagna and Parks, 1948). Anisotropy is not a physical property which allows specific identifications of lipids, but the manipulations mentioned above give it some characterizing value. The acicular crystals and the spherocrystals have different physical properties and may represent different substances. The parallelism between the presence of birefringent spherocrystals and the results with the Schultz test strongly suggest that these lipids in sebaceous glands represent esters of cholesterol.

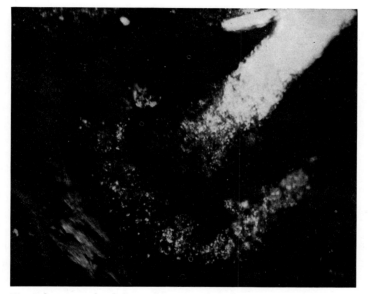

FIG. 13. Sebaceous gland from the external auditory meatus of the cat viewed under polarized light, showing birefringent lipids.

In the skin of genetically hairless mice, there is progressive increase in the amount of cholesterol as the animals become older (Montagna et al., 1952b). With advancing age, the skin acquires cysts. The early cysts are all sebaceous; later they become cornified. The sebaceous glands and the young sebaceous cysts contain birefringent crystals which become isotropic when warmed to 60°C; the lipids are sudanophilic and reactive to the Schultz test, but do not form chloroform-insoluble digitonin crystals. These properties suggest the presence of cholesterol esters. In this respect the sebaceous glands and sebaceous cysts are essentially similar to the sebaceous glands of the rat, the dog, the cat, the rabbit, the monkey, and man. The older corneal cysts contain, in addition to cholesterol esters, substances which are sudanophobic, birefringent, chloroform-soluble, and Schultz-reactive; these form chloroform-insoluble, birefringent, digitonide crystals. The birefringent digitonin crystals are reactive to the Liebermann-Burchard tests even after the tissues have been extracted with chloroform. These are properties of free cholesterol. Chemical analyses of the skin of young and old hairless mice confirm quantitatively these differences between the content of free and esterified cholesterol. The increase in free cholesterol, then, is associated with the increase in number of the keratinized cysts.

Viewed under near-ultraviolet light (3600Å), sebaceous glands emit a yellow-to-orange light which is usually comparable in distribution to the birefringence. The sebum in the terminal portions of the ducts emits a yellow light (Miles, 1958a, b). The new sebum and the degenerating sebaceous cells emit a yellow or white light of low intensity which fades toward the periphery of the glands. It is possible that the anisotropic, Schultz-positive cholesterol esters are responsible for the emission of the autofluorescent light. Not uncommonly, the sebaceous plugs in comedones emit a reddish fluorescence which is due to porphyrin.

Glycogen

With the exception of those of man and of the higher primates, the sebaceous glands of all other mammals studied contain practically no glycogen (Montagna and Ellis, 1959a, 1960a, b). However, in the fetal skin of other animals, as in all other epidermal appendages, the sebaceous glands contain glycogen. Those who claim that mature human sebaceous glands are free of glycogen except under pathologic conditions (Ludford, 1925; Sasakawa, 1921), are in error. Normal human sebaceous cells abound in glycogen; nearly all of the cells in the excretory ducts, and all of the peripheral, indifferent sebaceous cells of the glandular acini are rich in it (Fig. 14). In cells undergoing sebaceous transformation, glycogen decreases at the same rate that lipid increases (Montagna et al., 1951, 1952a). The distribution of glycogen is precisely correlated with lipid storage, and it is likely that sebaceous transformation takes place by a conversion of carbohydrates to lipids, rather than by an accumulation of "hemoconia" from the blood (Melczer and Deme, 1942).

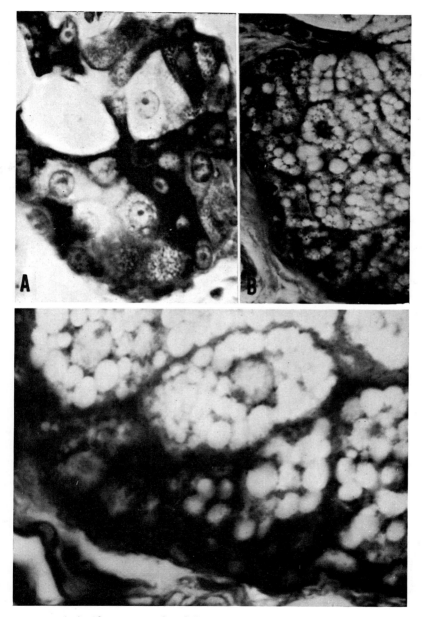

FIG. 14. (A) Glycogen in the differentiating sebaceous cells of the potto, a primitive primate. (B) Glycogen granules in the undifferentiated sebaceous cells of the scalp of man, and (C), the axilla.

Enzyme Systems

The chemical nature of the sebum of different animals is often very different and there are differences as well as similarities in their content of enzymes. For example, whereas the sebaceous glands of all animals we have studied contain such enzymes as succinic dehydrogenase and monoamine oxidase, some may be rich in alkaline phosphatases and phosphorylases, but others show no evidence of them. The differences in enzyme concentration must surely reflect the differences in the composition of the product that the glands manufacture.

Many of the histochemically demonstrable enzymes of the skin are heavily concentrated in the sebaceous glands. There is an intense reaction for cytochrome oxidase in the glands of man and all other mammals we have studied (Fig. 15D). The activity is in the form of granules, numerous in all cells, including those which are full of sebum, but are still apparently viable.

The sebaceous glands of all animals have heavy concentrations of succinic dehydrogenase activity, seen as granules, in the cytoplasm of the undifferentiated cells. The cells which are undergoing sebaceous transformation have a moderate amount of enzyme and the fully differentiated cells have none. Some reddish stain, indicative of monoformazans, appears in the mature sebaceous cells and in the sebum, but this indicates only that the formazans formed are soluble in fat, and is not an enzyme reaction. The distribution of succinic dehydrogenase activity in sebaceous glands is similar in all the animals that we have studied and seems to follow the pattern of the distribution of mitochondria (Montagna, 1955).

We have found large concentrations of peroxidase only in the sebaceous preputial glands in the rat and the mouse (Montagna and Noback, 1946a, b). The sebaceous glands of the general body surface, even in the rat (Montagna and Noback, 1947) have either scant activity or none.

The sebaceous glands in all of the animals we have studied contain very large amounts of monoamine oxidase (Fig. 15C). The enzyme is heavily concentrated throughout the gland and especially in the undifferentiated and immature sebaceous cells (Yasuda and Montagna, 1960).

Sebaceous glands have moderate amounts of aminopeptidase (Adachi and Montagna, 1961). Some reaction is localized in the new sebum in the center of the glands and in the mature sebaceous cells. Particularly strong activity is found in the periphery of the glands.

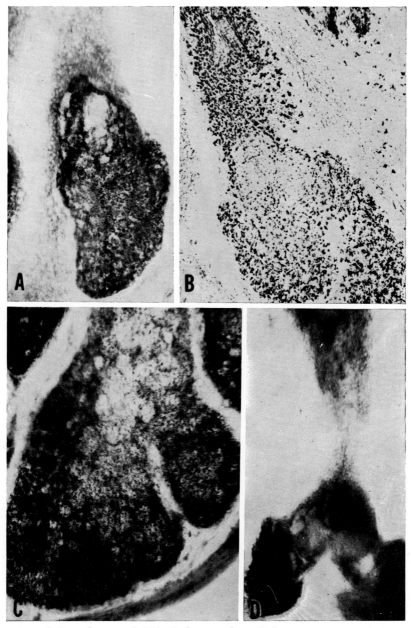

F<small>IG</small>. 15. Distribution of (A), β-glucuronidase, (B) tween esterase, (C) mono-amine oxidase, and (D) cytochrome oxidase. These sebaceous glands are from various regions of the body.

The glands of man and all animals studied, even those of *Ornitho-rhynchus,* contain large concentrations of β-glucuronidase activity (Braun-Falco, 1956b; Montagna, 1957), the distribution of which is similar to that of monoamine oxidase (Fig. 15A). All of the cells, undifferentiated and mature ones, contain large numbers of strongly reactive, coarse granules.

The sebaceous glands of man have very strong phosphorylase and amylo-1,4—1,6-transglucosidase activities, particularly in the undifferentiated cells and in the cells undergoing sebaceous transformation (Fig. 16) (Braun-Falco, 1956a; Ellis and Montagna, 1958; Takeuchi, 1958). The mature sebaceous cells are free of these enzymes. The distribution of these enzymes parallels the distribution of glycogen; the small sebaceous glands of the fetus and infant, which are laden with glycogen, have a much greater concentration of both of these enzymes than the glands of the adult. The presence of these enzymes in sebaceous glands in largely peculiar to the primates (Montagna and Ellis, 1959a), although of the animals we have studied, the lion and the goat show small amounts of them.

The distribution of alkaline phosphatase in the sebaceous glands shows enormous species differences. Even in closely related forms, as for instance the rat and the mouse, the sebaceous glands are very rich in enzymes in the former, but have practically none in the latter. The sebaceous glands of the cat, the raccoon, the dog, the seal, the weasel, and the lion, South American monkeys, lemurs, etc., are all very rich in alkaline phosphatase activity. Enzyme activity is concentrated at the periphery of the glands in all of the undifferentiated cells; cells undergoing sebaceous transformation have a weaker reaction, and the fully differentiated cells contain no enzymes. The cow, the pig, the rabbit, and the guinea pig have only moderate amounts of phosphatase in their sebaceous glands. In the mouse, in many of the primates, and in man, the sebaceous glands have no alkaline phosphatase activity, other than a few weakly reactive granules in the sebum. Although human sebaceous glands have no appreciable amounts of these enzymes, the endothelium of the numerous blood vessels around them is very strongly reactive (Fig. 17). In thick frozen sections, the patterns of these vessels can be studied with ease. The small sebaceous glands of children have relatively few vessels, and they arise from the arterioles around the middle part of the hair follicles. The larger, more complicated, glands are surrounded by intricate patterns of blood vessels which follow the contours of the glandular acini (Fig. 17). When the sebaceous glands become disproportionately large, as in the

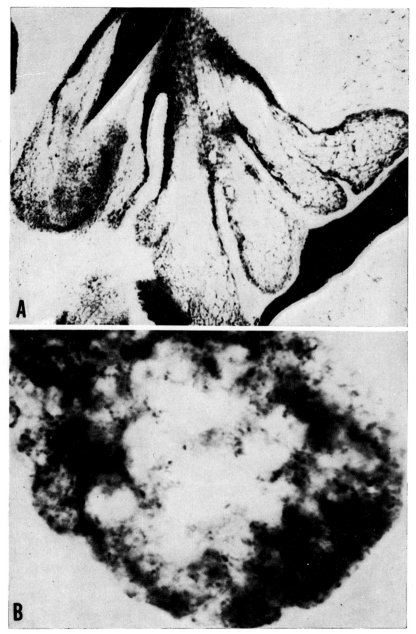

FIG. 16. (A) Amylophosphorylase in a sebaceous gland from the axilla. (B) En-larged detail of (A).

bald scalp, they also become more richly vascularized (Ellis, 1958). This is curious because whereas the entire senile scalp becomes gradually less vascularized, the sebaceous glands there actually attain a better vascular bed. During vasodilatation, or inflammation of the skin, the periphery of the sebaceous glands acquires some alkaline phosphatase activity, which, however, is diffuse and not neatly localized. The vessels surrounding the glands of other mammals may or may not have alkaline phosphatase, even in different species of primates (Montagna and Ellis, 1959a, 1960a, b).

The glands of man and of the other animals we have studied contain variable large amounts of acid phosphatase (Moretti and Mescon, 1956a, b). This enzyme is widespread and shows none of the species differences that one encounters in alkaline phosphatase. Acid phosphatase activity is strong at the periphery of the glands and diminishes in the differentiating cells; some remains even in the sebum. The glands of the hamster abound in acid phosphatase (Montagna and Hamilton, 1949). The reaction is strong throughout the acinus, but it is weak or absent at the periphery of the acini and in the center where the cells are undergoing degeneration. The newly-formed sebum in the center of the acini indicates intense activity; the old sebum shows less.

All sebaceous glands contain large amounts of esterases, but the presence or absence of the various classes of these enzymes depends upon the different techniques and substrates used. Since there are also species differences, it would be cumbersome to try to describe in detail the esterases in the glands of the major groups of mammals we have studied. The only generalization that can be made is that there are esterases in all glands. The descriptions which follow will deal only with the glands of man. There are moderate to strong amounts of tween esterase in the differentiating sebaceous cells at the periphery of the glands and in the sebum (Montagna and Ellis, 1958). The undifferentiated peripheral cells and the sebum are also rich in α-esterase; the mature sebaceous cells, however, contain little enzyme. The undifferentiated sebaceous cells have numerous small indoxyl esterase granules, the mature cells have clusters of coarse granules and the sebum is unreactive (Fig. 15B) (Montagna and Ellis, 1958). The distribution of AS esterase is similar to that of indoxyl acetate esterase, except that the sebum in the excretory duct has a strong reaction.

FIG. 17. (A) Alkaline phosphatase-reactive endothelium of the vessels around the glands associated with a vellus follicle. The arrow points to the dermal papilla of the hair follicle. (B) Rich capillary plexus around the glands from the scalp.

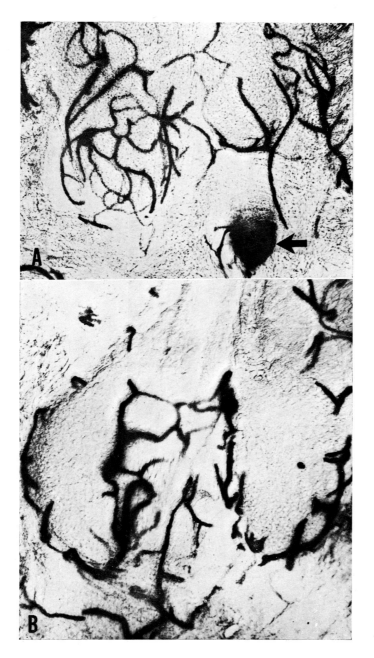

The sebaceous glands of the rat and the mouse and the preputial glands of the rat contain large amounts of cholinesterases (Montagna and Beckett, 1958; Montagna and Ellis, 1959b). The Meibomian glands of the dog, rat, goat, etc., are generally rich in nonspecific cholinesterase; there are probably other exceptions.

Those who have studied cutaneous nerves with modern methods agree that sebaceous glands are not surrounded by nerves, and it follows that no nerves containing cholinesterases have been found around them (Hurley *et al.*, 1953; Hellmann, 1955; Montagna and Ellis, 1957; Thies

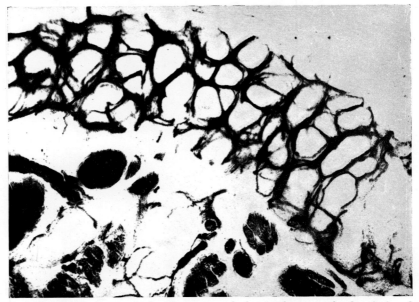

FIG. 18.   Cholinesterase-rich nerves around the Meibomian glands of the slow loris.

and Galente, 1957). In contrast with all of the other sebaceous glands, the Meibomian glands and some of the sebaceous glands associated with the hair follicles at the border of the palpebrae, are all surrounded by networks of cholinesterase-rich nerves (Fig. 18) (Montagna and Ellis, 1959b). It is difficult to say what value nerves could be to holocrine glands. Since many cutaneous nerves are rich in cholinesterases (Beckett *et al.*, 1956), and the conjunctival surface of the eyelid and the border of the eyelid are highly sensitive surfaces, the nerves around the Meibomian glands and the sebaceous glands in the eyelids could have a sensory, rather than a secretory function.

Growth and Proliferation

Since differentiating sebaceous cells ultimately die when mature, there is a mechanism that replenishes the cells lost in secretion. There has been an unnecessary amount of discord among the various authors concerning the mitotic activity in sebaceous glands. Some authors believe that mitotic division occurs in the cells at the periphery of the acini (Bizzozero and Vassale, 1887; Stamm, 1914; Kyrle, 1925; Schaffer, 1927). Others insist that mitotic activity occurs almost entirely in the

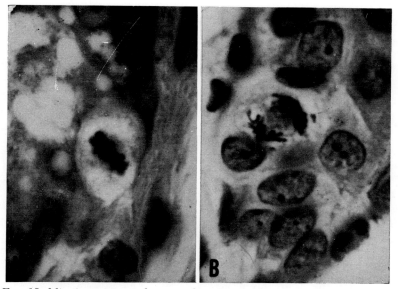

Fig. 19. Mitotic activity in human sebaceous glands. (A) Anaphase in an indifferent sebaceous cell between two acini. (B) Metaphase in an indifferent cell at the periphery of a large acinus.

epithelium of the ducts at their junction with the acini, and they envision that the new cells formed there glide down into the body of the glands (Bab, 1904; Brinkmann, 1912; Clara, 1929). Actually, mitotic activity is found in both of these places (Fig. 19), but it is unlikely that new cells glide down into the fundus of the glands. In mice, mitotic activity follows a cyclic diurnal rhythm similar to that of the epidermis. Also, mitotic division in the sebaceous cells of female mice is correlated with the ovarian cycle, being maximal at early proestrus and minimal in the first day of diestrus; injection of estrone induces a peak in mitotic activity (Bullough, 1946). Androgens also stimulate sebaceous activity (Ebling, 1948; Hamilton, 1941, 1947; Hooker and Pfeiffer, 1943; Lapiere, 1953; Montagna and Kenyon, 1949). After androgenic stimulation there is a sharp rise in sebaceous mitotic activity. Mitotic division can also occur in cells that have begun to differentiate. In the albino rat, the size of the sebaceous glands fluctuates together with the estrus cycle, being largest in proestrus and becoming reduced at estrus (Ebling, 1951, 1954). The mean mitotic incidence does not change in any phase of the cycle, however, and there is no correlation between mitotic incidence and the size of the gland. Oddly enough, although treatment with estrogen increases the mitotic incidence, the glands become smaller. In the rat, then, estrogen seems to stimulate mitotic incidence, sebaceous transformation, and secretion independently of one another.

Sebaceous acini are in a constant state of change. Epithelial buds, which grow from the walls of the excretory ducts, develop sebaceous kernels in their centers and then grow into new sebaceous units (Montagna and Noback, 1946a). As the new acini expand, they may encroach upon nearby acini, fuse with them, and become a part of larger units. In such sebaceous complexes, the periphery of the fused elements is still outlined by small epithelial cells and fibroblasts adhering to them, forming trabeculae which separate the sebaceous units into locules. Additional sebaceous acini also develop from the tabs of nonsebaceous cells at the periphery of the acini, protruding into the dermis as appendages of the parent acini. Such lateral buds grow and engulf smaller adjacent ones. Sebaceous kernels may develop anywhere along the acini, outside or in, where there are accumulations of undifferentiated cells. The fact that mitotic activity is abundant at the periphery of the acini, combined with the vicissitudes just described, militates against the static concepts usually described in textbooks. Furthermore, the inherent growth dynamics of these glands is demonstrated by their quick regeneration from the cells of the outer root sheath of hair follicles when the glands have been completely destroyed by chemical agents (Montagna and Chase, 1950).

All of our observations on the glands of man indicate that the individual acini are doomed to destruction once differentiation begins in them. The mitotic activity in the undifferentiated cells at their periphery is largely focal and related to the establishment of new acini; it is not a mechanism for replenishing cells lost in secretion within any one acinus.

A study of the skin of genetically hairless mice gives an interesting insight into the readiness with which other tissues transform into sebaceous cells (Montagna *et al.*, 1952b). At about 2 months of age some of the stranded cell aggregates derived from fragmented hair follicles in the dermis undergo sebaceous transformation. As these sebaceous clusters become older, the undifferentiated cells at the periphery begin to give rise to keratinized laminae, until cysts are formed that contain a sebaceous center surrounded by concentric layers of keratin. Regardless of the amount of keratinized exfoliation they contain, nearly all of the cysts retain some sebaceous cells at their periphery, or at least they possess appendages of sebaceous cells. The stranded part of the follicle in contact with the dermal papilla often becomes reorganized into a disoriented hair follicle, but after a brief period of growth the cells of such abortive follicles undergo sebaceous transformation, and the follicles are transformed into sebaceous cysts which contain hair fragments. These cysts, like all others, subsequently become cornified. Additional cysts also form from the sebaceous appendages of existing cysts.

The cells of the surface epidermis, when unduly irritated, may undergo sebaceous transformation. We have noted this on several occasions in the epidermis of the hamster, rabbit, and man after abrasions or other irritations. In such cases either single cells or clusters of three or more cells undergo typical sebaceous transformation. Sebaceous transformation occurs often in the epidermis of mice which have been treated repeatedly with methylcholanthrene, and occasionally in the epidermis of the hamster and the guinea pig after different kinds of injuries.

Eisen *et al.* (1955) produced shallow wounds in human skin by means of a rotary burr, destroying the proximal portion of pilosebaceous systems together with the surrounding epidermis. In the reparative changes that followed, they found first numerous mitotic figures in the basal cells of pilary canals and in the basal undifferentiated sebaceous cells and the cells of the ducts of sebaceous glands. From these proliferative foci, cells flowed to the surface of the wound and there differentiated into cells indistinguishable from epidermal cells. Some of the new "epidermal" cells, as if carrying with them an identifying mark, underwent sebaceous transformation on the surface.

Although sebaceous glands in the mucosa of the cheeks are still considered to be accidental and referred to as "Fordyce disease," they are common there, and the assignation should be dropped (Miles, 1958a, b). Sebaceous glands are common, even numerous, in both the vermilion surface of the upper lip and in the cheek mucosa (Fig. 20). The lower lip, and an area of the mucosa near the mucocutaneous junction of the upper lip, are free of them. Between childhood and adulthood, there is an increase in the prevalence and in the number of glands, related to the onset of puberty. There is a further increase

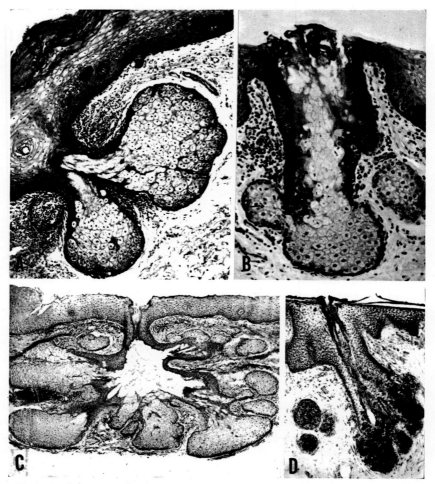

FIG. 20. Sebaceous glands from the cheek mucosa (A) and (B), gingiva (C), and upper lip (D). From Miles (1958a). (Reproduced by permission of the author and the *Brit. Dental J.*)

in buccal sebaceous glands in adults, after the age of 35. The differentiation of these glands from the epidermis reflects a type of embryonic potential of the mucosa. Granting that glands bud off from the ones already present, the widespread increase in the numbers of glands in the cheeks of subjects older than 35 years suggests that there is a real differentiation from the mucosa.

Differentiation of sebaceous glands occurs in a variety of organs. The most common such metaplasia is in the parotid and submaxillary glands of man, where typical sebaceous clusters have been found in a large per cent of glands inspected (Hartz, 1946; Andrew, 1952; Meza Chavez, 1949). The occurrence of sebaceous glands in salivary glands is not related to the age or the sex of the subjects. These sebaceous glands are identical to cutaneous sebaceous glands. Sebaceous metaplasias have also been reported in the cervix uteri of women (Nicholson, 1918-1919; Dougherty, 1948), and in the mammary glands of guinea pigs after injections of folliculin (Florentin and Binder, 1939). Sebaceous metaplasia in salivary glands is surprising only because of the high percentage of its occurrence, since salivary glands arise from buccal ectoderm. Similarly, it is not surprising to find such metaplasia in the mammary glands, which are cutaneous appendages. It is, however, remarkable to find sebaceous material in the epithelium of the cervix, which seems to have its origin in the entoderm of the urogenital sinus. All of these examples illustrate particularly well the readiness with which epidermal cells may transform into sebaceous cells.

Sebaceous Secretion

Long believed to be one of the factors that influences sebaceous secretion, the contraction of the arrectores pilorum muscles of the hair follicles has no effect upon the expulsion of sebum from the glands (Kligman and Shelley, 1958; Pontén, 1960). The viscosity of the sebum as influenced by the temperature of the skin could have some influence on the spread of sebum over the skin surface, but this factor is perhaps of minor importance. Some authors believe that sebaceous secretion ceases when a layer of sebum of a certain thickness has been accumulated over a surface, the cessation or inhibition of secretion being achieved either directly, by the pressure of the sebaceous layer (Emanuel, 1936, 1938), or by the mediation of nerves (Serrati, 1938). The first premise, however, is a misinterpretation of facts, and we know that the rate of sebaceous secretion, like hair growth and differentiation of epidermal cells, is unaffected by complete denervation of a skin area (Doupe and Sharp, 1943; Pontén, 1960).

Of all the suggested mechanisms of sebaceous secretion, none is more credible than that of Kligman and Shelley (1958). According to them sebaceous glands produce a continuous flow of secretion "without regard to what is on the surface." The quantity of lipid released in a given time per unit area is proportional to the total glandular volume, which is a function of the total number of differentiated sebaceous cells. A large part of the sebum on the forehead and face is apparently secreted by the very large sebaceous glands which are associated with the follicles of vellus hairs. These glands secrete a clear, fluid sebum. Sebaceous secretion is controlled neither by the surface lipids nor by nerves; rather, the stratum corneum acts as a wick that sucks up sebum from the ducts by capillary action.

It is difficult to observe the secretion from individual glands, and consequently, there is a controversy concerning the rate of sebaceous flow onto the skin. Observations on the effect of temperature, humidity, and altitude upon sebaceous secretion are largely empirical. The number and size of the sebaceous glands in a given area certainly must affect in some way the rate of secretion, and this would make the rate of secretion in the different parts of the body quite different. The rate of secretion of skin fats studied with the use of a monomolecular film technique shows a steady rate of secretion in the human forearm of the order of 0.1 µg per square centimeter per minute (Jones et al., 1951). This skin fat flows with a speed of 3.3 cm per second over a water film and presumably over wet skin. Thus it might be concluded that skin fat flows from areas of high sebaceous secretion to areas of low secretion and is constantly being removed by objects in contact with the skin. Sebum flows very slowly over dry skin.

The size and maturation of sebaceous glands are regulated by hormones (Rony and Zakon, 1943, 1945; Hamilton, 1941; Bullough and Laurence, 1960). The glands, small in childhood, attain full bloom at puberty. The pronounced increase in the size and activity at puberty is believed to be the principal factor in juvenile acne vulgaris. In men, testicular androgens have been implicated as the major incitant of puberal acne. Men castrated before puberty and eunuchoids do not develop acne or seborrhea, but they do so if they are treated with large doses of testosterone (Hamilton, 1941). Also, normal men and women may develop acne after treatment with large amounts of testosterone.

The administration of testosterone or progesterone to normal rats, produces a pronounced enlargement of sebaceous glands (Haskin et al., 1953). The removal of the pituitary and of the adrenal glands from ovariectomized rats results in an atrophy of sebaceous glands which is not counteracted by the administration of progesterone and which is counteracted only to a slight extent by testosterone (Lasher *et al.,* 1954). Hypophysectomy alone also results in a reduction of the size of the sebaceous glands; this is only partially counteracted by progesterone and testosterone therapy. The pituitary, then, is itself necessary for the proper maintenance of sebaceous glands.

Investigations by Strauss and Kligman (1958, 1961; Strauss, 1961) on the effects of hormones on the sebaceous glands of human beings are clarifying much of the confusion and controversy which has existed on this subject. It appears that the extent of development of acne is not an adequate end-point for determining the effect of hormones on the sebaceous glands, since acne is dependent on many other factors besides the size of the glands. These authors have confirmed the finding that androgens are the primary incitants for glandular development. As little as 5 mg of methyltestosterone daily was sufficient to cause marked enlargement of the glands in a group of children in the immediate prepuberal age, which is particularly susceptible to androgenic stimulation. The increase in size of the glands in such a group may be evident within 1 week. The fact that younger children do not consistently show these changes proves that there is a definite age factor. Androgens have no effect on the size of the glands of young men but they may cause a slight increase in the size of the glands of young women and postmenopausal women. Testosterone seems to act directly upon the sebaceous glands, and when applied topically, produces a local enlargement of the glands.

The administration of physiologic amounts of natural progesterone to prepuberal boys and girls, young men and women, and aged women, changes neither the size nor the function of their sebaceous glands. Furthermore, in women the production of sebum shows no fluctuations which can be correlated with the corpus luteum phase of the menstrual cycle, when the production of progesterone is high. These authors conclude that acne in women, and for that matter, the development of their sebaceous glands is not appreciably influenced by the effect of endogenous progesterone. They propose the alternate hypothesis that adrenal hormones play an important role in the control of the development of sebaceous glands in women, since large amounts of hydrocortisone do cause a glandular hyperplasia in them.

Estrogens suppress sebaceous secretion only when used in extremely large doses; physiological amounts are ineffective. The effect appears to be indirect, involving some central mechanism, since topical applications of estrogens induce no local effect. Furthermore, there is no local "antagonism" between estrogens and androgens. Small doses of exogenous androgens are capable of maintaining glandular enlargement in spite of concomitant overwhelming amounts of estrogen. This suggests that the hormonal control of the sebaceous glands is dependent only upon androgenic stimulation, and that the apparent "antagonistic" suppression of the sebaceous glands by high doses of estrogen could be due to a reduction in circulating androgens.

REFERENCES

Adachi, K. and W. Montagna. 1961. Histology and cytochemistry of human skin. XXII. Sites of leucine aminopeptidase. *J. Invest. Dermatol.* (In press.)

Andrew, W. 1952. A comparison of age changes in salivary glands of man and the rat. *J. Gerontol.* **7**: 178-190.

Bab, H. 1904. Die Talgdrüsen und ihre Sekretion. *Beitr. Klin. Med. Festschr. Senator,* **70** *Geburtstag,* pp. 1-37.

Baker, J. R. 1946. The histochemical recognition of lipine. *Quart. J. Microscop. Sci.* **87**: 441-470.

Beckett, E. B., G. H. Bourne and W. Montagna. 1956. Histology and cytochemistry of human skin. The distribution of cholinesterase in the finger of the embryo and the adult. *J. Physiol. (London)* **134**: 202-206.

Benfenati, A. and F. Brillanti. 1939. Sulla distribuzione delle ghiandole sebacee nella cute del corpo umano. *Arch. ital. dermatol. sifilog. e. venereol.* **15**: 33-42.

Bizzozero, G. and G. Vassale. 1887. Ueber die Erzeugung und die physiologische Regeneration der Drüsenzellen bei den Säugethieren. *Virchow's Arch. pathol. Anat. u. Physiol.* **110**: 155-214.

Bowen, R. H. 1926. Studies on the Golgi apparatus in gland-cells. II. Glands producing lipoidal secretions—the so-called skin glands. *Quart. J. Microscop. Sci.* **70**: 193-215.

Bowen, R. H. 1929. The cytology of glandular secretion. *Quart. Rev. Biol.* **4**: 484-519.

Braun-Falco, O. 1956a. Über die Fähigkeit der menschlichen Haut zur Polysaccharidsynthese, ein Beitrag zur Histotopochemie der Phosphorylase. *Arch. klin. u. exptl. Dermatol.* **202**: 163-170.

Braun-Falco, O. 1956b. Zur Histotopographie der β-Glucuronidase in normaler, menschlicher Haut. *Arch. klin. u. exptl. Dermatol.* **203**: 61-67.

Brinkmann, A. 1912. Die Hautdrüsen der Säugetiere (Bau und Secretionsverhältnisse). *Ergeb. Anat. u. Entwicklungsgeschichte* **20**: 1173-1231.

Bullough, W. S. 1946. Mitotic activity in the adult female mouse, *Mus musculus* L. A study of its relation to the estrous cycle in normal and abnormal conditions. *Phil. Trans. Roy. Soc. Ser. B* **231**: 453-516.

Bullough, W. S. and E. B. Laurence. 1960. Experimental sebaceous gland suppression in the adult male mouse. *J. Invest. Dermatol.* **35**: 37-42.

Cain, A. J. 1947. Demonstration of lipine in the Golgi apparatus in gut cells of *Glossiphonia. Quart. J. Microscop. Sci.* **88**: 151-157.

Cain, A. J. 1950. The histochemistry of lipoids in animals. *Biol. Revs.* **25**: 73-112.

Charles, A. 1960. Electron microscopic observations of the human sebaceous gland. *J. Invest. Dermatol.* **35**: 31-36.

Clara, M. 1929. Morfologia e sviluppo delle ghiandole sebacee nell'uomo. *Richerche morfol.* **9**: 121-182.

Dougherty, C. M. 1948. A sebaceous gland in the cervix uteri. *J. Pathol. Bacteriol.* **60**: 511-512.

Doupe, J. and M. E. Sharp. 1943. Studies in denervation G)—Sebaceous secretion. *J. Neurol. Psychiat.* **6**: 133-135.

Ebling, F. J. 1948. Sebaceous glands. I. The effect of sex hormones on the sebaceous glands of the female albino rat. *J. Endocrinol.* **5**: 297-302.

Ebling, F. J. 1951. Sebaceous glands. II. Changes in the sebaceous glands following the implantation of oestradiol benzoate in the female albino rat. *J. Endocrinol.* **7**: 288-298.

Ebling, F. J. 1954. Changes in the sebaceous glands and epidermis during the oestrous cycle of the albino rat. *J. Endocrinol.* **10**: 147-154.

Eisen, A. Z., J. B. Holyoke and W. C. Lobitz, Jr. 1955. Responses of the superficial portion of the human pilosebaceous apparatus to controlled injury. *J. Invest. Dermatol.* **25**: 145-156.

Ellis, R. A. 1958. Ageing of the human male scalp. In "The Biology of Hair Growth" (W. Montagna and R. A. Ellis, eds.), pp. 469-485. Academic Press, New York.

Ellis, R. A. and W. Montagna. 1958. Histology and cytochemistry of human skin. XV. Sites of phosphorylase and amylo-1,6 glucosidase activity. *J. Histochem. and Cytochem.* **6**: 201-207.

Emanuel, S. 1936. Quantitative determinations of the sebaceous glands' function, with particular mention of method employed. *Acta Dermato-Venereol.* **17**: 444-456.

Emanuel, S. 1938. Mechanism of the sebum secretion. *Acta Dermato-Venereol.* **19**: 1-15.

Engman, M. F. and D. J. Kooyman. 1934. Lipids of the skin surface. *Arch. Dermatol. and Syphilol.* **29**: 12-19.

Florentin, P. and C. Binder. 1939. Metaplasie sebacee de la glande mammaire du cobaye sous l'influence de la folliculine injectee a fortes doses. *Ann. endocrinol.* (*Paris*) **1**: 213-214.

Hamilton, J. B. 1941. Male hormone substance: a prime factor in acne. *J. Clin. Endocrinol.* **1**: 570-592.

Hamilton, J. B. 1947. Growth changes induced by androgens in the connective tissues, sebaceous glands, hairs, muscle, and melanoblasts of the skin (abstract). *Anat. Record* **97**: 340.

Hartz, P. H. 1946. Development of sebaceous glands from intralobular ducts of the parotid gland. *Arch. Pathol.* **41**: 651-654.

Haskin, D., N. Lasher and S. Rothman. 1953. Some effects of ACTH, cortisone, progesterone and testosterone on sebaceous glands in the white rat. *J. Invest. Dermatol.* **20**: 207-212.

Hellmann, K. 1955. Cholinesterase and amine oxidase in the skin: a histochemical investigation. *J. Physiol.* (*London*) **129**: 454-463.

Hooker, C. W. and C. A. Pfeiffer. 1943. Effects of sex hormones upon body growth, skin, hair, and sebaceous glands in the rat. *Endocrinology* **32**: 69-76.

Horner, W. E. 1846. On the odoriferous glands of the negro. *Am. J. Med. Sci.* **21**: 13-16.

Hurley, H. J., Jr., W. B. Shelley and G. B. Koelle. 1953. The distribution of cholinesterases in human skin, with special reference to eccrine and apocrine sweat glands. *J. Invest. Dermatol.* **21**: 139-147.

Johnsen, S. G. and J. E. Kirk. 1952. The number, distribution and size of the sebaceous glands in the dorsal region of the hand. *Anat. Record* **112**: 725-735.

Jones, K. K., M. C. Spencer and S. A. Sanchez. 1951. The estimation of the rate of secretion of sebum in man. *J. Invest. Dermatol.* **17**: 213-226.

Kligman, A. M. and W. B. Shelley. 1958. An investigation of the biology of the human sebaceous gland. *J. Invest. Dermatol.* **30**: 99-125.

Kvorning, S. A. 1949. Investigations into the pharmacology of skin fats and ointments. IV. Investigations into the composition of the lipids on the skin of normal individuals. *Acta Pharmacol. Toxicol.* **5**: 383-396.

Kyrle, J. 1925. "Vorlesungen über Histobiologie der menschlichen Haut und ihrer Erkrankungen." Springer, Wien und Berlin.

Lapiere, C. 1953. Modifications des glands sébacées par des hormones sexuelles appliquées localement sur la peau de souris. *Compt. rend. soc. biol.* **147**: 1302-1306.

Lasher, N., A. L. Lorincz and S. Rothman. 1954. Hormonal effects on sebaceous glands in the white rat. II. The effect of the pituitary adrenal axis. *J. Invest. Dermatol.* **22**: 25-31.

Lederer, E. and D. Mercier. 1948. Sur les constituants de la graisse de laine. IV. La peau de mouton comme organe de la biosynthese des alcools triterpeniques. *Biochem. et Biophys. Acta* **2**: 91-94.

Ludford, R. J. 1925. The cytology of tar tumors. *Proc. Roy. Soc.* **B98**: 557-577.

Machado de Sousa, O. 1931. Sur la présence de glandes sébacées au niveau du gland chez l'homme. *Compt. rend. soc. biol.* **108**: 894-897.

MacKenna, R. M. B., V. R. Wheatley and A. Wormall. 1950. The composition of the surface skin fat ("sebum") from the human forearm. *J. Invest. Dermatol.* **15**: 33-47.

MacKenna, R. M. B., V. R. Wheatley and A. Wormall. 1952. Studies of sebum. 2. Some constituents of the unsaponifiable matter of human sebum. *Biochem. J.* **52**: 161-168.

Melczer, N. and S. Deme. 1942. Beiträge zur Tätigkeit der menschlichen Talgdrüsen. I. Histologisch nachweisbare chemische Veränderungen während der Talgerzeugung. *Dermatologica* **86**: 24-36.

Melczer, N. and S. Deme. 1943. Beiträge zur Tätigkeit der menschlichen Talgdrüsen. I. Rolle und Formveränderungen des Golgi-Apparates während der Talgproduktion. *Arch. Dermatol. u. Syphilis* **183**: 388-395.

Meza Chavez, L. 1949. Sebaceous glands in normal and neoplastic parotid glands. Possible significance of sebaceous glands in respect to the origin of tumors of the salivary glands. *Am. J. Pathol.* **25**: 627-645.

Miles, A. E. W. 1958a. Sebaceous glands in the lip and cheek mucosa of man. *Brit. Dental J.* **105**: 235-248.

Miles, A. E. W. 1958b. The development and atrophy of buccal sebaceous glands in man. 6th Ann. Meeting of Brit. Div. of the Intern. Assoc. for Dental Research. *J. Dental Research* **37**(4): 757.

Montagna, W. 1949a. The glands in the external auditory meatus of the cat. *J. Morphol.* **85**: 423-442.

Montagna, W. 1949b. Anisotropic lipids in the sebaceous glands of the rabbit. *Anat. Record* **104**: 243-254.

Montagna, W. 1955. Histology and cytochemistry of human skin. VIII. Mitochondria in the sebaceous glands. *J. Invest. Dermatol.* **25**: 117-121.

Montagna, W. 1957. Histology and cytochemistry of human skin. XI. The distribution of β-glucuronidase. *J. Biophys. Biochem. Cytol.* **3**: 343-348.

Montagna, W. and E. B. Beckett. 1958. Cholinesterases and alpha esterases in the lip of the rat. *Acta Anat.* **32**: 256-261.

Montagna, W. and H. B. Chase. 1950. Redifferentiation of sebaceous glands in the mouse after total extirpation with methycholanthrene. *Anat. Record* **107**: 83-92.

Montagna, W. and R. A. Ellis. 1957. Histology and cytochemistry of human skin. XII. Cholinesterases in the hair follicles of the scalp. *J. Invest. Dermatol.* **29**: 151-157.

Montagna, W. and R. A. Ellis. 1958. L'histologie et la cytologie de la peau humaine. XVI. Repartition et concentration des esterases carboxyliques. *Ann histochimie* **3**: 1-17.

Montagna, W. and R. A. Ellis. 1959a. The skin of primates. I. The skin of the potto (*Perodicticus potto*). *Am. J. Phys. Anthropol.* **17**: 137-162.

Montagna, W. and R. A. Ellis. 1959b. Cholinergic innervation of the Meibomian gland. *Anat. Record* **135**: 121-128.

Montagna, W. and R. A. Ellis. 1960a. The skin of primates. II. The skin of the slender loris (*Loris tardigradus*) *Am. J. Phys. Anthropol.* **18**: 19-44.

Montagna, W. and R. A. Ellis. 1960b. The skin of primates. III. The skin of the slow loris (*Nycticebus coucang*). *J. Phys. Anthropol.* (In press.)

Montagna, W. and J. B. Hamilton. 1949. The sebaceous glands of the hamster. II. Some cytochemical studies in normal and experimental animals. *Am. J. Anat.* **84**: 365-396.

Montagna, W. and P. Kenyon. 1949. Growth potentials and mitotic division in the sebaceous glands of the rabbit. *Anat. Record* **103B**: 365-380.

Montagna, W. and C. R. Noback. 1946a. The histology of the preputial gland of the rat. *Anat. Record* **96**: 41-54.

Montagna, W. and C. R. Noback. 1946b. The histochemistry of the preputial gland of the rat. *Anat. Record* **96**: 111-128.

Montagna, W. and C. R. Noback. 1947. Histochemical observations on the sebaceous glands of the rat. *Am. J. Anat.* **81**: 39-62.

Montagna, W. and H. F. Parks. 1948. A histochemical study of the glands of the anal sac of the dog. *Anat. Record* **100**: 297-318.

Montagna, W., C. R. Noback and F. G. Zak. 1948. Pigment, lipids, and other substances in the glands of the external auditory meatus of man. *Am. J. Anat.* **83**: 409-436.

Montagna, W., H. B. Chase and J. B. Hamilton. 1951. The distribution of glycogen and lipids in human skin. *J. Invest. Dermatol.* **17**: 147-157.

Montagna, W., H. B. Chase and W. C. Lobitz, Jr. 1952a. Histology and cytochemistry of human skin. II. The distribution of glycogen in the epidermis, hair follicles, sebaceous glands and eccrine sweat glands. *Anat. Record* **114**: 231-248.

Montagna, W., H. B. Chase and H. P. Melaragno. 1952b. The skin of hairless mice. I. The formation of cysts and the distribution of lipids. *J. Invest. Dermatol.* **19**: 83-94.

Montagna, W., K. Yasuda and R. A. Ellis. 1961. The skin of primates. V. Skin of the black lemur (*Lemur Macaco*) *Am. J. Phys. Anthropol.* (In press.)

Moretti, G. and H. Mescon. 1956a. Histochemical distribution of acid phosphatases in normal human skin. *J. Invest. Dermatol.* **26**: 347-360.

Moretti, G. and H. Mescon. 1956b. A chemical-histochemical evaluation of acid phosphatase activity in human skin. *J. Histochem. and Cytochem.* **4**: 247-253.

Nicholson, G. W. 1918-1919. Sebaceous glands in the cervix uteri. *J. Pathol. Bacteriol.* **22**: 252-254.

Nicolaides, N. and S. Rothman. 1953. Studies on the chemical composition of human hair fat. II. The overall composition with regard to age, sex and race. *J. Invest. Dermatol.* **21**: 9-14.

Nicolaides, N. and G. C. Wells. 1957. On the biogenesis of the free fatty acids in human skin surface fat. *J. Invest. Dermatol.* **29**: 423-433.

Nicolas, J., C. Regaud and M. Favre. 1914. Sur les mitochondries des glandes sébacées de l'homme et sur la signification général de ces organites du protoplasma. *17th Intern. Congr. Med., Sect.* **13**, *Dermatol. Syphilis*, pp. 101-104.

Palay, S. L. (ed.). 1957. The cytology of secretion in holocrine glands. *In* "Frontiers in Cytology." Yale Univ. Press, New Haven, Connecticut.

Perkins, O. C. and A. M. Miller. 1926. Sebaceous glands in the human nipple. *Am. J. Obstet. Gynecol.* **11**: 789-794.

Pontén, B. 1960. Grafted skin. Observations on innervation and other qualities. *Acta Chir. Scand. Suppl.* **257**: 1-78.

Rogers, G. E. 1957. Electron microscope observations of the structure of sebaceous glands. *Exptl. Cell Research* **13**: 517-520.

Rony, H. R. and S. J. Zakon. 1943. Effect of androgen on the sebaceous glands of human skin. *Arch. Dermatol. and Syphilol.* **48**: 601-604.

Rony, H. R. and S. J. Zakon. 1945. Effect of endocrine substances on the adult human scalp. *Arch. Dermatol. and Syphilol.* **52**: 323-327.

Rothman, S. 1954. "Physiology and Biochemistry of the Skin." Univ. of Chicago Press, Chicago, Illinois.

Sasakawa, M. 1921. Beiträge zur Glykogenverteilung in der Haut unter normalen und pathologischen Zuständen. *Arch. Dermatol. u. Syphilis* **134**: 418-443.

Schaffer, J. 1927. Die Drüsen. I. Teil. *In* "Handbuch der mikroskopischen Anatomie des Menschen" (W. von Möllendorff, ed.), Vol. 2, Part 1, pp. 132-148. Springer, Berlin.

Schmidt-Nielsen, K., R. R. Suskind and E. Taylor. 1951. The chemistry of the human sebaceous gland. II. Analysis of human sebaceous material from individual orifices. *J. Invest. Dermatol.* **17**: 281-290.

Serrati, B. 1938. Infuenza del sistema nervoso sulla secrezione sebacea. Osservazioni e ricerche cliniche. *Rivista di Patologia Nervosa e Mentale* **52**: 377-423.

Stamm, R. H. 1914. Über den Bau und die Entwicklung der Seitendrüse del Waldspitzmaus (*Sorex vulgaris* L.) Mindeschrift for Japetus Steenstrup. København, pp. 1-24 (Cited from Schaffer, 1927).

Strauss, J. S. 1961. The control of human secretion by androgens and estrogens. *A.M.A. Arch. Dermatol.* (In press.)

Strauss, J. S. and A. M. Kligman. 1958. Pathologic patterns of the sebaceous glands. *J. Invest. Dermatol.* **30**: 51-61.

Strauss, J. S. and A. M. Kligman. 1961. The effect of progesterone and progesterone-like compounds of the human sebaceous gland. *J. Invest. Dermatol.* **36**: 309-319.

Suskind, R. R. 1951. The chemistry of the human sebaceous gland. I. Histochemical observations. *J. Invest. Dermatol.* **17**: 37-54.

Takeuchi, T. 1958. Histochemical demonstration of branching enzyme (amylo-1, 4-1, 6-transglucosidase) in animal tissues. *J. Histochem. and Cytochem.* **6**: 208-216.

Thies, W. and L. F. Galente. 1957. Zur histochemischen Darstellung der Cholines-terasen in vegetativen Nervensystem der Haut. *Hautarzt* **8**: 69-75.

Wheatley, V. R. 1952. The chemical composition of sebum. "Livre Jubilaire 1901-1951" de la Société Belge de Dermatologie et de Syphiligraphie, pp. 90-102. Imprimerie Medicale et Scientifique, Bruxelles.

Wheatley, V. R. 1953. Some aspects of the nature and function of sebum. *St. Bartholomew's Hosp. J.* **57**: 5-9.

Yasuda, K. and W. Montagna. 1960. Histology and cytochemistry of human skin. XX. The distribution of monoamine oxidase. *J. Histochem. and Cytochem.* **8**: 356-366.

Yun, J. S. and W. Montagna. 1961. The skin of hairless mice. III. The distribution of alkaline phosphatase. *Anat. Record.* **140**: 77-82.

CHAPTER 6

The Eccrine Sweat Glands

Introduction

Malpighi, who observed watery droplets issuing from from the pores on the surface of the skin deduced correctly that these were the orifices of sweat glands. More than a century later, Purkinje and his pupil, Wendt, in 1833, and Breschet and Roussel de Vouzzeme, in 1834, independently described the sweat glands. Eccrine glands were recognized to be different from apocrine glands in 1922 by Schiefferdecker. Eccrine glands are numerous and best developed in the higher primates. Other mammals have usually only a few of them, restricted to the volar surfaces of the paws and digits. Glabrous skin, in which the epidermis has a highly differentiated friction surface, is usually characterized by the presence of large numbers of eccrine sweat glands. The epidermis on the underside of the tip of the prehensile tail of some South American monkeys, and that over the knuckle pads of the gorilla is grooved with dermatoglyphics like that on the palms and soles, with the ridges pierced by the orifices of eccrine sweat glands.

Over the general body surface, eccrine glands are found only in the simian primates, and are most numerous in man. In other primates, the chimpanzee and the gorilla have more eccrine than apocrine glands over the body. Eccrine sweat glands are most highly developed in man and are sufficiently different from those of other mammals to be considered among his most characteristic organs. Man has two to five million glands over the surface of the body, with an average distribution ranging from 143 to 339 per square centimeter (Kuno, 1956). Only the lips, the glans penis, the inner surface of the prepuce, the clitoris, and the labia minora are free of eccrine glands.

In the adult body sweat glands are most numerous on the palms and soles, then, in decreasing order, on the head, the trunk, and the extremities. There are more glands on the flexor and ventral surfaces than on the extensor and dorsal surfaces. Those who have studied the actual numbers of sweat glands per square centimeter of surface have found great individual variations. Accurate studies are largely wanting and data available are fragmentary. Although it is believed that Negroes have more eccrine sweat glands than Europeans do (Rose, 1948), there is no significant difference between the number of sweat glands that can be activated thermally in Europeans and in African Negroes. The mean number of such glands is 130 and 127, respectively, per square centimeter of skin (Thomson, 1954). Some data suggest that fewer sweat glands can be activated in white subjects than in Japanese (Kuno, 1956). Japanese have more sweat glands on the extremities than on the trunk, a condition that may be the reverse of that found in the Europeans.

Since sweat glands are not formed after birth, the density of their population is greatest at birth, and gradually decreases as a result of dilution due to the growth of the body (Szabó, 1958). The skin of an infant one year old contains 8 to 10 times as many sweat glands per unit area as are found in an adult (Thomson, 1954). This agrees with the fact that the body surface area of the adult is about 7 times that of a newborn and 5.5 times more than that of an infant one year old. The density of population of sweat glands in the adult shows high individual differences which could be due to differences in body size; the larger surface areas are probably associated with smaller count, and vice versa. This, however, may not be the whole answer; since the total number of sweat glands does not change after birth, a small man should have a relatively larger output of sweat than a large one, but this is not the case. Other factors, such as changes in the secretory activity of each gland, may counterbalance this relationship (Kuno, 1956). The actual number of sweat glands present does not correspond to the number of active glands. Only some of the apparently anatomically perfect glands are functional. Dobson is of the opinion that the glands which rest in the upper part of the dermis are not functional.

Development

The first anlagen of eccrine sweat glands appear in the fourth fetal month, in the palms and soles. During the early part of the fifth fetal month, anlagen of glands appear in the axilla, and from the later part of the fifth month they appear over the parts of the skin, arranged in characteristic patterns around hair follicles (Horstmann, 1952). This chronology of events suggests a classification of sweat glands into three groups; the glands on the palms and soles, those of the axilla, and the glands over the general body surface. The development of glands in the general body surface is also dyschronous; anlagen are formed first in the forehead and scalp and then gradually over the rest of the body. The subsequent function of sweat glands may in some way also reflect developmental events. Sweating, for instance, varies between the palms and soles, and the general body surface. Kuno (1956) suggests that the sweat glands that develop earlier in fetal life may have arisen from a more primitive stem than those that develop later.

Beginning in fetuses 16 to 19 weeks of age, proliferative buds of cells grow down from the crests of the ridges on the underside of the volar surface of the pes and manus. Similar buds of cells are also found on the nail folds and eponychium, and the entire dorsal surface of the distal phalanx. There are no gland anlagen anywhere else on the body surface although hair follicles have well-formed hairs in them and differentiated sebaceous glands. The gland anlagen begin as epidermal buds, similar to but narrower than the primordia of hair follicles; the latter can be recognized by the aggregate of dermal papilla cells at their bases. The cords of cells extend gradually downward into the dermis and attain a clavate end. The swollen end is the growing part of the cord, since mitotic figures are numerous only there. Also glycogen, which is abundant throughout the narrow, straight part of the cord, is not present in the bulbous portion. The cords gradually become tortuous, twisted, and glomerate distally. Glands develop dyschronously even in the same body region where some glands have progressed much farther than others. At the end of the fifth month, the cells in the center of the straight part of the cord become keratinized and shrink, establishing a lumen there. Later, in the seventh and eighth months, "vacuoles" appear in the center of the twisted cords. Adjacent vacuoles coalesce and form elongated clefts. When the clefts also coalesce they form a lumen, which by the end of the seventh month is continuous with that in the duct, and the entire gland is hollow. The lumen broadens during the eighth month, and the presumptive secretory cells assume some of the characteristic appearance of the cells in adult glands (Tsuchiya, 1954).

The myoepithelial cells, which in functional glands resemble smooth muscle fibers insinuated between the epithelium and the basement membrane, are not recognizable during fetal life. Even the characteristic loose connective tissue stroma around the entire gland is not fully differentiated until after birth. The morphology of the glands begins to resemble that of adults in fetuses 9 months old (Borsetto, 1951; Tsuchiya, 1954).

From birth to 10 months of age the glands become gradually active, and attain the characteristic cytological features which will be described later. Nearly all of the histochemical attributes of the adult glands become discernible from late fetal life through the first postnatal year. These details will be described under the various subsections that follow.

FIG. 1. Stereogram of two adjacent sweat glands surrounded by blood vessels. This diagram was reconstructed from thick frozen sections treated for the demonstration of alkaline phosphatase.

Vascularization

The blood vessels that surround eccrine sweat glands have usually been studied with the use of opaque injections; Eichner (1954) used a silver impregnation method and iron hematoxylin. The study of blood vessels injected with colored or opaque substances is limited to the flow of these materials; also, most available specimens are not suitable for these studies. The most convenient and generally satisfactory methods to visualize capillaries are the techniques for alkaline phosphatase which capitalize on the fact that the endothelium of terminal arterioles and capillaries, whether they are dilated or collapsed, is strongly reactive for alkaline phosphatase.

Thick preparations treated for alkaline phosphatase show the path of the capillaries and arterioles that surround the gland outlined as clearly as if the vessels had been injected with opaque substances. The entire glomerate portion of the gland, secretory segment, and coiled duct is richly and intimately supplied with blood vessels, which closely follow its contours (Ellis et al., 1958). All of the vessels to one gland frequently arise from one arteriole; the vessels to the larger glands may come from several arterioles (Fig. 1). In the scrotum, where the glomerate part of the glands is loosely coiled, the capillaries around the different loops can be seen giving off branches and shunts which connect the vessels around adjacent loops. In the tightly coiled tubules of the glands in the scalp, the axilla, or the arm, the blood vessels form a denser plexus around them.

Two or more capillaries or arterioles wind loosely around the straight portion of the excretory duct as it ascends toward the surface (Fig. 1). Cross-shunts connect these roughly parallel vessels. At the base of the papillary body the parallel vessels branch, giving off capillary loops around the cone of the epidermis that contains the terminal coiled intraepidermal portion of the duct. Capillary loops around this part of the duct also come from the arcades of vessels that lie under the epidermis. The capillary networks around the sweat glands remain relatively unaltered even in the skin of senile individuals.

Histological Features

Eccrine sweat glands are simple tubes that extend from the epidermis to midway in the dermis, or to the tela subcutanea. Thus, the glands are separable into groups: shallow ones and deep lying ones. The gross morphology can be appreciated by isolating glands from skin digested with collagenase, or by staining the glands selectively in very thick sections (Fig. 2). Each tubule consists of an irregularly and tightly coiled basal portion, a straight segment that extends from the coil to the epidermis, and a proximal coiled segment that lies within the epidermis. The superficial and deep portions of each tubule, then, are coiled, and the middle portion is relatively straight. The basal coil consists of about one-third duct in the more superficial part, and two-thirds secretory portion in the basal part. Thick sections prepared for alkaline phosphatase show the relative proportions of the two segments. The duct, in turn, consists of three segments: the helical segment that lies within the epidermis, so-called "epidermal sweat duct unit"; the straight

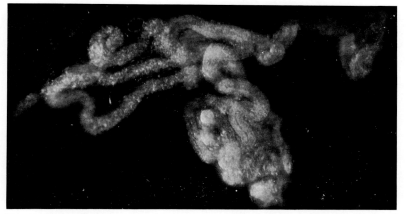

FIG. 2. The coiled segment of an eccrine sweat gland from the skin of the chest, teased after treatment with collagenase and viewed under dark-field illumination. From Hambrick and Blank (1954). (Reproduced by permission of the authors and the Waverly Press.)

portion that traverses the dermis approximately perpendicular to the surface, and the coiled basal portion.

The diameter of the duct is variably smaller than that of the secretory coil. Among other peculiarities, the glands in the palms and soles have a duct which is less than one-third the diameter of the secretory coil, making the transition between duct and gland somewhat abrupt, as in apocrine glands. Although not as prominent, the eccrine glands of the axilla also show this difference between the two segments. Elsewhere the differences in the diameter of the two segments are not as pronounced. The extent and the compactness of the basal coil are also different, the difference usually being associated with the level of the dermis in which the glands are located; those about midway in the dermis are smaller and more compact.

Histological sections cut the nests of tubules at different angles. Depending upon the angle, each nest is composed of different proportions of duct and secretory tubules. Sections through the higher levels of the coil contain more duct than secretory tubule, and sections through

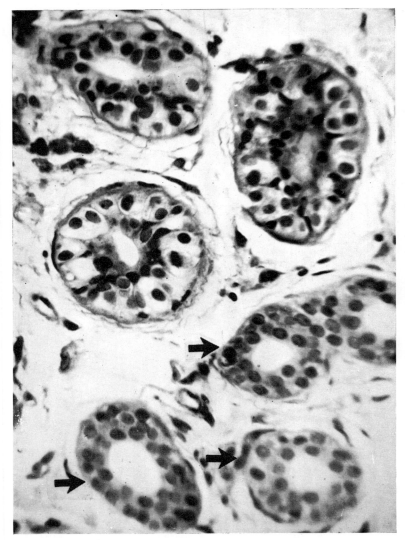

Fig. 3. Section through the basal coil of an eccrine sweat gland in the axilla. There are as many sections of the coiled duct (arrows) as there are of the secretory segment. Stained with toluidine blue buffered to pH 5.0.

the lower levels may contain all secretory tubules (Fig. 3). The epithelium has an uneven free border and occasional cytoplasmic blebs protrude into the lumen. A number of Japanese authors have believed that such processes are indicative of apocrine secretion and that differentiation of sweat glands into eccrine and apocrine types on the basis of their secretory mechanism is not valid (Ito, 1943; Ito and Iwashige, 1951; Ito *et al.*, 1951; Iwashige, 1952; Kuno, 1956). Ito *et al.* (1951) even state that the basophil, RNA-containing granules, normally in the apices of eccrine cells, are discharged into the lumen. Blebs and ripples of epithelium are often found on the luminal border of any serous secreting glands, but to consider this a basis for "apocrine type" of secretion is a misinterpretation of facts.

Ito (1943), who first recognized two kinds of secretory cells in eccrine glands, saw the epithelial cells arranged as "superficial cells" and "basal cells," the basal cells not reaching the lumen, but connecting with it by way of intercellular canaliculi. Other Japanese investigators have confirmed the presence of superficial and basal cells both in the glands of man (Kuno, 1956), and in those of other mammals (Tsukagoshi, 1951, 1953, 1955). The eccrine secretory cells are friable and upon fixation become collapsed, distorted and piled up on each other. The "superficial" cells in one section often have a broad cytoplasmic base in another, and most "basal" cells reach the lumen. Thus "basal" and "superficial" cells both rest upon the myoepithelial cells and all reach the surface (Fig. 4). Basal and superficial cells, therefore, are unfortunate names since they convey the impression that there are two layers of cells. The two types of cells are nevertheless very distinct. The smaller superficial cells, largely displaced toward the lumen, have cytoplasmic granules that stain avidly with basic dyes, and are, for this reason, called *dark cells* (Montagna *et al.*, 1953). The larger basal cells have small, sparse, and slightly acidophil cytoplasmic granules, and should be called *clear cells*.

Treatment of sections with ribonuclease before staining abolishes only some of the cytoplasmic basophilia of the granules in the dark cells; these cells, then, contain ribonucleic acid and other basophil substances (Ito *et al.*, 1951; Montagna *et al.*, 1953). The residual basophilic substance which stains a moderate to strong metachromatic color and is PAS-reactive, probably contains acid mucopolysaccharides (Montagna *et al.*, 1953; Formisano and Lobitz, 1957). Lee (1960), unaware of the well-documented evidence that the dark cells contain and secrete mucopolysaccharides (Formisano and Lobitz, 1957; Dobson and Lobitz, 1958; Dobson *et al.*, 1958), proposes to call the dark cells "mucin cells" and the clear cells "chief cells." The practice of some investigators of giving a new name to every structure they study is deplorable, and only adds to the list of meaningless synonyms. These names, therefore, are regrettable. When stained with Giemsa or with eosin-methylene blue the apices of the dark cells have a mixture of basophil and acidophil granules. The clear cells have very small acidophil and some basophil granules evenly distributed in the cytoplasm. The

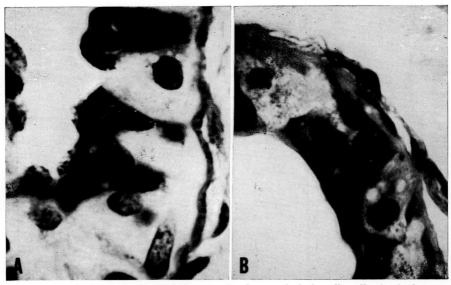

FIG. 4. (A) Secretory epithelium with clear and dark cells, all of which rest upon the basement membrane and myoid cells, and all reaching the lumen. From the axilla, stained with toluidine blue buffered to pH 5.0. (B) The cuticular border, distinct in the clear cells, is poorly defined in the dark cells. Stained with toluidine blue buffered to pH 5.0.

proportion of dark to clear cells is variable, but it is somewhat consistent in the glands of the same specimen. While distinct in most specimens, dark and clear cells may not be conspicuous in others; when this is the case most of the cells appear to belong to the clear type. The eccrine glands of the chimpanzee have a striking differentiation of clear and dark cells. Occasionally the secretory cells have a clear cytoplasm riddled with evenly spaced vacuoles, and resemble sebaceous cells; the vacuoles, however, contain neither glycogen nor lipid. These glands may be encountered in individuals of all ages and in normal or in abnormal skin (Holyoke and Lobitz, 1952). When this condition is found in one gland, all of the glands in a given specimen of skin show it. Subsequent biopsy specimens removed several weeks apart from individuals whose sweat glands are composed of cells with "clear reticulated cytoplasm," all show this peculiarity. The functional significance of this condition is not known.

Under the electron microscope, the cytoplasm of the clear cells extends into slender microvilli of uniform diameter, into the luminal border. The elongated microvilli of adjacent cells interdigitate and give rise to a complex, tortuous intercellular boundary (Kurosumi *et al.*, 1960). According to the functional state of the gland or the tonicity of the fixing solution, there are intercellular spaces of varying sizes (Figs. 5 and 6). In some sections the villous processes of apposed cells are clearly separated; in others the microvilli are tightly meshed with scarcely any space between them. Adjacent clear cells have occasional desmosomes between them that usually mark the sites of the intercellular canaliculi (Fig. 7). The microvilli that extend into the canaliculi are shorter than those which interdigitate along the borders of adjacent clear cells, but they are of the same diameter.

The cytoplasm of the clear cells is full of formed elements, the osmiophilia of which make the clear cells moderately electron dense (Fig. 8). The cytoplasmic matrix of the clear cells, then, is markedly different from that of the dark cells. Clear cells have numerous, clumped glycogen units associated with smooth-surfaced membranes, larger and more numerous mitochondria, and an organized Golgi zone. There is no organized ergastoplasm. Nearly every part of the cell contains glycogen units. Some of the clear cells contain much more glycogen than others do. The round or rod-shaped mitochondria are everywhere in the cytoplasm. They contain lamellar cristae embedded in a moderately electron-dense matrix. The cristae and the mitochondrial walls are composed of unit membranes (Fig. 9).

The Golgi zone of the light cell is located near the nucleus. It has paired parallel, smooth-surfaced membranes, small vesicles, and occasional larger vacuoles. Small lipid droplets, with a moderately electron-dense interior and an adielectronic outer rim, are also associated with the Golgi zone. These are probably the lipochondria that Baker has associated with the Golgi complex (Palay, 1957). The Golgi apparatus seems to be oriented toward the intercellular canaliculi, and is never located near the interfaces of myoepithelial or dark cells. Small smooth-surfaced vacuoles similar to those in the Golgi zone may also be found in the cytoplasm bordering the intercellular canaliculi.

Under the electron microscope, the supranuclear portions of the

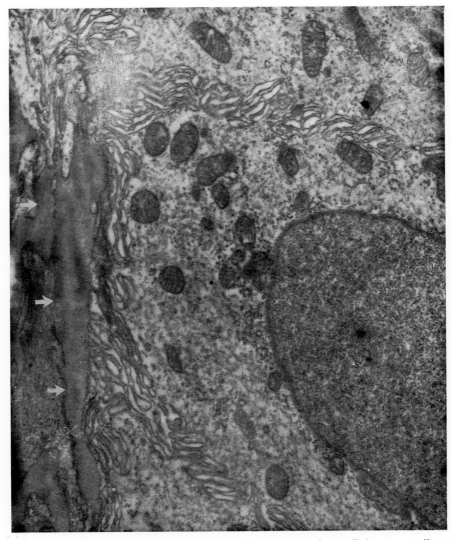

Fig. 5. Electron micrograph of the basal portion of a clear cell from an axillary eccrine gland. The cell rests upon an amorphous basement membrane (arrows); the cloudy cytoplasm is characteristic of glycogen. Ovoid mitochondria and scattered rough-surfaced endoplasmic reticulum are also present. The plasma membranes of the basal and lateral faces of the cell are plicated, and the processes of adjacent cells are interdigitated. The slightly hypertonic fixing solution has exaggerated the intercellular spaces (see Fig. 6 for comparison). (Courtesy of Dr. R. A. Ellis.)

dark cells have abundant endoplasmic reticulum, organized ergastoplasm, and one or more small, but well-organized Golgi apparatus (Figs. 10 and 11). Some small, clear, membrane-bounded vacuoles may be found in the apical cytoplasm, often just beneath the plasma membrane of

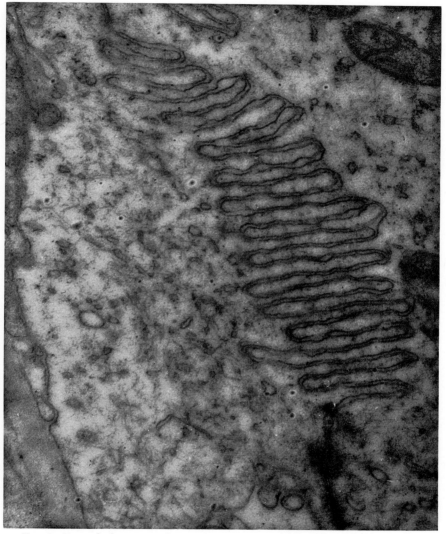

Fig. 6. Typical plasma membranes between two adjacent clear cells. The folded borders of the cells interdigitate with each other, and the intercellular spaces are irregular. (Courtesy of Dr. R. A. Ellis).

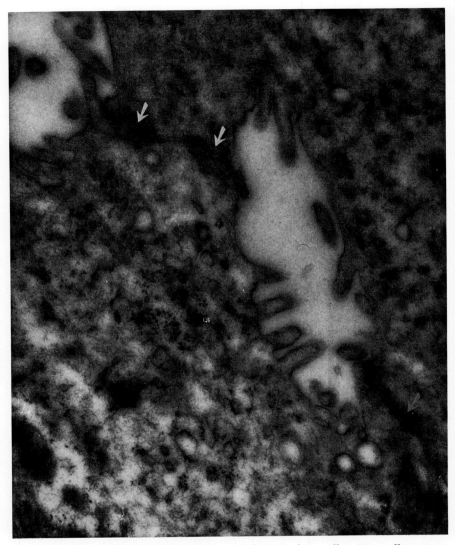

Fɪɢ. 7. Intercellular canaliculi between adjacent clear cells. Microvilli project into the lumen of the canaliculi and prominent terminal bars (arrows) isolate the canalicular system from the luminal surface of the cell. Many smooth-surfaced and a few rough-surfaced profiles of the endoplasmic reticulum can be seen. (Courtesy of Dr. R. A. Ellis.)

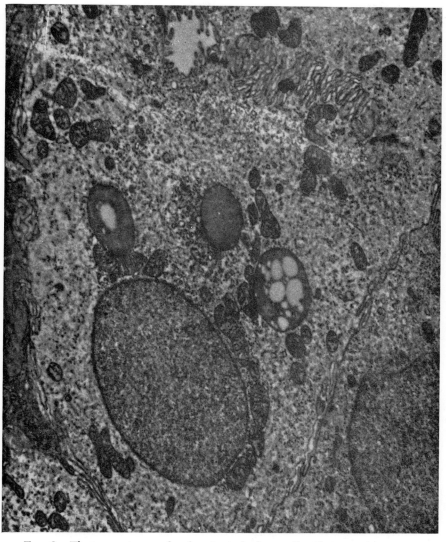

Fig. 8. Electron micrograph of a typical clear cell. The cytoplasm contains numerous ovoid mitochondria, lipid droplets, and a prominent Golgi zone. The cloudy appearance of the cytoplasm is characteristic of glycogen. Folded plasma membranes and an intercellular canaliculus are also shown. (Courtesy of Dr. R. A. Ellis.)

the luminal border. The nucleus is rounded or oval, but its periphery is irregularly indented.

During secretion, the apical cytoplasm of the dark cells is filled with electron-clear, membrane-bound vacuoles of various sizes, frequently

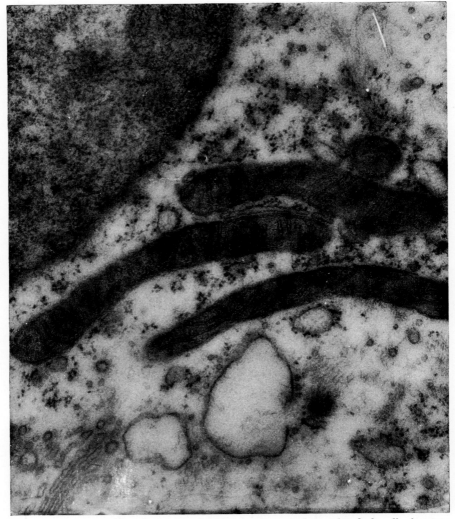

Fig. 9. Long, filamentous mitochondria in the cytoplasm of a dark cell, showing internal and external membranes, as well as regularly spaced cristae. Numerous RNP particles, associated with the membranes of the endoplasmic reticulum, are also visible in the cytoplasm. (Courtesy of Dr. R. A. Ellis.)

crowded together, and closely packed near the plasma luminal membrane (Fig. 10). A narrow, moderately electron-dense region, which corresponds to the terminal web, separates the vacuoles from the plasma membrane along most of the luminal interface. The plasma membrane occasionally protrudes into the lumen in the form of blebs. These cytoplasmic extrusions contain the same membranous fragments as they appear in the lumen of the secretory coil. During the formation of the bleb, the membrane-bound vesicles must lose their identity, since they are never seen intact within the cytoplasmic extrusion.

Occasional cells, smaller than the dark cells may be found. These contain a few membrane-bound vacuoles, some rough-surfaced endoplasmic reticulum, and a small pycnotic nucleus. These relatively rare cells seem to be degenerating dark cells.

Rarely, cells that resemble dark cells are found in pairs, and may be newly divided cells. These cells have a relatively electron-clear cytoplasm, have only a few mitochondria, and contain few elements of the endoplasmic reticulum.

A layer of myoepithelial cells is sandwiched between the thick hyalin basement membrane and the secretory cells. Although in histological preparations these cells seem to be loosely dove-tailed, with large interstices between them, the electron microscope shows that these cells form a fairly complete sheet under the secretory cells. Myoepithelial cells are aligned parallel to the axis of the tubule. Since the myoepithelial cells in eccrine glands are structurally like those in apocrine glands, the details described in the chapter on apocrine glands will not be repeated here.

Under the electron microscope, the flat attenuated base of myoepithelial cells rests directly upon a moderately electron-dense and homogeneous basement membrane (Fig. 12). In cross sections, the cells are curved along the base, forming the outer smooth contours of the gland; they are arched at their inner surface, particularly over the nucleus, providing a ribbed pavement for the cells that lie over them (Ellis and Montagna, 1961). In longitudinal sections, the strap-like myoepithelial cells are nearly the same width along their entire length, being slightly wider at the level around the nucleus. Adjacent myoepithelial cells overlap more frequently toward their ends than they do near the nucleus.

The secretory segment is surrounded by a fairly thick basement membrane, which in unstained preparations is yellowish, hyalin, and refractile. Under polarized light it is birefringent when the tubules are sectioned transversely. It does not stain with basic dyes; with

Van Gieson's or Mallory's triacid stain it stains like the collagenous fibers. That part of the membrane which adheres to the myoepithelial cells reduces ammoniacal silver nitrate, but the outer collagenic part does not. Similarly, the inner, nonfibrillar part of the basement

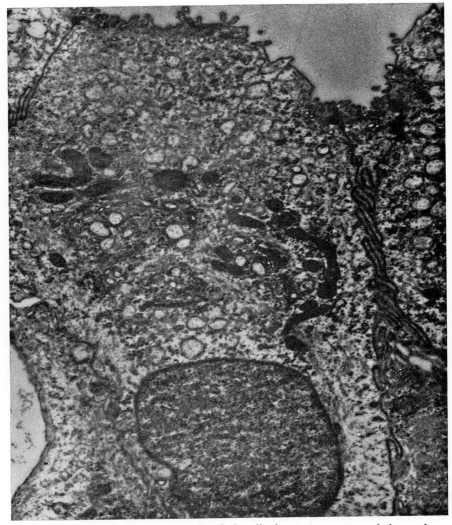

FIG. 10. Electron micrograph of a dark cell, showing a portion of the nucleus, the prominent Golgi zone, dense filamentous mitochondria, and numerous clear vesicles containing mucopolysaccharide. Microvilli are present on the luminal border. (Courtesy of Dr. R. A. Ellis.)

membrane against the myoepithelial cells has a strong PAS reactivity, but the outer, hyalin layer does not. The basement membrane around the eccrine glands is similar to that around other glandular tubules or

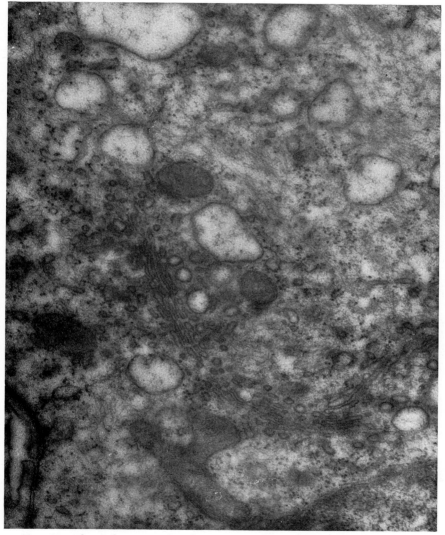

FIG. 11. The Golgi zone of a dark cell. Parallel smooth-surfaced membranes, small vesicles, and larger secretory vacuoles show a characteristic pattern. Mitochondria, RNP particles, and elements of the endoplasmic reticulum are also shown. (Courtesy of Dr. R. A. Ellis.)

FIG. 12. Myoepithelial cell in the secretory segment of a human eccrine sweat gland. The cell rests upon the amorphous basement membrane; the basal cytoplasm is filled with fibrils oriented longitudinally. The nucleus occupies the apical portion of the cell. Small mitochondria are present both in the fibrous and vesicular cytoplasm. The basal portions of several clear cells are also shown. (Courtesy of Dr. R. A. Ellis.)

around the seminiferous tubules (Montagna and Hamilton, 1952). In the skin of aged subjects the outer, hyalin, collagenic layer becomes thicker, but the thinner, PAS-reactive, inner portion remains approximately the same thickness. At the transition between the secretory segment and the duct the basement membrane becomes abruptly thin and remains inconspicuous along the entire duct.

Loewenthal (1960, 1961) has named the terminal segment of the secretory coil at the junction with the duct, the "ampulla." This segment is 33 to 80 μ in length; it may be contracted or dilated, and when contracted resembles the duct. When dilated it should have a distinctive appearance, being often marked by a spiral shelf, which in longitudinal sections appears as a spur on either side. In the wall of the ampulla, a single layer of cuboidal cells rests upon attenuated myoepithelial cells. Even canaliculi have been described between the cells of the ampulla. The ampulla, opens into the "sphincter," which is about the same length as the ampulla. The wall of the sphincter is said to consist of a basal layer of large myoepithelial cells and cuboidal cells on the luminal border. The myoepithelial cells are said to be arranged transversely to the axis of the tubule. Loewenthal states that it is not possible to show unerringly these myoepithelial cells. Surely, it should not be difficult to unveil such large "myoepithelial" cells when very small ones offer no challenge. The state of dilatation of the sphincter and the ampulla are said to be independent of that of the remainder of the gland. Loewenthal speculates that the ampulla is important in the reabsorption of "sweat constituents," and the sphincter is important as a contractile element. Yet, intradermal injections of various drugs caused no visible alterations in the size of the ampullae. It is unfortunate that the illustrations in these two papers are of a very poor quality. If these are samples of the best histological material used by the author, the rest of it must have been even poorer and unintelligible. It is my impression that Loewenthal has overemphasized the eminence of these two structural entities.

Since the secretory segment of the tubule is lined with a simple epithelium, and the duct with two layers of cuboidal cells, the transition between the two segments is abrupt. The luminal cells in the first portion of the duct, however, contain granules that resemble those in the secretory cells; the duct attains its characteristic epithelium gradually. The basal cells of the epithelium of the duct are cuboidal; the surface cells are also cuboidal but they may be slightly flattened. The luminal surface is differentiated into a hyalin, faintly yellow cuticular border. The hyalin border varies in thickness in different glands; it becomes distinct above the short transition segment of the coiled duct, and is most marked in the straight segment of the duct. The cuticle is, in effect, a keratinization of the cytoplasm at the luminal border of each cell (Ellis and Montagna, 1961), and shows many minor structural variations in the sweat ducts of normal skin (Holyoke and Lobitz, 1952).

The straight segment of the duct has a narrower diameter than that of any other portion of the duct, and its cuboidal or columnar luminal cells, which are larger than those elsewhere in the duct, have a very well-developed cuticle. In surface view the cuticle cells have a pentagonal configuration and between the cells is an easily demonstrable cementum substance (Fig. 13).

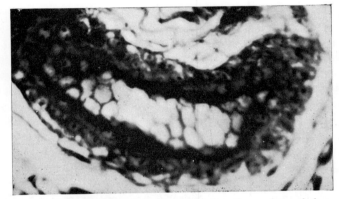

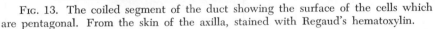

FIG. 13. The coiled segment of the duct showing the surface of the cells which are pentagonal. From the skin of the axilla, stained with Regaud's hematoxylin.

Under the electron microscope the luminal surface of the surface cells has low microvilli that are surrounded by a plasma membrane composed of two adielectronic lines separated by a light band (Ellis and Montagna, 1961). There are a few agranular membranous vesicles in the cytoplasm beneath the microvilli, and partially closed vesicles are occasionally found in the crypts between the short microvilli. The cytoplasm of the microvilli just beneath the plasma membrane is filled with moderately electron-dense, coarse, tonofilaments, similar to filaments inserted on the attachment plaques along the lateral borders of adjoining luminal cells. These tonofilaments are coarser than those described in epidermal cells (Brody, 1959). They are similar to the filaments seen in the cells of human cervical epithelium (Karrer, 1960).

The wavy, rarely straight, tonofilaments measure 35 to 70 Å in diameter; in longitudinal sections they appear as parallel strands with small irregular enlargements along one surface; in cross sections they look like small irregular rings with an electron-light center. The filaments, being loosely organized, give a spongy appearance to the cuticular border. Some filaments appear to be continuous with the inner adielectronic line of the plasmalemma. Near the attachment zone, beaded filaments become closely aggregated and form compact, moderately adielectronic zones. Deeper in the cell, just above the level of the nucleus, the filaments are straighter and less numerous, giving the cytoplasm a fibrous appearance. This zone also contains a few small mitochondria, some smooth-surfaced vesicles, and strands of agranular reticulum. The more basal cytoplasm of the luminal cells contains randomly scattered mitochondria of various shapes and sizes, some granular and agranular reticulum, glycogen units, and a moderate number of Palade particles. There is no evidence of organized ergastoplasm and Golgi elements.

The elaborately interdigitated plasma membranes of adjoining superficial cells have numerous attachment zones. At the attachment zones the plasma membranes are separated by an electron-dense line, forming quintuple-layered cell interconnections (Karrer, 1960). Attachment zones, which become increasingly larger and more numerous near the luminal interface, are usually oriented somewhat parallel to it. The attachment plaques of apposed cells are 120–140 Å wide and they are separated by a gap 200–220 Å wide. Within this gap are distinguished three dense lines which correspond to the intermediate dense layers and the intercellular contact layer described by Odland (1958) in epidermal cells.

Adjacent basal cells of the duct are separated by an intermembranous space 100–170 Å in width. The boundaries between adjacent cells are convoluted. The cytoplasm near the plasma membranes has a fibrous appearance and is denser than that nearer the center of the cell. Desmosomes, smaller and fewer than those of the luminal cells, are found along the plasma membranes. The cytoplasm of the cell consists of membranous and granular components embedded in a predominantly amorphous matrix. The granular and agranular membranes are not organized into ergastoplasm or in a Golgi complex. Palade granules and glycogen units occur frequently. Numerous round granular or short rod-shaped mitochondria have no particular orientation in the cytoplasm.

The nuclei of the basal cells frequently have deep invaginations, and the cytoplasm in these infoldings usually contains mitochondria and Palade granules. Aside from this the nuclear envelope and the nucleoplasm show no peculiarity. Compared with the nuclei of the luminal cells, the nuclei of the basal cells have prominent nucleoli.

The basal borders of the peripheral cells are relatively smooth, but the other borders of these cells have intricate convolutions. There is no distinct basement membrane around the coiled duct; a thin, electron-light line occasionally separates the plasma membrane from the

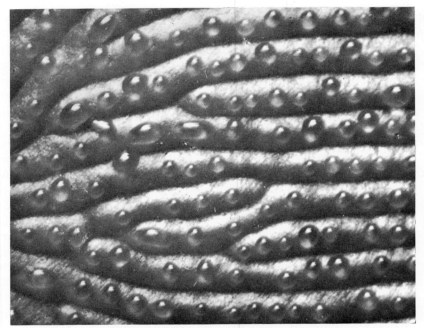

FIG. 14. Beads of sweat gathered at the orifices of the sweat ducts in the epidermal ridges of the palm. (Courtesy of Dr. W. C. Lobitz, Jr.)

underlying collagen. Over most of the interface, however, small loosely packed collagen fibrils with no particular orientation seem to be attached directly to the basal membranes.

The ducts open onto the surface of the palms and soles through the ridges of the epidermis, the openings being very regularly spaced in the centers of the epidermal ridges (Fig. 14) (Hambrick and Blank, 1954). The stratum corneum at the periphery of the orifices is elevated to form cup-shaped craters or "beakers." The average diameter of the outer orifice and that of the duct are 60 and 15 μ, respectively, in the palm, 80 and 16 in the sole, and 70 and 14 on the general body surface (Kuno, 1956). If the mean diameter of the orifices is calculated to be 72 μ, and the total number of sweat glands is in the vicinity of 2, 3 millions, the total surface area of the orifices is about 94 square centimeters. The ducts join the epidermis at the apices of its rete ridges. In the palms and soles the ridges have a flattened base, each

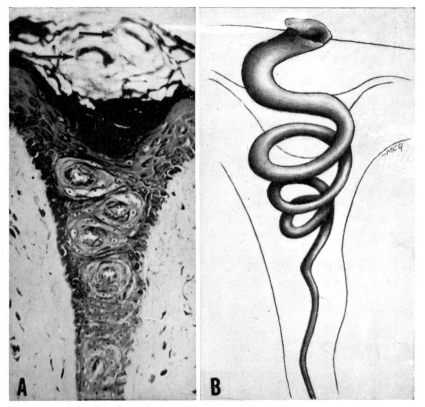

FIG. 15. (A) "Epidermal sweat duct unit" from the skin of the scalp. The spiral duct has been cut many times, four times in the stratum corneum. Stained with Regaud's hematoxylin. (B) A three-dimensional representation of the path of the duct through the epidermis showing a left-handed coiling.

ridge corresponding to the "fingerprint" ridge. As soon as they enter the epidermal ridges the ducts become spiraled (Fig. 15). The majority of the helices have a right-handed, or clockwise coiling, which may be regarded as normal (Takagi, 1952). In various regions, however, some ducts have a left-handed coiling, or they may coil in irregular directions.

Such aberrations are few, but when they occur, they are seen in groups. The ducts become helical as soon as they enter the epithelial ridges. The coils of the spiral are small at the narrow base and become progressively larger as they approach the surface of the epidermis. Similarly, the lumen becomes increasingly larger near the orifice (Hambrick and Blank, 1954). In the thick epidermis of the palms and soles the duct traverses the epidermis as a steep helix; in thin epidermis it may be more tortuous. This suggests that the intraepidermal portion of the sweat duct is a distinct entity, with a specific length which must adjust its shape to fit the various thicknesses of the epidermis (Pinkus, 1939). However, in thin epidermis the duct may have only two to three coils, whereas in the palms or soles it may have many. It is controversial whether the cells which line the intraepidermal part of the duct are a part of the epidermis or part of the duct itself.

An idea, which was apparently first voiced by Unna in 1882, is that the part of the duct which passes through the epidermis possesses no wall of its own, and that there is free communication between the lumen of the duct and the interepidermal spaces. Some authors believe that the passage through the epidermis is only a channel excavated between the epidermal cells. Others deny this and believe that the channel has a wall composed of two layers of cuboidal cells.

When thin slices of the fresh stratum corneum are viewed under the microscope, with the surface up, the orifices of the lumen of the distal portion of the ducts are seen to be surrounded by three or more layers of closely packed, flattened cells (Takagi, 1952). The cells of the inner layer pave the inside of the duct so closely that they leave no observable interstices between them. The duct is similar as it traverses the middle and deepest parts of the stratum corneum. In the deepest parts of the stratum corneum the cells begin to show traces of a nucleus as do the cells of the epidermis around them.

Pinkus (1939) expresses the opinion that the epidermis is like a plate which is pierced by biologically separate structures, the ducts, around which the epidermis is molded. Since the cells of the intraepidermal portion of the duct seem to have different cytological features from those of the epidermis around them, the intraepidermal portion of the duct together with a layer of cells immediately around it was named "the epidermal sweat duct unit" (Lobitz et al., 1954a). In tissue cultures of human skin, the cells of the syringeal epithelium seem to be endowed with greater mitotic propensities than those of the epidermis around it. In epidermal lesions, such as senile keratosis, the intraepidermal part of the ducts remain relatively unaltered. These, however, are not sufficient reason for coining this name. All of the cells of the duct in the middle of the stratum corneum contain fine filaments, and the cells within the deepest layer have tonofibrils similar to those in the epidermal cells around them. The part of the duct within the malpighian layer is made of nucleated cells that contain keratohyalin granules in the region of the granular layer and tonofibrils and intercellular bridges in the spinous layer.

Biologically, the cells of the ducts are identical with those of the epidermis; for instance, during wound healing they participate in repairing the denuded surface, and the epithelial cells which they contribute are indistinguishable from those that proliferate from the epidermis (Lobitz et al., 1954b). Mitotic figures are found only in the basal cells of the epidermal cone, at the junction of the duct with the epidermis and at no other place along the spiral intraepidermal path (Lobitz et al., 1954b). These basal cells, then, comprise the germinative layer, or "matrix" of the helical duct. The cells must glide upwards in a spiral fashion, arranging themselves in two or more concentric rows around the lumen.

The cells of the duct have no pigment in them. In the skin of Negroes, the nonpigmented ducts are clearly outlined against a highly melanized epidermis. Pigmented epidermal cells form a ring around the base of the duct, and in some cases pigment cells may extend a short distance below the junction of the duct with the epidermis.

The cells of the intraepidermal part of the duct undergo keratinization. The lumen itself is encircled by a keratinized "ring" within which may occasionally be found a ring of hyalinized cells, which probably represent the keratinized luminal cells from farther down in the duct; these may have been pushed upwards into the keratinized ring. In the base of the spiral the luminal cells have only the keratinized hyalin border and contain no keratohyalin. The progress of keratinization in the cells of the duct is not unlike that of the surrounding epidermal cells; it is more precocious, however, than that in the cells around it. Keratinization in the cells of the duct in the middle of the malpighian layer, for example, corresponds to that of the epidermal cells in the stratum granulosum. The type of keratin formed by the cells of the duct has different properties from that formed by the epidermis. If sections of stratum corneum are boiled in sodium hydroxide, for example, the epidermal cells become swollen and translucent, but the cells of the duct retain their integrity (Kuno, 1956).

When the intraepidermal duct is removed surgically together with the surrounding epidermis, the terminal stump does remarkable things

(Lobitz *et al.*, 1954b). Shortly after the infliction of the wound, the exposed dermis and the terminal stumps of the ducts within it form a thin necrotic crust. It must be emphasized that by now the top of the stump of the duct is below the original site of the epithelial ridge. Three days after the injury the basal cells near the end of the stump become swollen and crowded around the lumen, causing the lumen to attain some tortuosity. Cells streaming from the end of the stump become continuous with the luminal cells and outline a single-layered tortuous tube in the shape of a cone under the necrotic layer which covers the wound. Since little or no mitotic activity can be seen in the cells of the duct at this time, the fashioning of this apical cone must be attributed principally to the increase in volume of the cells already there. After the third day there is a burst of mitotic activity, but only in the basal cells of the duct, at the base of the flimsy terminal cone under the crust of the wound. Many of these new cells radiate from the cone and come to foim epithelial tongues under the crust. Continued proliferation of cells radially results in the formation of an epithelial covering under the crust. When the crust is eventually sloughed off, the epithelium under it looks and behaves exactly like epidermis.

The Nucleus and Mitotic Activity

The nuclei of the secretory cells are strongly reactive to the Feulgen technique. The nuclei of the dark cells are oval and very compact; a chromatin network is seldom clearly shown. The nuclei of the clear cells are round and densely stippled with Feulgen-reactive granules. Two or more small nucleoli are usually close together. The nuclei of eccrine glands are different from those of apocrine glands which are larger, usually spherical, only moderately Feulgen-reactive, and possess conspicuous nucleoli. In the duct the basal cells have strongly Feulgen-reactive nuclei and the surface cells have moderately to weakly reactive ones. The strength of the reaction in the nuclei of the surface cells is inversely related to the degree of cuticular development in the cells.

Now and then cells in the secretory tubules contain more than one nucleus. This has given rise to the belief that these cells, particularly the clear cells, undergo division by amitosis (Ito and Iwashige, 1951). Searches in numerous samples of skin from different regions of the body, however, have yielded not one case of recognizable amitosis. This is not surprising since even in the liver, where polynucleated cells are common, multiple nuclei result not from amitosis, but from division

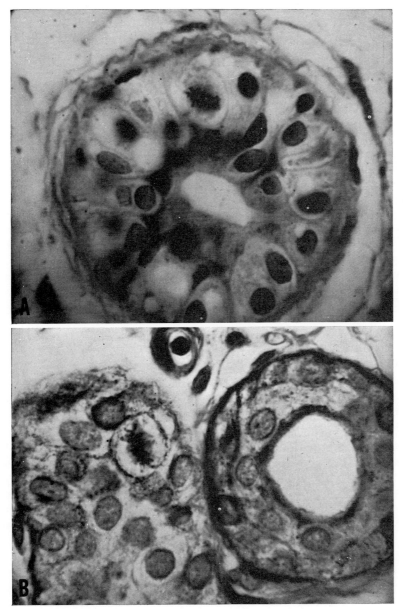

Fig. 16. Mitosis in the eccrine gland: metaphase in (A) a secretory cell, and (B) in a cell of the coiled duct. From the skin of the axilla, stained with toluidine blue buffered to pH 5.0.

of the nucleus. Binucleate cells could thus be formed from the result of "cytoplasmic lag" in mitotic division, that is, the cytoplasm lagging behind the nucleus to a point where it does not divide until the next division, or does not divide at all (Wilson and Leduc, 1948).

Mitotic activity in the cells of the secretory tubules is said to be rare (Bunting et al., 1948; Holyoke and Lobitz, 1952). Yet cell division is occasionally encountered in both clear and dark cells (Fig. 16). Unlike other cutaneous appendages, most of which are characterized by a loss and replacement of cells, there is little need for cell replacement in eccrine sweat glands. The cells of the duct, which are normally also mitotically inert, retain the ability to proliferate rapidly when the need arises. When needed, mitotic activity occurs only in the basal cells of the duct, where the loss of cells at the luminal side may provide the stimulus for replacement. The potentialities of sweat glands to regenerate after injury are particularly interesting (Lobitz et al., 1954b). Injury gives great impetus to the proliferative ability of these cells. Injury to the duct, however, has little effect on the mitotic activity of the glandular portion.

Mitochondria

The mitochondria as seen under the electron microscope have already been described. We include here only a description of their structure as seen in stained preparations.

Although mitochondria are demonstrated easily in eccrine glands very few have studied them (Ito and Iwashige, 1951; Tsukagoshi, 1953, 1955; Iwashige, 1952). The Japanese investigators see mitochondria mostly as rod-like and filamentous, distributed throughout the cytoplasm, and concentrated around the nuclei. They believe also that since the numbers of secretion granules and mitochondria appear to have an inverse relation in each cell, secretion granules are formed by a direct transformation of mitochondria. The mitochondria in the glands of old human beings are said to be rod-like and granular, and never filamentous (Iwashige, 1952).

In general, mitochondria are in the form of short, stout rods, with a few long filamentous ones radiating in the distal part of the cytoplasm toward the lumen (Montagna, 1955). Mitochondria tend to be clustered around the nucleus, and often completely encircle it. In the clear cells mitochondria are somewhat evenly distributed in the cytoplasm, but tend to be aggregated toward the basal part. They seem to bear no direct relationship to the intercellular canaliculi, but may be found clustered around cytoplasmic vacuoles, often making loops around them. In the dark cells filamentous mitochondria are crowded between the cytoplasmic granules. When one appreciates the restlessness of mitochondria complexes in living cells, it is not difficult to understand such pleomorphism in active cells. There is a disparity in the distribution of mitochondria between the dark and clear cells, and between the individual cells in each group; some cells contain many, and others very few. Both mitochondria and cytoplasmic granules may be numerous or scant in the same cell. Mitochondria may mediate the metabolic activities of these cells, but there is no proof that they change into, or form secretion products. The difference in the number of mitochondria in the various cells of the same tubule may reflect differences in the physiological states of the cells.

All the cells of the duct contain some mitochondria. In the short transition segment of the coiled dermal portion of the duct, the superficial cells have numerous mitochondria around the nucleus and extend to just below where the cytoplasm is differentiated into a cuticle. Some mitochondria may even extend into the partially differentiated cuticular border. In the basal cells of this segment of the duct, mitochondria are finer and less numerous than in the superficial cells. In the more distal parts of the duct, where the superficial cells have attained a distinct cuticular cap, there are only a few fragmented mitochondria, but the basal cells abound in them. Unlike the mitochondria in the secretory cells, which are often stout, those in the cells of the duct are very small.

Histochemistry

The cytoplasm in the clear secretory cells of the eccrine glands is stippled with delicate lipid granules; the dark cells contain few such granules. Variations in the amount of lipid occur in individual glands and the glands of different individuals. The glands of children contain fewer lipid granules than those of adults, and those of old subjects may abound in them (Kano, 1951). Lipids are apparently stable, additive components of apocrine cells; they are not secreted, even when the glands are stimulated to sweat (Shelley and Mescon, 1952; Dobson and Lobitz, 1958; Dobson et al., 1958).

Most eccrine cells have a diffuse yellow pigment, probably a carotinoid, in their cytoplasm (Bunting et al., 1948). The glands also have variable numbers of pigment granules that fluoresce with a yellow or orange light under near ultraviolet light, resist extraction, contain no iron, are not reactive to the PAS test, and are firmly bound to a lipid. The number of pigment granules increases with age, there being none in infants and many in old subjects.

Eccrine sweat glands contain large quantities of glycogen (Tsukagoshi, 1951; Montagna *et al.*, 1952), more of it in the clear cells than in the dark cells (Fig. 17). The distribution of glycogen in the cells of any one tubule is uneven; some cells are laden with it and others may contain none. In the clear cells glycogen is often piled up

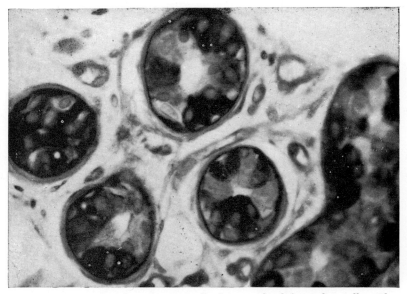

Fig. 17. Glycogen in the secretory cells from a gland from the axilla. There is a disparity in the distribution of glycogen from cell to cell.

against the walls of intercellular canaliculi (Fig. 18). The dark cells also contain a substance which is PAS-reactive but resistant to digestion in saliva or diastase. This corresponds to the basophil material which is not hydrolyzed by ribonuclease and which often stains metachromatically; it is probably a mucopolysaccharide (Formisano and Lobitz, 1957). The epithelium of the duct routinely contains glycogen, mostly concentrated in the basal cells (Montagna, 1955; Lobitz *et al.*, 1955). In the luminal cells glycogen is uniquely distributed in a fine line that marks the separation of the cuticle from the basal cytoplasm (Lobitz *et al.*, 1955).

Eccrine glands abound in cytochrome oxidase (Fig. 19A). Large concentrations of reactive granules are found in the cytoplasm of the cells of the duct as well as those of the secretory cells. This is concordant with the fact that the basal cells of the duct are as rich in mitochondria as those of the secretory coil.

The glands have very large amounts of succinic dehydrogenase (Fig. 19B) (Braun-Falco and Rathjens, 1954; Serri, 1955; Montagna and Formisano, 1955). The basal cells of the duct are homogeneously

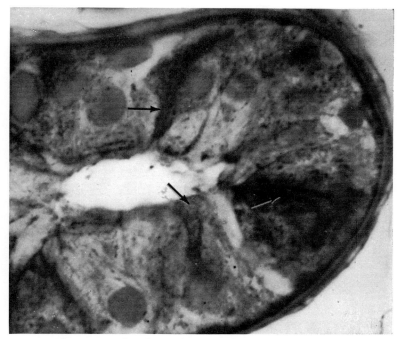

Fig. 18. Glycogen in the clear cells is piled up against the walls of the intercellular canaliculi (arrows). From the skin of the inguen.

strongly reactive, but the reaction in the luminal cells is proportional to the degree of differentiation of a cuticular border. Reactive granules are aggregated around the nucleus of the luminal cells and in a delicate band parallel to the surface of the lumen, and at about the level where the cytoplasm becomes cuticular (see glycogen) (Lobitz et al., 1955). The reaction in the secretory cells is occasionally uneven; the clear cells seem to have a stronger concentration of coarse and fine reactive granules than the dark cells do. Although the enzyme is said to reside only in the mitochondria (Schneider and Hogeboom, 1950), histochemical enzyme activity in the secretory cells is found in granules and also diffusely in the cytoplasm. The myoepithelial cells have practically no reaction. All eccrine glands on the body are strongly reactive, but those in the palms and soles and the axilla have more enzyme than those elsewhere. Entire glands can be seen in thick frozen sections prepared for succinic dehydrogenase activity; in the palms and soles the glands are different from those elsewhere in that the diameter of their secretory coil is

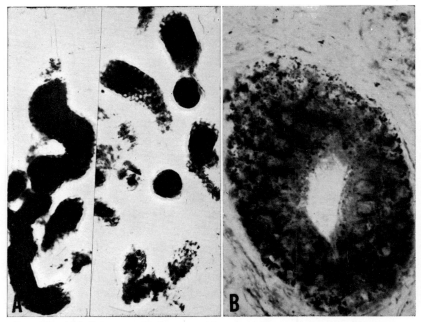

FIG. 19. (A) Intense cytochrome oxidase activity in the entire glomerate segment of a gland. (B) Succinic dehydrogenase activity in the coiled portion of the duct.

twice to three times that of the duct. In other regions the differences in diameter in the two portions of the glands are less pronounced. The eccrine sweat glands of all the animals we have studied, including those on the bill of the platypus, have as intense a reaction for succinic dehydrogenase activity as those of man.

Large amounts of carbonic anhydrase have been demonstrated in the eccrine glands of man (Braun-Falco and Rathjens, 1955). The reaction is strong in both the duct and in the secretory coil; in the secretory epithelium, there is a greater concentration of it in the clear cells than in the dark cells. Since eccrine sweat glands are rich in glycogen, and glycogen disappears during excessive secretion of sweat, the disappearance of glycogen in the secretory portion, on the one hand, and the presence of lactic and citric acids in the sweat, on the other, have suggested an aerobic glycolysis following the Krebs citric acid cycle (Braun-Falco and Rathjens, 1955). The strong concentration of carbonic anhydrase in the secretory cells could insure a rapid hydration of the CO_2 liberated; the enzyme could play an important role in the regulation of acidity, and in the composition of electrolytes in sweat. These hypotheses are based on the principle that glycogen always vanishes from the sweat glands during excessive sweating. However, Dobson (1961) now finds that after the initial period of stress, sweat glands become acclimatized and no longer lose glycogen when subjected to further stress. Also the technique which has been used for the demonstration of the enzyme is completely unreliable.

Other investigators have found only a moderate amount of monoamine oxidase in eccrine sweat glands (Hellmann, 1955; Shelley *et al.*, 1955). Using the method of Glenner *et al.* (1957), we now find the concentration and distribution of this enzyme in eccrine glands as strong as that of succinic dehydrogenase (Yasuda and Montagna, 1960). The cytoplasm of the cells of the duct is crowded with delicate reactive granules (Fig. 20). In the secretory cells the reactive cytoplasm contains large reactive granules. The secretory segment, then, is quite distinct from the duct. The myoepithelial cells are weakly reactive. The eccrine sweat glands of every animal we have studied, including those of the duck-billed platypus, have similar concentrations of monoamine oxidase.

The entire glandular unit of eccrine sweat glands contains more phosphorylase than any other cutaneous appendage (Braun-Falco, 1956a; Ellis and Montagna, 1958; Yasuda *et al.*, 1958). The coiled and the straight portions of the duct stain an intense blue-black (Fig. 21); at the place where the duct joins the epidermis, the duct attains the same intensity of reaction as the epidermis. In the palms and soles the coiled intraepidermal part of the duct is strongly reactive up to the level of the stratum granulosum, where it stops abruptly; the portions of coils within the stratum corneum have no enzyme activity. In the secretory coil, enzyme reaction is so strong that the details of its distribution are masked. Whereas fresh sections must be incubated for 10 to 25 minutes in the buffered substrate to show enzyme activity in the epidermis and the sebaceous glands, sweat glands show intense activity after an incubation of only $2\frac{1}{2}$ minutes. Since the end-point of this reaction is a blue-black color it is not possible to discriminate between the various intensities of reaction. The cytoplasm of both

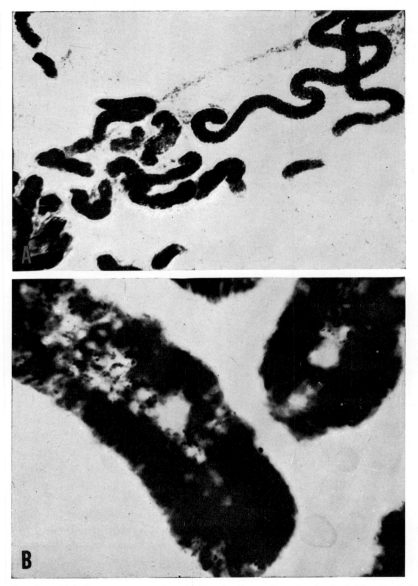

Fig. 20. (A) Strong monoamine oxidase in the entire gland. (B) Detail of the distribution of the enzyme in the secretory coil.

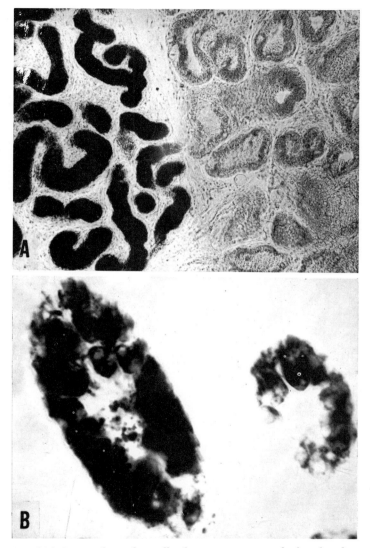

Fig. 21. (A) Section from the axilla showing strong amylophosphorylase activity in an eccrine gland, on the left, but none in the apocrine gland on the right. (B) Detail of the distribution of amylophosphorylase in the secretory epithelium.

the clear and dark cells is equally rich in phosphorylase, the reaction being particularly strong in the apical portion of the cells. Since the preparations fade after a few days, they become more useful for the study of intracellular localization. When fading, the clear cells

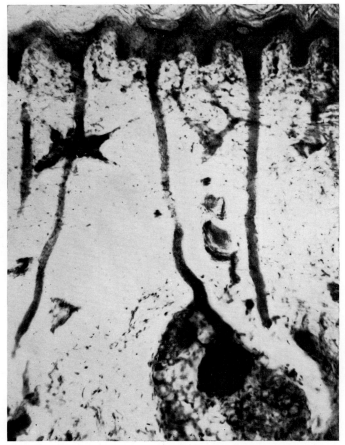

FIG. 22. Intense aminopeptidase activity in the sweat glands of the palm of a newborn infant.

retain the color longer than the dark cells; this may indicate that they have greater enzyme activity.

Human eccrine sweat glands abound in β-glucuronidase activity (Braun-Falco, 1956; Montagna, 1957). The duct and secretory coil of the glands in all mammals studied contain equal concentrations of enzymes. In contrast, the glands have only scant amounts of acid phosphatase. This is strange since both of these enzymes are supposed to be present in a masked form within the lysosomes.

Aminopeptidase activity is readily demonstrated in the secretory coil of the eccrine sweat glands of man. The reaction results in the formation of coarse granules along the entire length of the secretory segment (Fig. 22). Precise intracellular localization is not yet possible. The duct has less activity or may be unreactive (Fig. 23).

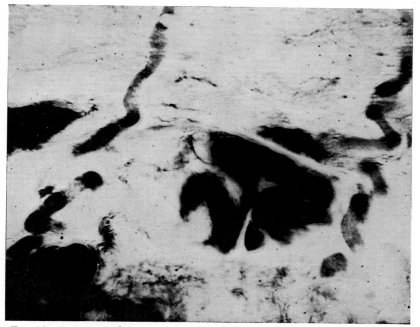

Fig. 23. Aminopeptidase activity in the coiled secretory segment, but not in the duct of a gland from the palm.

Reports on the distribution of alkaline phosphatase in eccrine glands are based on overincubated paraffin sections of tissues fixed in acetone; these are of little value. When frozen sections of tissues fixed not longer than 4 hours in unbuffered 4% neutral formaldehyde are used, the results are clear and repeatable, whether one uses the method of Gomori or one of the azo-dye coupling methods (see Gomori, 1952). Enzyme activity is found only in the deeper coils of the glomerate portion of the gland; the superficial coils, which consist of duct, lack phosphatase. Phosphatase reaction is slight in the myoepithelial cells; the cytoplasm

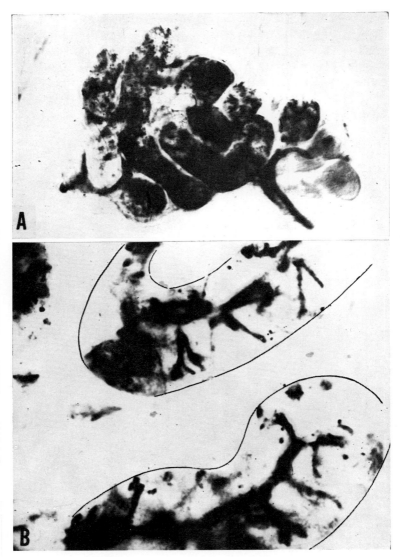

Fig. 24. (A) Alkaline phosphatase activity in the secretory segment of a sweat gland but not in a coiled part of the duct. (B) Detail of two secretory segments, outlined in ink, showing the concentration of alkaline phosphatase in the intercellular canaliculi.

of the clear cells has no reaction except for variable numbers of discrete granules. Between the clear cells are branching, anastomosing intercellular canaliculi, the walls of which are so intensely reactive that they appear much larger than they are (Fig. 24). Several canaliculi can be seen converging toward, and emptying into, a common excretory "pore" at the surface of the epithelium. The dark cells seem to have

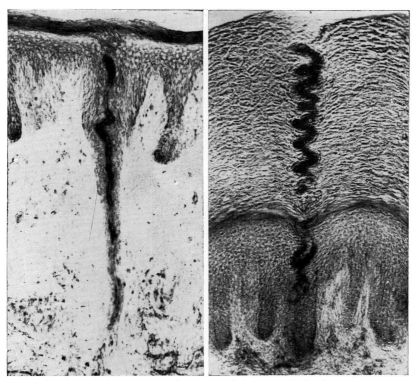

FIG. 25. AS esterase activity in the terminal segment of the duct from the axilla on the left, and in that of the palm on the right.

no enzyme activity, other than at the superficial border. Some enzyme reaction can occasionally be seen extracellularly, within the lumen. The cells of the straight part of the duct are very weakly or not at all reactive. The localization of alkaline phosphatase described is approximately similar in specimens of skin from all ages. In specimens from older subjects, however, the number of reactive granules in the clear cells is progressively greater.

The presence and distribution of alkaline phosphatase are variable in the eccrine glands of other animals. In the glands of the apes, the distribution of alkaline phosphatase is similar to that of man. The glands of the Lemuridae have intense alkaline phosphatase activity.

Eccrine glands have a moderate amount of esterase activity (Montagna and Ellis, 1958). Both the secretory cells and those of the duct show some reaction. There seems to be a slightly greater concentration of tween esterase in the dark than in the clear cells. After profuse sweating, the secretory coil has an apparent increase in tween esterase

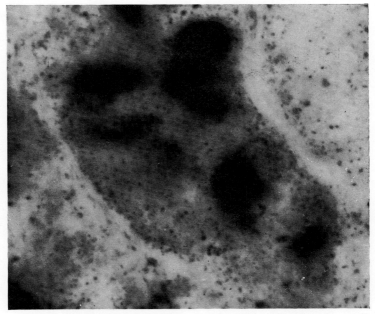

FIG. 26. Concentration of AS esterase in the dark cells; the clear cells show practically no reaction.

activity (Dobson and Lobitz, 1958; Dobson *et al.*, 1958). The distribution and concentration of α-naphthol esterase is similar to that of tween esterases. The cuticle of the duct is strongly reactive. The keratinized cells that line the terminal part of the duct within the epidermis are so strongly reactive for nonspecific esterase and AS esterase that they outline the path of the sweat duct clearly (Fig. 25) (Steigleder and Schultis, 1957; Montagna and Ellis, 1958). A moderate concentration of indoxyl acetate esterase can be seen throughout the gland in the form of coarse indigo blue granules. AS esterase is conspicuously concentrated in the dark cells, while the clear cells show only a slight reaction (Fig. 26). The cells of the duct are full of very fine granules, but the cuticle of the luminal cells is strongly reactive (Montagna and Ellis, 1958). There are minor variations in the concentration of all these esterases in different individuals and in the skin of different parts

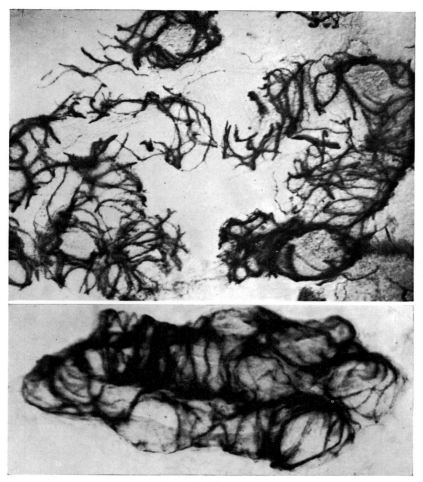

FIG. 27.   Two sections from the axilla showing cholinesterase-rich nerves around the secretory coils of eccrine glands.

of the body. The glands in the palms and soles are consistently more strongly reactive than those elsewhere. In other animals, esterases in eccrine glands are extremely variable.

The cells of eccrine glands of man contain no cholinesterases. Those of some other mammals, notably the platypus, the dog, and the marmosets, however, have moderate concentrations of nonspecific cholinesterase. The secretory coils of the eccrine glands of man are surrounded by nerves rich in specific cholinesterases (Hurley *et al.*, 1953; Hellmann,

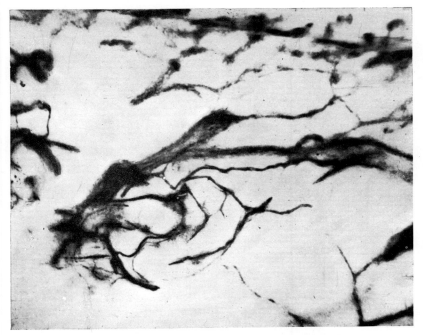

Fig. 28. Cholinesterase-rich nerves around the glands in the palm of a fetus 4½ months old.

1955; Beckett *et al.*, 1956; Thies and Galente, 1957; Montagna and Ellis, 1958). Delicate, strongly reactive nerve fibers are wound around the coils of the secretory segment (Fig. 27) (Montagna and Ellis, 1958). Some of the coils of the duct, but not the straight segments, are also surrounded by nerves that contain specific cholinesterases. In contrast with all other mammals we have studied, the straight duct of the glands on the surface of the bill of the platypus is also surrounded by cholinesterase-containing nerves. In man the relation of sweat glands with cholinesterase-rich nerves is established as soon as the glands are formed in 4½-month-old fetuses (Fig. 28) (Beckett *et al.*, 1956). The nerves around the sweat glands of man contain only specific cholinesterase, and this is typical of the nerves around most mammalian sweat glands. Species differences, however, do occur: the sweat glands in the digital pads of the dog, the cells of which contain nonspecific cholinesterase, have no such nerves around them, and there are wide differences among the primates we have studied. In some of them, the nerves contain specific cholinesterase; in other primates, notably those from South America, the nerves may contain both specific and nonspecific cholinesterases.

Relation of Structure to Function

The secretory epithelium of eccrine glands consists of *dark* and *clear* cells which are very different from one another. The dark cells contain ribonucleic acid and mucopolysaccharides, both of which are stainable with basic dyes; mucopolysaccharides usually stain metachromatically, and are PAS-positive and saliva-resistant (Formisano and Lobitz, 1957). The dark cells secrete these substances into the lumen, and variable amounts of it may be found anywhere in the duct, particularly in the coiled terminal portion within the epidermis. The clear cells may contribute very small amounts of these substances, or none at all. Both clear and dark cells contain glycogen, but only the clear cells abound in it. Thus, the two types of cells have a distinct dichotomy and they must have different functional significance.

Glycogen disappears from the cells after profuse sweating. When subjects are kept in a temperature of approximately 105°F, sweating reaches maximal profusion in 80 minutes, remains at this high level for 4 hours and then declines (Dobson *et al.*, 1958). Six hours after the initiation of sweating, the sweat glands contain no glycogen. Even the Schiff-positive, nonglycogen material normally found in the apical cytoplasm of the dark cells is mostly secreted and rests in the excretory duct, or over the free surface of the skin around the opening of the pores. If there is poral occlusion, this material is dammed in the last portion of the duct. Small vacuoles appear first at the base of both the secretory cells and in the cells of the duct about 1 hour after the initiation of sweating; the vacuoles become progressively larger until after 6 hours.

Profuse sweating causes marked changes in the nuclei of the secretory cells. Those of dark cells become larger and their nuclear membranes become very distinct; in contrast, the nuclei of the clear cells become progressively more pale. Twenty-four hours after this period of profuse sweating great quantities of glycogen reappear in the clear cells; none reappears at this time in the dark cells and in the cells of the duct. Nonglycogen PAS-positive material is also reaccumulated at the apices of the dark cells; this material, however, is in finer granules than in resting glands and it does not stain metachromatically. After 48 hours most glands have largely recovered, having abundant glycogen and PAS-positive diastase-resistant material that does not stain metachromatically; some glands are still damaged; with some exceptions, the glands are recovered from the damage of the profuse sweating after 72 hours. Thus, one finds an orderly progression in the development of injury with continued stimulation and a similar orderly but slow recovery sequence.

When the same subjects are again placed in the sweat chamber at 106°F, the following day the secretory cells remain smaller than normal, they are vacuolated and are distorted (Dobson and Lobitz, 1958; Dobson *et al.*, 1958). Neither the PAS-positive, nonglycogen material in the dark cells, nor glycogen is depleted. Adjacent clear cells, however, seem to coalesce and often contain two or three nuclei. When these subjects are placed in the sweat chamber for another 6-hour period on the third day, the clear cells become more atrophied; in some segments they even seem to disappear completely. The remaining clear cells often have as many as six nuclei, but they still contain glycogen, particularly piled up against the periphery of the vacuoles. The dark cells contain considerably less PAS-positive nonglycogen material. When the same subjects are placed in the sweat chamber for similar periods of time on the fourth and fifth days, the changes do not progress beyond those on the third day. Successive episodes of profuse sweating, then, produce the greatest changes in the clear cells, which show progressive vacuolization, distortion, coalescence of adjacent cells, becoming multinucleated, but the cells retain large amounts of glycogen.

Thus, several major cytological changes occur more or less simultaneously as a result of consecutive daily episodes of profuse sweating: degenerative changes, consisting of vacuolization, fusion of adjacent cells, and nuclear changes, and even total atrophy take place mostly in the clear cells. The general decrease in the severity of the damage caused by each subsequent episode of sweating in many of the glands shows an adaptive mechanism.

The stress of the first day results in the loss of glycogen; the clear cells, however, reacquire it and do not lose it again, despite additional periods of profuse sweating. Once the cells of the duct have regained their content of glycogen, they also no longer lose it, in spite of continued periods of sweating.

Despite degenerative and adaptive changes, there is some recovery from the effects of the first episode of sweating. Glycogen reappears in the cells of the secretory coil within 18 hours after the first episode of sweating; it reappears in the basal cells of the duct after 48 hours, and in the luminal cells after 72 hours. PAS-positive, nonglycogen material reaccumulates in the dark cells at about the same rate. Recovery from damage induced by a single episode of sweating seems to be an inherent property of the eccrine sweat gland and is independent of subsequent stress (Dobson, 1961).

These changes are probably related to the process of acclimatization, which seems to be controlled by a pituitary-adrenal cortical mechanism (Conn and Louis, 1950). Since both desoxycorticosterone acetate (DOCA) and adrenocorticotropic hormone (ACTH) depress the sodium chloride concentration of sweat, acclimatization could involve a response to chronic stress, such as repeated profuse sweating in a hot environment (Dobson, 1961). This stress could result in an increase in the production of salt-retaining corticosteroids, and lead to the reduction of salt in the sweat. Acclimatization, however, could be independent of adrenal activity, and the changes in functional activity could be the result of the cytologic alterations caused by repeated profuse sweating.

The secretory cells often contain delicate vacuoles in their cytoplasm, larger in the clear cells than in the dark cells. Although we have not succeeded in staining the content of these vacuoles, they occur so regularly, particularly after stress, that they must be associated with the process of secretion.

Cytoplasmic granules aggregate above the nucleus; this is more conspicuous in the dark cells where the granules are coarse and densely packed. The concept that the filamentous mitochondria break down and are transformed into cytoplasmic granules is not tenable (Ito and Iwashige, 1951; Iwashige, 1952). Mitochondria, in the form of rodlets and filaments, are found largely around the nucleus, aligned vertically toward the surface of the cells. Neither cytological methods nor the electron microscope have ascertained that the mitochondria decrease with the formation of granules, which, indeed, they would do if they transformed into granules. In fact, as in all other organs studied, the population of mitochondria remains fairly constant, regardless of its state of activity.

Until recently, the canaliculi visible between the secretory cells might have been considered artifacts. Secretory cells are friable, and fixation fluids could cause splits between them. However, even if they were artifacts, the cytoplasm should have a basic structural pattern which would allow the formation of such predictable structures. Intercellular canaliculi are demonstrated best in tissues which have been excellently preserved; they are seen in preparation for alkaline phosphatase; they have a definite structure with microvilli lining their walls, as seen with the electron microscope; they are found only between the clear cells and they must be an important part of the mechanism of sweat secretion. They open to the surface between clear cells, and the sweat from the clear cells is probably secreted through these structures. The basal part of each canaliculus is divided into a maze of tributaries which are continuous with, or attached to, the numerously plicated adjacent cell membranes.

If the secretion from the clear cells is by way of the canaliculi, one might ask what happens to the so-called secretory granules. Since there in no visible relationship between granules and canaliculi, and the granules are really secretion products, the granules must be secreted in a liquid form. There seems to be no relationship between the mitochondria and the canaliculi; their proximity may be accidental, but one cannot be sure of this. The only positive morphological clues to the functional dynamics of the canaliculi are the distribution of glycogen and alkaline phosphatase, and the presence of numerous microvilli lining their lumina. Glycogen is piled up against the walls of each canaliculus, and the walls are intensely alkaline phosphatase-positive; it is self-evident that these substances might aid the mediation of transfer of sweat from the cytoplasm.

The cytoplasm of the dark cells occasionally terminates in blebs, containing granules and vacuoles, which protrude into the lumen. Influenced by the thought that apocrine glands secrete by the breaking off of similar processes, the Japanese investigators have deduced that the separation of eccrine and apocrine glands in man in inappropriate, that they are all apocrine (cf. Kuno, 1956). This is neither good observation nor good reasoning; it is unlikely that cytoplasmic blebs pinch off into the lumen. Furthermore, they may be fixation artifacts.

Several bits of evidence suggest that the duct is an active part of eccrine glands, perhaps in the reabsorption of water (Lloyd, 1959). Urea secreted in the secretory segment becomes more concentrated in the duct (Nitta, 1953; Schwartz et al., 1953). The total length of the duct may be equal to or even greater than that of the secretory segment; if the duct had no function this would seem to be an unnecessary mechanism in such metabolically active organs. Histophysiological observations provide further presumptive evidence (Lobitz et al., 1955). Moderate sweating results in a depletion of the glycogen only from the luminal cells of the ducts, but in severe sweating it is depleted from all of the cells. This may not constitute proof of functional activity, but it nonetheless indicates that changes take place during functional stress. The presence of basophil granules in some of the cells of the duct, as well as an adundance of succinic dehydrogenase (Montagna and Formisano, 1955) and phosphorylase (Ellis and Montagna, 1958) in the entire duct leads one to conclude that this is not a passive structure as is generally assumed. The rich capillary plexus around the duct strongly supports the conclusion that the duct may function as a reabsorption mechanism (Lobitz and Mason, 1948). Thompson (1960) has made some observations on sweat glands buried in the skin for 4 years that are pertinent. Glands in autogenous dermis grafts survive and even though they do not open to the surface retain the histological and histochemical characteristics of normal glands. After injections of pilocarpine glycogen is depleted from the secretory cells, as in normal glands. This suggests to the author that secretion occurs and that the sweat may be reabsorbed largely by the remaining duct.

The electron microscopic studies do not add appreciably to our understanding of the function of the duct. The presence of microvilli and occasional smooth-surfaced vesicles on the luminal surface of the duct suggests that some pinocytotic activity may occur there. Since the cells have neither a Golgi complex nor an organized ergastoplasm, they are not primarily secretory cells. The numerous tonofilaments, continuous with the inner layer of the luminal plasmalemma could comprise a selective filter for the reabsorption of specific substances from the sweat in the lumen of the gland. But, the most likely function of the tonofilaments in the cuticular border is to form a rigid ring that prevents the collapse and occlusion of the lumen of the duct (Fig. 29). The extended attachment plaques probably serve as buttressing and insertion points that strengthen the border architecturally. The cuticular border can thus be considered as a hypertrophied terminal web furnishing a rigid lining for the lumen of the gland. Cross sections of the lumen of the coiled duct are always circular whereas those of the secretory coil, which have no cuticular border, are variable in shape. A concept of architectural support does not necessarily negate a physiological function (Palay and Karlin, 1959).

The luminal and peripheral cells of the coiled duct do not seem to be particularly modified for the reabsorption of water. The mitochondria and other cytoplasmic elements are not obviously oriented parallel to a supposed direction of flow. The basal membranes of the cells of the duct are remarkably regular and have no complex infoldings such as those found in epithelia which are known to transport water (Pease, 1956). The convoluted boundaries between adjacent cells might indicate that they have absorptive capacity, but they could also be responsible for the rigid interlocking of the duct cells or adaptations for flexibility to accommodate modest changes in cell volume (Palay and Karlin, 1959). The presence of glycogen in these cells also seems to be inconsistent with water transport, but until we know more about the morphological features of the cell that are specialized for the absorption and transport of water, it is impossible to exclude this function for the cells of the duct.

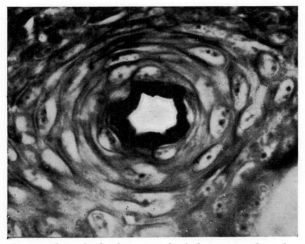

FIG. 29. Section through the lowest coil of the intraepidermal part of a sweat duct from the scalp, showing strongly —S—S— reactive cuticle.

During the first 2½ years of life, sweat glands secrete meagerly and irregularly, and the total number of active glands is small. After 2½ years of age all of those glands that will be active in the adult became functional, and the number remains relatively unchanged after this epoch (Kuno, 1956). If there is an average of about 2.3 millions active glands over the human body, they would have an approximate length of about 53 kilometers, a total surface of about 0.92 square meters, and a volume of about 34 cc (Kuno, 1956).

The ability of an individual to sweat is dependent on factors other

FIG. 30. Sparse sweating in the right axilla of a subject in a heat chamber. Compare with Fig. 31. (Courtesy of the Colgate-Palmolive Biological Research Laboratory.)

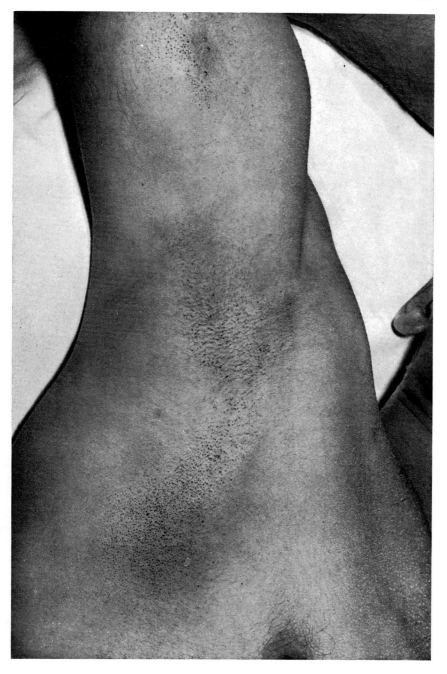

than the density of population of sweat glands (Figs. 30 and 31). There is considerable variation in the amount of sweat that different sweat glands discharge, and many glands do not secrete at all. Six out of nine glands on the tips of the fingers, for example, are inactive; there are sweat glands, then, which although morphologically indistinguishable from active ones, cannot be activated (Ogata and Ichihashi, 1935). For this reason eccrine glands are *active* or *inactive*, the total ratio being in the vicinity of 16 to 14, respectively, although there are regional and individual differences (Kuno, 1956). Inactive sweat glands do not respond to any kind of stimulation.

The maximum amount of sweating evoked by heat and pilocarpine are identical (Ogata and Ichihashi, 1935), although individual glands have different levels of responsiveness. In response to heat, the body sweats profusely first on the forehead, the neck, the larger areas of the ventral and dorsal parts of the trunk, lumbar region, and the back of the hands (Kuno, 1956). The sides of the chest and the extremities sweat less, and the inner surface of the thighs and the axilla sweat even less. Actually, there are so many individual differences that these sequences have little meaning. The axillary glands, for example, respond readily to thermal stimuli in some individuals, and practically not at all in others. The palms and soles respond very weakly to thermal stimuli. When the surrounding temperature is raised, sweating appears after a long latent period, which varies according to the intensity of the heat. Even when the temperature is very high the rate of sweat increases gradually. Thus, external factors alone are not sufficient to cause sweating, and intrinsic changes in the body may also be necessary. In the summer, when the required bodily changes are already present, exposures to heat cause immediate sweating (Kuno, 1956).

Emotional stress, and sensory stimulation, which have little bearing on body temperatures, also incite sweating. Under emotional stress, sweating appears at once in the palms and soles, and in the axilla without a latent period. The secretion corresponds to the intensity of the stimulation, and subsides immediately after the stimulation ceases. In some individuals, if the stimulus is strong enough, psychic sweating also occurs on the forehead. Gustatory stimulation, such as that caused by some spices may induce variable amounts of sweating on the face.

Fig. 31. Profuse sweating in the left axilla of the same subject in Fig. 30. Evidently, the same thermal stimulus that causes profuse sweating in the left axilla was ineffective in the right axilla. (Courtesy of the Colgate-Palmolive Biological Research Laboratory.)

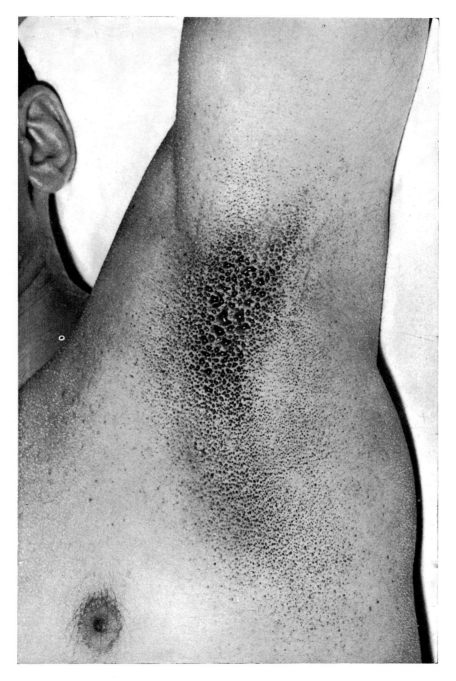

Sweating caused by muscular exercise seems to result from a combination of thermal and psychic stimulation (Kuno, 1956).

According to their responses, then, there are three general categories of sweat glands: the glands in the palms and soles, which respond well only to psychic stimuli; those of the axillae and forehead, which respond to both thermal and psychic stimuli, and those on the rest of the body, which respond almost entirely to thermal stimuli. These differences must be brought about by the central nervous system.

Since ordinary sweating in man appears all over the body, there is probably no restricted spinal reflex; if there are sweat centers in the spinal cord, they must be inactive under normal conditions. Spinal sweat centers become active when the cord is isolated from cerebral control. Probably only those individuals who have hyperhydrosis of the face have a bulbar sweat center. Since the centers that control body temperature reside in the hypothalamus, the principal centers for the regulation of sweat are probably also located in the hypothalamus, near the temperature centers; their precise locations are not known. The center that controls sweating in the palms and soles is located in the premotor area of the cortex. The cortex may also have a center that inhibits sweating.

After injections of epinephrine or acetylcholine, or after thermal stimulation, some individual glands can be stimulated on one occasion but not on another (Mellinkoff and Sonnenschein, 1954), and the period of refractivity may persist even after the reapplication of the same stimulus. Since epinephrine, acetylcholine, and heat bring about similar patterns of response, each stimulus probably controls the same glands. Even though it is widely agreed that eccrine glands are innervated largely, if not entirely, by cholinergic fibers (mostly postganglionic fibers arising from the paravertebral ganglia), they may have a double innervation (Kuno, 1956).

Summary of the Responses of Eccrine Sweat Glands to Pharmacological Stimuli

Dale and Feldberg in 1934 first demonstrated that eccrine sweat glands are supplied with nerves that, although belonging anatomically to the sympathetic nervous system, are cholinergic. Human eccrine sweat glands are very sensitive to acetylcholine, and spontaneous sweating, whether thermal or emotional, is strongly and selectively inhibited by atropine. The minimum effective concentration of acetylcholine required to produce definite local sweating when injected intradermally in human skin is as low as 10^{-12} (Wada and Takagaki, 1948).

There are many natural and synthetic cholinergic substances. The well-known alkaloid, pilocarpine, is a potent sudorific substance. Among many other synthetic cholinergic compounds, acetyl-β-methylcholine (Mecholyl) and carbamylcholine (carbachol) have powerful eccrine sudorific effects (Brun and Favre, 1954; Kernen and Brun, 1953; Randall and Kimura, 1955). The responses of the sweat glands to these substances are strongly suppressed by atropine and by other anticholinergic agents.

The sudorific effect of acetylcholine is enhanced and prolonged by physostigmine (eserine), a strong inhibitor of cholinesterase, but physostigmine itself, when injected intradermally, causes a local sweating. It is not known, however, whether the sudorific action of this substance is due to its direct stimulation of the sweat gland, or simply to its potentiating the action of acetylcholine, which might exist in the skin in subthreshold amounts (Randall and Kimura, 1955).

Intradermal injections of adrenergic compounds such as adrenaline, noradrenaline, or isopropylnoradrenaline also produce local eccrine sweat responses (Barnett, 1951; Chalmers and Keele, 1951; Haimovici, 1948, 1950; Kisen, 1948; Sonnenschein, 1949; Sonnenschein et al., 1949, 1951; Wada, 1950; Wada and Takagaki, 1948), but this response is not as pronounced as the responses to cholinergic agents. The eccrine sweat glands in the footpad of the cat also respond to adrenaline (Nakamura and Hatanaka, 1958). Unlike the response to cholinergic stimulation, the response to adrenaline is not inhibited by atropine, but is selectively annulled by such antiadrenergic agents as Dibenamine, Priscol, dihydroergotamine, or tolazoline (Chalmers and Keele, 1951; Haimovici, 1950; Sonnenschein, 1949; Sonnenschein et al., 1951). A single intradermal injection of adrenaline in concentrations of 10^{-3} to 10^{-4} causes eccrine sweating which continues for several hours (Wada, 1950); the phenomenon cannot be explained as the result of contraction of the myoepithelial cells, which would cause only an expulsion of sweat already formed and pooled in the sweat gland tubule. Thus, sweating induced by these high doses of adrenaline and allied substances is probably due to an activation of the secretory cells of the eccrine sweat glands.

These facts suggest the possibility that the eccrine sweat glands are innervated by both cholinergic and adrenergic sudorific nerve fibers (Haimovici, 1948, 1950). Convincing evidence for adrenergic innervation, however, is lacking (Chalmers and Keele, 1951, 1952; Patton, 1949; Sonnenschein et al., 1951), and the physiological significance of adrenergic eccrine sweating awaits further investigation. Systemic administrations of adrenaline, unlike such cholinergic agents as pilocarpine, Mecholyl and carbachol, do not usually evoke eccrine sweating (Chalmers and Keele, 1951; Haimovici, 1950).

Histamine has no sudorific action on the eccrine sweat glands (Manuila, 1952). There are sexual differences in the sensitiveness of human eccrine glands to pharmacological stimulations. Women have a definite lower responsiveness to acetylcholine, pilocarpine, or Mecholyl than men do (Gibson and Shelley, 1948; Janowitz and Grossman, 1950; Kahn and Rothman, 1942). Chalmers and Keele (1952), however, failed to find any significant difference between the sexes in their sensitiveness to acetylcholine.

The sensitivity of human eccrine sweat glands to adrenaline varies considerably with age (Wada, 1950). The minimum effective concentration of adrenaline for eliciting local sweating responses by intradermal injection is 10^{-7} in most subjects 14 to 24 years of age, while in young subjects 1 to 12 years old, and in old ones 60 to 70 years, the sensitivity of eccrine sweat glands to adrenaline is much lower, rarely showing a threshold concentration lower than 10^{-4}. On the other hand, the sweat glands of new born infants show a sensitivity to adrenaline almost as high as that in young adults. Similar observations have been made on the responsiveness of the apocrine sweat glands in the hairy skin of the dog. The apocrine sweat glands of week-old puppies are highly sensitive to both adrenaline and acetylcholine; the sensitivity gradually decreases reaching the lowest level after a few months. It increases again and attains high normal levels in puberal animals about one year of age. The mechanism involved in such variations in the sensitivity of the glands is not clear, but humoral or hormonal influences might be presumed in controlling and maintaining the sensitivity of the sweat glands (Wada, 1950).

Severance of the postganglionic sympathetic nerves to the eccrine sweat glands of man causes a prompt and remarkable decrease in their responsiveness to direct pharmacological stimulations (Chalmers and Keele, 1952; Janowitz and Grossman, 1950, 1951; Kahn and Rothman, 1942; Randall and Kimura, 1955). Kahn and Rothman (1942) found a decrease in sweat response to intradermal injection of acetylcholine a few hours after denervation, but the response was completely abolished after a few days. This is contradictory to the general concept of Cannon's (1939) law of denervation. Such hyposensitive sweat glands appear to have no morphological changes (Gurney and Bunnell, 1942; Löfgren, 1950). In contrast, Nakamura and Hatanaka (1958) have shown that the eccrine sweat glands in the footpads of the cat become hypersensitive to the actions of adrenaline, nicotine, and Mecholyl after denervation, this being compatible with Cannon's law of denervation. So far, no explanation is available for this discrepancy. If both of these findings are true, some differences in the mode of cholinergic innervation might be expected between the eccrine sweat glands of man and those of the cat. The nerves around the eccrine sweat glands in the footpads of the cat contain pseudocholinesterase (Hellmann, 1952, 1955), whereas those around human glands contain true cholinesterase (Montagna and Ellis, 1958; Hurley et al., 1953).

An axon reflex response can be induced in the skin of man and in the cat's paw either by faradic or by pharmacological stimulations. The local sweat response elicited by faradic stimulation to the skin is due to an axon reflex mechanism (Bickford, 1938; Wilkins et al., 1938; Hanawoka, 1958). At least in the footpads of the cat, axon reflex sweating depends upon the integrity of the peripheral sympathetic sudomotor fibers, as shown by Wada et al. (1955). Coon and Rothman reported that intradermal injections of nicotine or other substances with nicotine-like action such as acetylcholine and lobeline produces a similar local sweat response in man (Coon and Rothman, 1939, 1941; Rothman and Coon, 1940). The following agents are also effective in producing axon reflex sweating: Carbamylcholine (Wada, 1960), tetramethylammonium (Bernstein and Sonnenschein, 1958; Wada et al., 1958b), hordenine methiodide (Tashiro, 1960), high concentrations of sodium chloride (Wada et al., 1952) and certain other sodium and potassium salts (Wada, 1960), as well as sodium cyanide (Wada et al., 1958a). At least in the footpads of the cat, the axon reflex sweating was conclusively proved to depend upon the integrity of the peripheral sympathetic sudomotor fibers (Wada et al., 1955).

The physiological importance of the axon reflex sweating is still far from clear. It seems significant that acetylcholine, a chemical mediator liberated at the terminals of cholinergic sudomotor nerves, has the property of causing sweat gland activity by direct muscarinic action of the sweat glands, and by nicotinic axon reflex on the sudorific nerve fibers. Wada et al. (1952) suggest that the axon reflex mechanism may subserve a peripheral control in physiological sweating under certain conditions.

REFERENCES

Barnett, A. J. 1951. Sweating in man from the intradermal injection of nor-adrenaline. Nature 167: 482-483.
Beckett, E. B., G. H. Bourne and W. Montagna. 1956. Histology and cytochemistry of human skin. The distribution of cholinesterase in the finger of the embryo and the adult. J. Physiol. (London) 134: 202-206.

Bernstein, M. and R. R. Sonnenschein. 1958. Local potentiation by tetrathylammonium ion of central tonic impulses to human sweat glands and piloerector muscles. *J. Appl. Physiol.* **12**: 408-412.

Bickford, R. G. 1938. The mechanism of local sweating in response to faradism. *Clin. Sci.* **3**: 337-341.

Borsetto, P. L. 1951. Osservazioni sullo sviluppo delle ghiandole sudoripare nelle diverse regioni della cute umana. *Arch. ital. anat. e embriol.* **56**: 332-348.

Braun-Falco, O. 1956a. Über die Fähigkeit der menschlichen Haut zur Polysaccharidsynthese, ein Beitrag zur Histotopochemie der Phosphorylase. *Arch. klin. u. exptl. Dermatol.* **202**: 163-170.

Braun-Falco, O. 1956b. Zur histotopographie der β-Glucuronidase in normaler menschlicher Haut. *Arch. klin. u. exptl. Dermatol.* **203**: 61-67.

Braun-Falco, O. and B. Rathjens. 1954. Histochemische Darstellung der Bernsteinsäuredehydrogenase in der menschlichen Haut. Dermatol. *Wochschr.* **130**: 1271-1276.

Braun-Falco, O. and B. Rathjens. 1955. Über die histochemische Darstellung der Kohlensäureanhydratase in normaler Haut. *Arch. klin. u. exptl. Dermatol.* **201**: 73-82.

Brody, I. 1959. An ultrastructure study on the role of the keratohyalin granules in the keratinization process. *J. Ultrastruct. Research* **3**: 84-104.

Brun, R. and F. Favre. 1954. Experiences sur la transpiration. 7. Examens semi-quantitatifs de la sudation provoquee par certaines substances: suivi d'une analyse statistique par A. Linder. *Dermatologica* **108**: 257-270.

Bunting, H., G. B. Wislocki and E. W. Dempsey. 1948. The chemical histology of human eccrine and apocrine sweat glands. *Anat. Record* **100**: 61-77.

Cannon, W. B. 1939. A law of denervation. *Am. J. Med. Sci.* **198**: 737-750.

Chalmers, T. M. and C. A. Keele. 1951. Physiological significance of the sweat response to adrenaline in man. *J. Physiol. (London)* **114**: 510-514.

Chalmers, T. M. and C. A. Keele. 1952. The nervous and chemical control of sweating. *Brit. J. Dermatol.* **64**: 43-54.

Conn, J. W. and L. H. Louis. 1950. Production of endogenous "salt-active" corticoids as reflected in concentrations of sodium and chloride of thermal sweat. *J. Clin. Endocrinol.* **10**: 12-23.

Coon, J. M. and S. Rothman. 1939. Nature of the sweat response to drugs with nicotine-like action. *Proc. Soc. Exptl. Biol. Med.* **42**: 231-233.

Coon, J. M. and S. Rothman. 1941. The sweat response to drugs with nicotine-like action. *J. Pharmacol. Exptl. Therap.* **73**: 1-11.

Dale, H. H. and W. Feldberg. 1934. The chemical transmission of secretory impulses to the sweat glands of the cat. *J. Physiol. (London)* **82**: 121-128.

Dobson, R. L. 1961. The effect of repeated episodes of profuse sweating on the human eccrine sweat glands. *J. Invest. Dermatol.* (In press.)

Dobson, R. L. and W. C. Lobitz, Jr. 1958. Some histochemical observations on the human eccrine sweat glands. IV. The recovery from the effects of profuse sweating. *J. Invest. Dermatol.* **31**: 207-213.

Dobson, R. L., V. Formisano, W. C. Lobitz, Jr., and D. Brophy. 1958. Some histochemical observations on the human eccrine sweat glands. III. The effect of profuse sweating. *J. Invest. Dermatol.* **31**: 147-159.

Eichner, F. 1954. Zur Frage der Motivbildung in der menschlichen Haut. *Anat. Anz.* **100**: 303-310.

Ellis, R. A. and W. Montagna. 1958. Histology and cytochemistry of human skin. XV. Sites of phosphorylase and amylo-1,6-glucosidase activity. *J. Histochem. and Cytochem.* **6**: 201-207.

Ellis, R. A. and W. Montagna. 1961. Electron microscopy of the duct, and especially the cuticular border of the eccrine sweat glands in *Macaca mulatta. J. Biophys. Biochem. Cytol.* **9**: 238-242.

Ellis, R. A., W. Montagna and H. Fanger. 1958. Histology and cytochemistry of human skin. XIV. The blood supply of the cutaneous glands. *J. Invest. Dermatol.* **30**: 137-145.

Formisano, V. and W. C. Lobitz, Jr. 1957. "The Schiff-positive, nonglycogen material" in the human eccrine sweat glands. I. Histochemistry. *A.M.A. Arch. Dermatol.* **75**: 202-209.

Gibson, T. E. and W. B. Shelley. 1948. Sexual and racial differences in the response of sweat glands to acetylcholine and pilocarpine. *J. Invest. Dermatol.* **11**: 137-142.

Glenner, G. G., H. J. Burtner and G. W. Brown, Jr. 1957. The histochemical demonstration of monoamine oxidase activity by tetrazolium salts. *J. Histochem. and Cytochem.* **5**: 591-600.

Gomori, G. 1952. "Microscopic Histochemistry. Principles and Practice." University of Chicago Press, Chicago, Illinois.

Gurney, R. and I. L. Bunnell. 1942. The study of the reflex mechanism of sweating in the human being: effect of anesthesia and sympathectomy. *J. Clin. Invest.* **21**: 269-274.

Haimovici, H. 1948. Evidence for an adrenergic component in the nervous mechanism of sweating in man. *Proc. Soc. Exptl. Biol. Med.* **68**, 40-41.

Haimovici, H. 1950. Evidence for adrenergic sweating in man. *J. Appl. Physiol.* **2**: 512-521.

Hambrick, G. W., Jr. and H. Blank. 1954. Whole mounts for the study of skin and its appendages. *J. Invest. Dermatol.* **23**: 437-453.

Hanawoka, N. 1958. Sweating axon reflex produced by faradic stimulation and the site of its initiation. *Japan. J. Physiol.* **8**: 114-122.

Hellmann, K. 1952. The cholinesterase of cholinergic sweat glands. *Nature* **169**: 113-114.

Hellmann, K. 1955. Cholinesterase and amine oxidase in the skin: A histochemical investigation. *J. Physiol. (London)* **129**: 454:463.

Holyoke, J. B. and W. C. Lobitz, Jr. 1952. Histologic variations in the structure of humane eccrine sweat glands. *J. Invest. Dermatol.* **18**: 147-167.

Horstmann, E. 1952. Über den Papillarkörper der menschlichen Haut und seine regionalen Unterschiede. *Acta Anat.* **14**: 23-42.

Hurley, H. J., Jr., W. B. Shelley and G. B. Koelle. 1953. The distribution of cholinesterases in human skin, with special reference to eccrine and apocrine sweat glands. *J. Invest. Dermatol.* **21**: 139-147.

Ito, T. 1943. Über den Golgiapparat der ekkrinen Schweissdrüsenzellen der menschlichen Haut. *Okajimas Folia Anat. Japon.* **22**: 273-280.

Ito, T. and K. Iwashige. 1951. Zytologische Untersuchung über die ekkrinen Schweissdrüsen in menschlicher Achselhaut mit besonderer Berücksichtigung der apokrinen Sekretion derselben. *Okajimas Folia Anat. Japon.* **23**: 147-165.

Ito, T., K. Tsuchiya and K. Iwashige. 1951. Studien über die basophile Substanz (Ribonukleinsäure) in den Zellen der menschlichen Schweissdrüsen (in Japanese). *Arch. Histol. japon.* **2**: 279-287.

Iwashige, K. 1952. Zytologische und histologische Untersuchungen über die ekkrinen Schweissdrüsen der Achselhaut von gesunden Menschen höheren Alters (in Japanese). *Arch. Histol. japon.* **4**: 75-90.

Janowitz, H. D. and M. I. Grossman. 1950. The response of the sweat glands to some locally acting agents in human subjects. *J. Invest. Dermatol.* **14**: 453-458.

Janowitz, H. D. and M. I. Grossman. 1951. An exception to Cannon's law. *Experientia* **7**: 275.

Kahn, D. and S. Rothman. 1942. Sweat response to acetylcholine. *J. Invest. Dermatol.* **5**: 431-444.

Kano, K. 1951. Zytologische und histologische Untersuchungen über die Schweissdrüsen in Greisenaltern. Beobachtungen der ekkrinen Schweissdrüsen bei den an Krankheit gestorbenen Fällen (in Japanese). *Arch. histol. japon.* **3**: 91-105.

Karrer, H. E. 1960. Cell interconnections in normal human cervical epithelium. *J. Biophys. Biochem. Cytol.* **7**: 181-184.

Kernen, R. and R. Brun. 1953. Experiences sur la transpiration. 5. Examens pharmacodynamiques au niveau de la glande sudoripare de l'homme. *Dermatologica* **106**: 1-13.

Kisen, E. E. 1948. A method of pharmacological study of the sweating function of the skin *in situ. Vestnik Venerol. i Dermatol.* **No. 5**: 27-31. (Cited from *Chem. Abstr* **43**: 2323, 1949.)

Kuno, Y. 1956. "Human Perspiration." C. C Thomas, Springfield, Illinois.

Kurosumi, K., T. Iijima and T. Kitamura. 1960. Electron microscopy of the human eccrine sweat gland with special reference to the folding of plasma membrane. Fourth Intern. *Kongr. Electronenmikroskopie 4. Kongr., Berlin, 1958* **2**: 361-365.

Lee, M. M. C. 1960. Histology and histochemistry of human eccrine sweat glands, with special reference to their defense mechanisms. *Anat. Record* **136**: 97-105.

Lloyd, D. P. C. 1959. Average behavior of sweat glands as indicated by impedance changes. *Proc. Natl. Acad. Sci. U.S.* **45**: 410-413.

Lobitz, W. C., Jr. and H. L. Mason. 1948. Chemistry of palmar sweat. VII. Discussion of studies on chloride, urea, glucose, uric acid, ammonia nitrogen, and creatinine. *Arch. Dermatol. and Syphilol.* **57**: 907-915.

Lobitz, W. C., Jr., J. B. Holyoke and W. Montagna. 1954a. The epidermal eccrine sweat duct unit. A morphologic and biologic entity. *J. Invest. Dermatol.* **22**: 157-158.

Lobitz, W. C., Jr., J. B. Holyoke and W. Montagna. 1954b. Responses of the human eccrine sweat duct to controlled injury. Growth center of the "epidermal sweat duct unit." *J. Invest. Dermatol.* **23**: 329-344.

Lobitz, W. C., Jr., J. B. Holyoke and D. Brophy. 1955. Histochemical evidence for human eccrine sweat duct activity. *A.M.A. Arch. Dermatol.* **72**: 229-236.

Loewenthal, L. J. A. 1960. The human eccrine sweat gland ampulla. *J. Invest. Dermatol.* **34**: 233-235.

Loewenthal, L. J. A. 1961. The eccrine ampulla: morphology and function. *J. Invest. Dermatol.* **36**: 171-182.

Löfgren, L. 1950. Reappearance of sweat secretion in denervated areas after sympathectomy: A sign of regeneration of the sympathetic system. *Ann. Chir. et Gynaecol. Fenniae* **39**: 105-125.

Manuila, L. 1952. Effet of pharmacodynamique de quelques substances sur la glande sudoripare. *Schweiz. med. Wochschr.* **82**: 104-106.

Mellinkoff, S. M. and R. R. Sonnenschein. 1954. Identity of sweat glands stimulated by heat, epinephrine, and acetylcholine. *Science* **120**: 997-998.

Montagna, W. 1955. Histology and cytochemistry of human skin. VIII. Mitochondria in the sebaceous glands. *J. Invest. Dermatol.* **25**: 117-121.

Montagna, W. 1957. Histology and cytochemistry of human skin. XI. The distribution of β-glucuronidase. *J. Biophys. Biochem. Cytol.* **3**, 343-348.

Montagna, W. and R. A. Ellis. 1958. L'histologie et la cytologie de la peau humaine. XVI. Repartition et concentration des esterases carboxyliques. *Ann. histochim.* **3**: 1-17.

Montagna, W. and V. R. Formisano. 1955. Histology and cytochemistry of human skin. VII. The distribution of succinic dehydrogenase activity. *Anat. Record* **122**: 65-77.

Montagna, W. and J. B. Hamilton. 1952. Histological studies of human testes. II. The distribution of glycogen and other H10$_4$-Schiff reactive substances. *Anat. Record* **112**: 237-249.

Montagna, W., H. B. Chase and W. C. Lobitz, Jr. 1952. Histology and cytochemistry of human skin. II. The distribution of glycogen in the epidermis, hair follicles, sebaceous glands, and eccrine sweat glands. *Anat. Record* **114**: 231-248.

Montagna, W., H. B. Chase and W. C. Lobitz, Jr. 1953. Histology and cytochemistry of human skin. IV. The eccrine sweat glands. *J. Invest. Dermatol.* **20**: 415-423.

Nakamura, Y. and K. Hatanaka. 1958. Effect of denervation of the cat's sweat glands on their responsiveness to adrenaline, nicotine, and mecholyl. *Tôhoku J. Exptl. Med.* **68**: 225-237.

Nitta, H. 1953. On the possibility of a resorption in the excretory duct of the sweat gland. Experiments on the changes in sweat constituents resulting from the application of collodion membrane on the skin. *Nagoya Med. J.* **1**: 59.

Odland, G. F. 1958. The fine structure of the interrelationship of cells in the human epidermis. *J. Biophys. Biochem. Cytol.* **4**: 529-539.

Ogata, K. and T. Ichihashi. 1935. Sweat reflexes due to changes in the posture of the human body. (In Japanese.) *J. Orient. Med.* **23**: 95-97.

Palay, S. L. (ed.). 1957. "Frontiers in Cytology." Yale Univ. Press, New Haven, Connecticut.

Palay, S. L. and L. J. Karlin. 1959. An electron microscopic study of the intestinal villus. I. The fasting animal. *J. Biophys. Biochem. Cytol.* **5**: 363-372.

Patton, H. D. 1949. Effect of autonomic blocking agents on sweat secretion in cat. *Proc. Soc. Exptl. Biol. Med.* **70**: 412-414.

Pease, D. C. 1956. Infolded basal plasma membranes found in epithelia noted for their water transport. *J. Biophys. Biochem. Cytol.* **2**: 203-208.

Pinkus, H. 1939. Notes on the anatomy and pathology of the skin appendages. I. The wall of the intra-epidermal part of the sweat duct. *J. Invest. Dermatol.* **2**: 175-186.

Randall, W. C. and K. K. Kimura. 1955. Pharmacology of sweating. *Pharmacol. Revs.* **7**: 365-397.

Rose, A. M. 1948. "The Negro in America." Harper, New York.

Rothman, S. and J. M. Coon. 1940. Axon reflex responses to acetylcholine in the skin. *J. Invest. Dermatol.* **3**: 79-97.

Schiefferdecker, P. 1922. Die Hautdrüsen des Menschen und des Säugetieres, ihre Bedeutung sowie die Muscularis sexualis. *Zoologica* **72**: 1-154.

Schneider, W. C. and G. H. Hogeboom. 1950. Intracellular distribution of enzymes. VI. The distribution of succinoxidase and cytochrome oxidase activities in normal mouse liver and in mouse hepatoma. *J. Natl. Cancer Inst.* **10**: 969-975.

Schwartz, I. L., J. H. Thaysen and V. P. Doyle. 1953. Urea excretion in human sweat as a tracer for movement of water within the secreting gland. *J. Exptl. Med.* **97**: 429-437.

Serri, F. 1955. Note de enzimologia cutanea. II. Ricerche bio ed istochimiche sull'attivita succinodeidrasica della cute umana normale. *Bol. soc. med.-chir. Pavia* **69**: 3-19.

Shelley, W. B. and H. Mescon. 1952. Histochemical demonstration of secretory activity in human eccrine sweat glands. *J. Invest. Dermatol.* **18**: 289-301.

Shelley, W. B., S. B. Cohen and G. B. Koelle. 1955. Histochemical demonstration of monoamine oxidase in human skin. *J. Invest. Dermatol.* **24**: 561-565.

Sonnenschein, R. R. 1949. Local sweating in man induced by intradermal epinephrine. *Proc. Soc. Exptl. Biol. Med.* **71**: 654-656.

Sonnenschein, R. R., H. Kobrin and M. I. Grossman. 1949. Further observations on local action of epinephrine on human sweat glands. *Am. J. Physiol.* **159**: 591-592.

Sonnenschein, R. R., H. Kobrin, H. D. Janowitz and M. I. Grossman. 1951. Stimulation and inhibition of human sweat glands by intradermal sympathomimetic agents. *J. Appl. Physiol.* **3**: 573-581.

Steigleder, G. K. and K. Schultis. 1957. Zur Histochemie der Esterasen der Haut. *Arch. klin. u. exptl. Dermatol.* **205**: 196-211.

Szabó, G. 1958. The regional frequency and distribution of hair follicles in human skin. *In* "The Biology of Hair Growth" (W. Montagna and R. A. Ellis, eds.), pp. 33-38. Academic Press, New York.

Takagi, S. 1952. A study on the structure of the sudoriferous duct transversing the epidermis in man with fresh material by phase contrast microscopy. *Japan. J. Physiol.* **3**: 65-72.

Tashiro, G. 1960. Effects of hordenine sulfate and methiodide on the receptors for the sweating axon reflex and on the sweat glands in the human skin. *Arch. intern. pharmacodynamie* **129**: 131.

Thies, W. and L. F. Galente. 1957. Zur histochemischen Darstellung der Cholinesterasen im vegetativen Nervensystem der Haut. *Hautarzt* **8**: 69-75.

Thompson, N. 1960. Tubular resorption of secretion in human eccrine sweat glands. Based on a histochemical study of buried autogenous dermis grafts in man. *Clin. Sci.* **19**: 95-107.

Thomson, M. L. 1954. A comparison between the number and distribution of functioning eccrine sweat glands in Europeans and Africans. *J. Physiol.* (*London*) **123**: 225-233.

Tsuchiya, K. 1954. Über die ekkrine Schweissdrüse des menschlichen Embryo, mit besonderer Berücksichtigung ihrer Histo- und Cytogenese. (In Japanese.) *Arch. histol. japon.* **6**: 403-432.

Tsukagoshi, N. 1951. Zur zytologie der ekkrinen Schweissdrüsen der Tiere mit besonderer Berücksichtigung des Vorkommens der zwei Arten Drüsenzellen und ihrer apokrinen Sekretion. *Arch. histol. japon.* **2**: 481-497.

Tsukagoshi, N. 1953. Zur zytologie der ekkrinen Schweissdrüse der Tiere. Über die e-Schweissdrüsen der Handtellerhaut der Affen. *Arch. histol. japon.* **4**: 381-396.

Tsukagoshi, N. 1955. Zur Zytologie der ekkrinen Schweissdrüse der Tiere. Über die e-Schweissdrüsen in den Sohlenballen der Ratte. *Arch. histol. japon.* **9**: 313-342.

Wada, M. 1950. Sudorific action of adrenalin on the human sweat glands and determination of their excitability. *Science* **111**: 376-377.

Wada, M. 1960. Local sweating produced by axon reflex mechanism. "Essential Problems in Climatic Physiology," pp. 185-195. Nankodo, Tokyo.

Wada, M. and T. Takagaki. 1948. A simple and accurate method for detecting the secretion of sweat. *Tôhoku J. Exptl. Med.* **49**: 284.

Wada, M., T. Arai, T. Takagaki and T. Nakagawa. 1952. Axon reflex mechanism in sweat responses to nicotine, acetylcholine, and sodium chloride. *J. Appl. Physiol.* **4**: 745-752.

Wada, M., Y. Nakamura, K. Hatanaka and T. Aoki. 1955. On the axon reflex sweating in the toe-pads of the cat. *Arch. intern. physiol. et biochem.* **63**: 203-212.

Wada, M., T. Aoki and W. Koyama. 1958a. The axon reflex sweating produced by potassium and sodium cyanides. *Experientia* **14**: 102-103.

Wada, M., H. Kikuchi, G. Tashiro, and M. Takahashi. 1958b. "Symposium on Sweat Secretion." Kyoto, Japan.

Wilkins, R. W., H. W. Newman and J. Doupe. 1938. The local sweat response to faradic stimulation. *Brain* **61**: 290-297.

Wilson, J. W. and E. H. Leduc. 1948. The occurrence and formation of binucleate and multinucleate cells and polyploid nuclei in the mouse liver. *Am. J. Anat.* **82**: 353-391.

Yasuda, K. and W. Montagna. 1960. Histology and cytochemistry of human skin. XX. The distribution of monoamine oxidase. *J. Histochem. and Cytochem.* **8**: 356-366.

Yasuda, K., H. Furusawa and N. Ogata. 1958. Histochemical investigation on the phosphorylase in the sweat glands of axilla. *Okajimas Folia Anat. Japon.* **31**: 161-169.

CHAPTER 7

The Apocrine Sweat Glands

Introduction

Many distinctly different organs are called apocrine sweat glands. In man apocrine glands occur in the axilla, the mons pubis, the external auditory meatus, the eyelids, the circumanal area, the aureola and nipple of the breast and the labia minora of the female, and in the prepuce and scrotum of the male. Some "ectopic" glands may also be found in the face, the scalp, and on the abdomen around the umbilicus (Pinkus, 1958). Apocrine sweat glands occur in the skin of most mammals. The glands of the horse, though apocrine, are very different organs. The prosimian primates have only apocrine glands on the body surface; the simian primates have both eccrine and apocrine sweat glands in such proportions that they suggest a gradual phylogenetic replacement of apocrine glands with eccrine glands (Schiefferdecker, 1922).

Schiefferdecker suggested that Europeans, allegedly having the fewest apocrine glands, belong to the highest order of human races, whereas the Australian Negroes, with the most glands, belong to the lowest. This is hearsay, since in the case of the Australians, Schiefferdecker studied only one sample of skin from the cheek, in which by coincidence apocrine glands were numerous. From this, Schiefferdecker inferred that they must be equally numerous in all Australian aboriginals. Actually, the distribution of apocrine sweat glands on the bodies of Australian aboriginals is not different from that of Europeans, and has the same differences in frequency as is found in European races (Woollard, 1930). Apocrine glands are better developed and may be more numerous in Negroes than they are in Caucasians, and more numerous in the women than in the men of both races (Homma, 1926).

A thorough consideration of each of the various apocrine glands in man is outside the scope of this book. The apocrine glands in some of the regions of the body of man are different enough for each to warrant special attention; basically, however, they are similar enough to have their general properties illustrated by a description of the glands in the cavum axillae.

Krause (1844) first observed that the glands in the axilla, the external auditory meatus, the circumanal region, and the eyelids are larger than the other sweat glands. The large apocrine sweat glands of the axilla were clearly described and recognized to be different from the general sudoriparous glands by Horner (1846) and Rolin (1846).

Kölliker (1853) described the histology of these glands with perspicacious clarity, and Schiefferdecker (1917), years later, called them *epicrine* or *apocrine* glands.

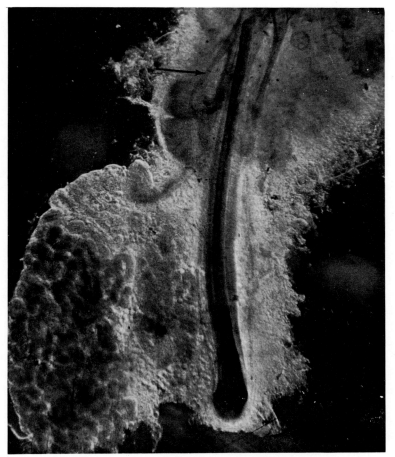

FIG. 1. An axillary apocrine gland and the hair follicle with which it is associated, macerated and dissected to show its coil on the left of the picture, its duct (arrow) opening into a pilary canal, and its relative size in comparison with a hair follicle. (Courtesy of Dr. W. B. Shelley.)

The apocrine glands in the axillary organ of man are such flourishing organs that they cannot be considered rudiments of a waning organ system. They have peculiarities not found in the glands of other mammals, and they are as numerous and well-developed in this area as they are in the skin of any other mammal. It is singularly significant that these glands are as different from those of more primitive primates as the eccrine glands of man are.

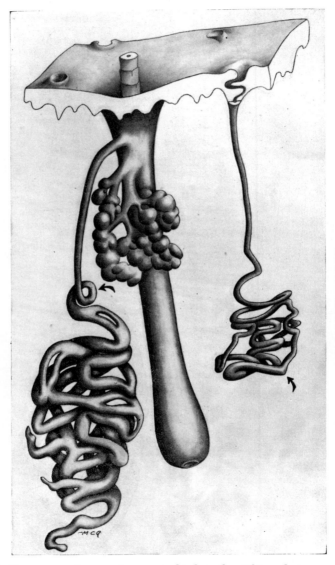

Fig. 2. Stereogram of an eccrine sweat gland on the right, and an apocrine sweat gland on the left of a hair follicle.

Wax model reconstructions and teased whole apocrine glands from the axilla show them to be simple, coiled tubular glands (Horn, 1935; Sperling, 1935; Hurley and Shelley, 1954, 1960). The secretory portion of each gland is compactly coiled, and adjacent loops may be joined by shunts; diverticula extend from the tubules (Figs. 1 and 2). The secretory segments of the smaller glands are entirely within the dermis; those of the large glands may extend into the subcutaneous fat. There may be a distance of about 5 mm or more from the surface of the

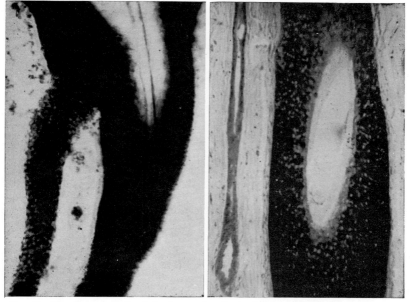

Fig. 3. The figure on the left shows the duct of an axillary sweat gland opening into a pilary canal. The figure to the right shows a duct parallel to a hair follicle.

axilla to the lowermost glandular coil. If an entire tubule could be stretched, its length would be considerable. At the widest part, the glands may measure as much as 2 mm in diameter; the glands, therefore, are macroscopically visible on the underside of the skin, as was shown over one hundred years ago by Horner (1846). The duct of the axillary glands, which lie close to and parallel to a hair follicle, usually opens inside of the pilary canal, above the entrance of the duct of sebaceous glands(Fig. 3). Occasionally two glands may open into one pilary canal (Hurley and Shelley, 1960). Some ducts may open directly onto the surface. The diameter of the duct is much narrower than that of the secretory coil, and the transition between the two segments is abrupt.

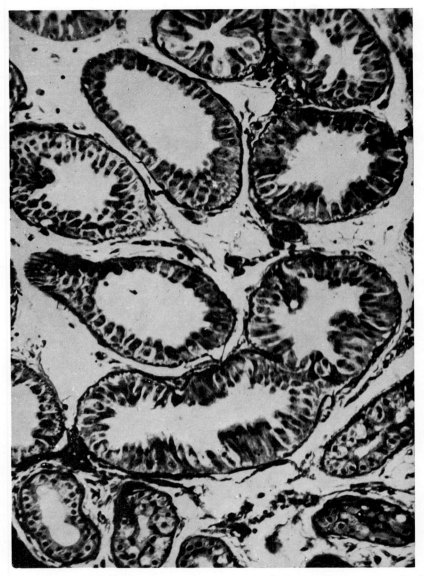

Fig. 4. General field of segments of a secretory coil of an axillary apocrine gland. At the bottom of the field are segments of an eccrine sweat gland.

The epithelium of the secretory tubule is simple columnar, but that of the duct is a double layer of cuboidal cells. The glandular units are surrounded by a loose connective tissue bed rich in blood vessels.

The secretory epithelium is irregularly columnar; the terminal portion of some cells is elongated and projects into the lumen, giving the luminal border an irregular surface (Fig. 4). The free edge of some of these cells is differentiated into a cuticular or brush border; that of others is not. Segments of some tubules, or entire tubules are often dilated, and lined with simple cuboidal epithelium; in excessively dilated tubules the epithelium is so flat as to appear squamous. All of the epithelial cells

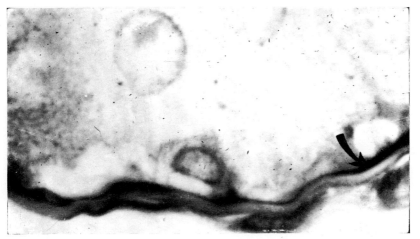

FIG. 5. Basement membrane of an axillary gland. The arrow indicates the inner, PAS-reactive layer. The thicker, outer, hyalin layer is PAS-negative.

rest upon a bed of myoepithelial cells, outside of which is a thick, hyalin basement membrane (Fig. 5).

Only the apocrine glands of the axilla have been studied with the electron microscope (Laden et al., 1955; Charles, 1959; Kurosumi and Kitamura, 1958; Kurosumi et al., 1959; Yasuda and Ellis, 1961). In the lumen of the glands, electron micrographs show material that is vesiculated, or sprinkled with amorphous opaque masses and fine granules of moderate density (Charles, 1959); these may correspond to PAS-positive substances often found there. Blood vessels are frequently seen in contact with the basement membrane, but nerves are not. The luminal border of the cells, which under the light microscope appears as a brush border (Minamitani, 1941a, b; Ito, 1949; Montagna et al., 1953) consists of microvilli about 1 μ long and 100 Å wide (Kurosumi

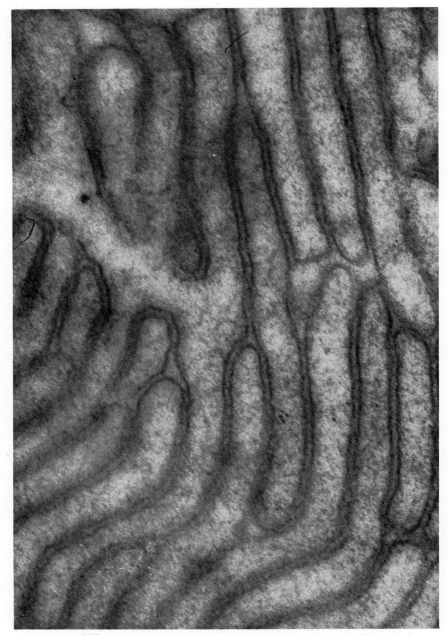

FIG. 6. Infoldings of the basal plasma membrane of a secretory cell from a human apocrine sweat gland. The intercellular spaces and the intracellular spaces are remarkably regular. Magnification: × 76,000.

et al., 1959). The apical cytoplasm of the microvilli contain granules and "vacuoles" attached close to the luminal membrane. The apical, hyalin cytoplasm of mature apocrine cells contains clusters of small vesicles, fine and moderately electron-dense granules, and a ground substance slightly denser than that elsewhere in the cell.

Except at the apical surface, which is covered with a single membrane, apocrine cells are surrounded by double membranes. Adjacent cells make contact in a straight line with practically no membrane interdigitation. Infoldings and denticulations, however, are found at the base of the cells where they dovetail with both myoepithelial cells and with the basement membrane (Kurosumi and Kitamura, 1958) (Fig. 6). The so-called "intercellular spaces" described by Charles (1959) are probably the cross sections of the deeply infolded basal cell membranes (Yasuda and Ellis, 1961).

The basement membrane has a thin, dense, homogeneous inner layer with an irregular surface at the junction with either the myoepithelial cells or the glandular cells, and an outer, collagenous fibrillar layer (Fig. 5) (Yasuda and Ellis, 1961).

Development

The development of sweat glands has been studied systematically by several authors, and the brief account which follows is a summary of some of their findings supplemented with our own observations (Carossini, 1912; Steiner, 1926; Borsetto, 1951; Pinkus, 1958).

The primordia of eccrine sweat glands first appear in the palms and soles of the 4-month-old fetus, but the glands over the rest of the body begin to develop in the fifth fetal month, between the more precociously developed primordia of hair follicles. Somewhat later the anlagen of the presumptive apocrine glands grow from the side of hair follicles, as solid epithelial buds above the sebaceous gland. It is important to emphasize the dyschrony in the development of these cutaneous appendages; when the anlagen of apocrine glands appear, the hair follicles are fully formed, having already produced a hair that may even emerge through the surface of the skin, and the sebaceous glands are partially differentiated. Some authors state that in the scalp and face the hair follicles of the fetus always develop an apocrine gland anlage that later regresses. We have confirmed the presence of numerous glandular anlagen in these areas but only a small number of follicles have them. The flask-shaped gland anlagen become elongated into solid cords, and by the sixth fetal month, the base of each cord begins to be coiled. A lumen appears first in the presumptive duct by a partial keratinization and shriveling up of the cells in the center. Later, clefts appear in the center of the coil; the clefts become more extensive and confluent, forming a lumen in the presumptive secretory coil. The glands gradually become larger and more convoluted, attain a larger lumen, and resemble apocrine sweat glands in the seventh and eighth months. In the newborn the glands have some of their characteristic morphology; the secretory coil is enveloped in a connective tissue capsule, but myoepithelial cells are yet not recognizable. Thus, the glands are still incompletely formed at birth.

Apocrine glands, which develop as adventitious appendages of hair follicles, open into pilosebaceous canals, some ducts, however, occasionally open directly onto the surface of the epidermis. In such instances, either the excretory ducts have become separated from their points of origin, or the glands may have developed from the epidermis. Phylogenetic studies throw some light on this. All of the apocrine glands of the *Lemuridae* open directly onto the surface of the epidermis. Even in the anthropoid apes, the glands often open near the lip of the pilary canal, and not inside it. The shift in position of the orifice of the duct deep into the pilary canal may be of secondary phylogenetic significance, and more characteristic of the glands of man.

Since apocrine glands are not large at birth, some authors have assumed that they are formed after birth. Although, the characteristic properties of functioning apocrine glands develop slowly, one who is familiar with the histology of sweat glands would never confuse these with eccrine sweat glands. Unless the specimen of skin studied has been removed from the cavum axillae proper, a very small area in children, apocrine glands are likely to be missed altogether; this has given rise to unnecessary confusion about the identity of the two types of glands. In children up to 1 year of age, the coils of the apocrine glands lie deep in the dermis, whereas those of the eccrine gland are nearer to the surface (Montagna, 1959). The diameter of the two types of glands in the axilla remains about the same during infancy, but the apocrine glands have a lumen that is larger and lined with cuboidal cells which are all alike (Fig. 7). Eccrine glands have a very small lumen lined with pyramidal dark and clear cells. Whereas the basement membrane of the apocrine glands is very thick, that of the eccrine glands is thin. Although the axillary apocrine glands remain small and relatively undifferentiated up to 7 years of age, some individual glands develop precociously even in children 5 years old. There is an incipient accumulation of fluid in the lumen, and some of the glands become distended, perhaps due to a blockage of the duct even in preadolescent children (Montagna, 1959). Beginning in the seventh year and continuing through adolescence, the glands become progressively larger and

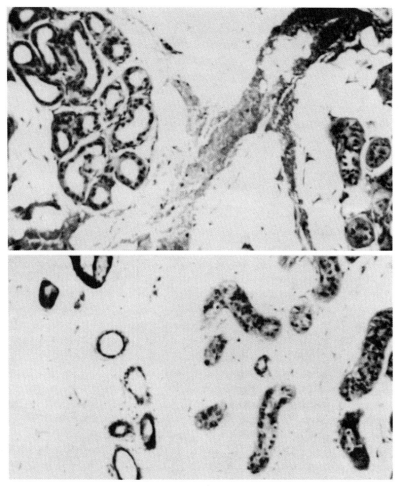

FIG. 7. The figure at the top shows eccrine and apocrine glands from the axilla of a boy 4 years old; that at the bottom is from one 5 years old. In both tissues the apocrine glands are to the left, the eccrine glands to the right.

gradually attain the structure and histochemical properties of functional glands. Actually, the glands of children around 10 years of age are large and well enough differentiated to be functional. Morphology, however, could be deceptive; limited pharmacological observations in the glands of a few children 10 years old has thus far given negative results (Hurley and Shelley, 1960). It is a common observation of alert parents that girls attain a characteristic body odor, presumably due to axillary secretion, around 9 years of age. In spite of their small size, the glands of infants and children are similar to those of adults, and have largely similar histochemical properties. In old age they undergo gradual involution, but this is not strictly related to the fading of the sex hormones (Montagna, 1959; Hurley and Shelley, 1960). The details of aging changes will be discussed later in this chapter.

The Excretory Duct

The upper part of the secretory segment, which has a diameter less than one third that of the lower coils, becomes abruptly attenuated and emerges into the very narrow duct (Fig. 2). There is no transition between the epithelium of the duct and that of the secretory segment. Running a relatively straight course along the hair follicle, the duct is composed of two layers of cells, the luminal ones being flattened and often having a cornified border, or cuticle. The terminal portion of apocrine ducts is slightly dilated and multilayered.

The Nucleus

One, or rarely two, large spherical nuclei are located in the basal part of the cells. The large nucleus stains deeply with most basic dyes and with the Feulgen reaction. One or two large nucleoli are flanked by two strongly basophil, Feulgen-positive satellite bodies. The basophil property of the nucleolus is abolished by digestion with ribonuclease, whereas that of the rest of the nucleus is only slightly diminished. The nucleus of healthy glands, when well-fixed, is always turgid and particles or fragments have never been observed escaping from it.

Under the electron microscope, the nucleus of the secretory cells is surrounded by an envelope composed of an inner thick and an outer thin membrane, both laden with fine granules (Yasuda and Ellis, 1961). The granules attached to the outer membrane are approximately 150 Å in diameter, and those on the inner membrane are so small that they are difficult to distinguish from the particulate chromatin (Kurosumi et al., 1959). The narrow space between the two membranes varies in width, and is occasionally vesiculated. Nuclear pores, occasionally covered by indefinite single membranous diaphragms, can also be seen (Watson, 1955).

Cell division is not common in adult apocrine cells, but when one mitotic figure is found, others are usually present in nearby cells in the same tubule. During mitosis, cells become roughly spherical and relatively free from cytoplasmic granules (Fig. 8). In spite of comparatively high

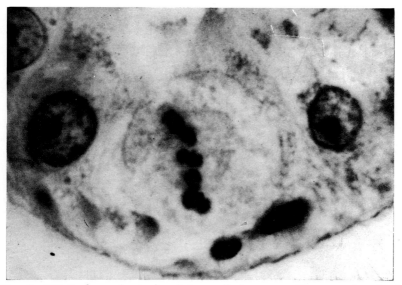

Fig. 8. Mitotic figure (metaphase) in a cell, from an axillary apocrine gland of a 24-year-old woman.

cytoplasmic turbulence, apocrine cells seem not to perish readily, and rarely need to be replaced.

Cytoplasmic Basophilia

When stained with variants of Heidenhain's hematoxylin, the secretory cells show some siderophily in the cytoplasm at the base of the nucleus and particularly around the nucleus. All other basic dyes used, toluidine blue, methylene blue, azure B, etc., demonstrate a certain amount of cytoplasmic basophilia. We prefer to use the dyes named above in solutions of 1/5000 to 1/2000, buffered to pH 4.0 or 5.0, at which values little else is stained in tissues except nucleic acids. At higher pH values proteinous substances show progressive stainability, and even enzymatic control with ribonuclease is of little value.

The cytoplasm at the base of each apocrine cell is usually stippled with fine basophilic granules. Such granules are copious in some cells and aligned in such a way at their base as to give them a longitudinal striation, or outline a fine reticulum. The cytoplasm lateral to and above the nucleus is weakly basophil. The negative image of Golgi zone and the terminal cytoplasm of each cell is relatively free of basophil granules. The cytoplasmic basophilia, as well as that of the nucleoli, is abolished by incubation in ribonuclease, and must be due to ribonucleic acids.

The large pigmented granules are stained a blue-green with the dyes named above, whereas the smaller yellow granules remain unstained. Chromophobe (acidophil) secretion granules in the supranuclear cytoplasm are surrounded by a film that stains a delicate metachromatic color. Neither the basophil staining of the pigmented granules nor the metachromasia on the outside of the chromophobe granules is abolished by previous digestion of tissues with ribonuclease.

The apical and terminal cytoplasm of apocrine cells is almost chromophobic. Yet, some authors believe that apocrine cells which contain very few secretion granules, actually secrete into the lumen a basophilic substance alleged to be ribonucleic acid (Ito and Iwashige, 1953). The secretion substances in the lumen of some tubules stain weakly with basic dyes only if the dyes are buffered to pH 6.0 or above. Ribonuclease has no effect upon the stainability of these substances, and it is unlikely that the secretion contains ribonucleic acid (see also Montes et al., 1960).

The intensity of the basophil staining of the cytoplasm of the secretory cells is inversely proportional to the number of recognizable secretion granules present, and directly proportional to the number of mitochondria. On morphological grounds it appears that nucleic acid together with mitochondria may be involved in the synthesis of the secretion granules, pigmented or chromophobe (cf. Montes et al., 1960).

In the excretory duct, both layers of cells are intensely basophil, but the luminal border of each cell in the inner layer is hyalin and free of basophilia.

Under the electron microscope the cytoplasm of the secretory cells resembles that of other glandular cells, except that it contains large, characteristic granules. Moderate amounts of both rough-surfaced and smooth-surfaced endoplasmic reticulum (Palade, 1955) tend to be concentrated in the basal part of the cell. Since the rough-surfaced reticulum is laden with RNA particles, it probably constitutes the stainable basophil substances of the cytoplasm. The "chromophobic" granules, surrounded by a delicate film that stains somewhat metachromatically, correspond to the light granules seen in electron micrographs; these are frequently surrounded by a flattened rough-surfaced reticulum (Yasuda and Ellis, 1961). Although Kurosumi et al. (1959)

found none, stacks of ergastoplasmic lamellae may be found in the apical cytoplasm, or rarely in the other parts of the cells. The Golgi apparatus is surrounded by characteristic aggregations of vacuoles of various sizes, some of which extend around and below the nucleus. Kurosumi *et al.* (1959) believe that these vacuoles have their origin in the Golgi apparatus, and that they give rise to the dark secretory granules.

Mitochondria and Cytoplasmic Granules

Mitochondria can be demonstrated with relative ease in the axillary apocrine glands, even in tissues fixed in Zenker-formol without post-

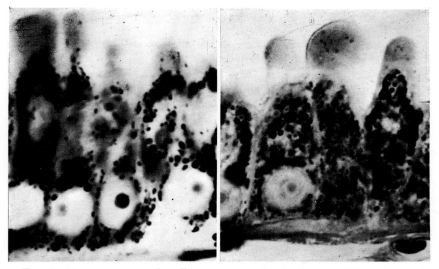

Fig. 9. Two specimens of axillary apocrine glands showing differences in the number, shape, and size of mitochondria. The clear, oval area above the nucleus is the negative image of the Golpi apparatus.

chromation. The choice of specific techniques, then, is unimportant; Heidenhain's hematoxylin, Regaud's hematoxylin, aniline acid fuchsin-methyl green, or a variety of other methods all demonstrate mitochondria well in these glands. The mitochondria are large, numerous, and pleomorphic (Fig. 9).

Brinkmann (1908), who studied them in the glands of other animals, believes that mitochondria are replaced by, or transformed into, secretion granules. Nicolas *et al.* (1914) perceived a relationship between mitochondria and cytoplasmic granules in both the eccrine and apocrine glands of man, and stated that granules arise directly from mitochondria.

Mitochondria seem to be most numerous in cells which have few or no granules; they are few or absent in cells replete with granules (Mina-mitani, 1941a, b; Ota, 1950).

The tall columnar cells which contain few or no cytoplasmic granules have numerous rodlet, filamentous, granular, and spherular mitochondria. They are in the form of long filaments in the cytoplasm above the nucleus and around the nucleus. Both rodlets and filaments are aligned parallel to the axis of the cell. The granular mitochondria seem to arise from condensations at both ends of the rodlets (Minamitani, 1941a, b), and the beaded and ring-shaped ones seem to develop from the filaments. The basal part of the cells has the most mitochondria; the rounded, negative image of the Golgi region above the nucleus, and the terminal part of the cells have none. Even the cuboidal, or very flat, cells which line the dilated tubules have numerous, large, and pleomorphic mito-chondria.

The tall columnar cells which contain discernible granules in the cytoplasm above the nucleus have fewer mitochondria and they look like large granules and moniliform filaments. In some cells, the entire cyto-plasm, with the exception of the apical hyalin border and the area of the Golgi apparatus, is filled with round granules larger than the granular mitochondria but smaller than the recognizable, so-called "secretion" granules. It is difficult to be sure whether most of these elements are large mitochondria or small granules. In preparations stained with Altmann's technique, these granules, like mitochondria, are fuchsinophil. The intermediate-sized granules stain purple and the large ones stain a dark blue-green. The majority of the recognizable mitochondria appear granular; some are in the shape of rodlets and dumbbells. It has been suggested that rodlet and filamentous mitochondria change into granular and beaded ones. The granular mitochondria would then gradually increase in size and transform directly into "secretion" granules. This process is said to take place throughout the cytoplasm, with the exception of the Golgi zone and the hyalin terminal border of the cell. More often than not, however, the large granules are found only in the cytoplasm above the nucleus, with the largest granules always around the Golgi region. In the glands of aged individuals the number of mitochondria and cytoplasmic granules is conspicuously reduced.

Although one cannot overlook a possible relationship between mito-chondria and secretory activity, one cannot assume that the mitochondria transform directly into granules. The number and the shape of mito-chondria in each cell seem to change according to the size of the cell and according to the number and size of the granules in the cytoplasm.

In contrast with what one sees under the light microscope, under the electron microscope, mitochondria are relatively few and small. They are somewhat elongated, and occasionally dumbbell-shaped and mostly located near the base of the cells and around the nucleus (Fig. 9). Mitochondria have three fundamental features: they have an outer limiting double membrane, double-membraned cristae mitochondriales, and a matrix (Palade, 1952). The few cristae are ill-developed, short, and occasionally take an arch-like course, being attached at both ends on the same wall (Kurosumi *et al.*, 1959; Yasuda and Ellis, 1961). Dense and fine granules are homogeneously distributed through the matrix. The number of mitochondria recognizable under the electron microscope is much smaller than that seen in stained preparations. Thus, many of the stained elements may not be mitochondria.

The Golgi Apparatus

Bergen (1904) first described a "canalicular system" or Golgi apparatus in apocrine sweat glands between the nucleus and the free border of the cells. Osmium tetroxide reveals a system of twisted osmiophil rodlets and granules above the nucleus, which covers an area about the size of the nucleus (Melczer, 1935; Minamitani, 1941b; Mitchell and Hamilton, 1949; Ota, 1950). This corresponds to the area free of mitochondria and of secretion granules, which was described earlier as the negative image of the Golgi apparatus (Fig. 9). In tall columnar cells the osmiophil bodies lie between the nucleus and the large secretion droplets dammed at the distal part of the cells. In the low cuboidal cells or in the flattened cells of dilated tubules, osmiophil filaments and granules lie directly above the nucleus or along its sides. In cells laden with granules the general configuration of the Golgi apparatus is lost; the filamentous osmiophil skein is fragmented and the granules in the vicinity may be surrounded by semilunar osmiophil caps. In some cells, twisted filaments are found together with clusters of osmiophil granules, some of them with eccentric osmiophobe vacuoles. The distribution of the Golgi element between the ripened secretion granules distally and the nucleus proximally, suggested to Minamitani (1941b) that the secretion granules are formed below the Golgi apparatus, at the expense of the mitochondria, and that the Golgi element is concerned with the maturation of the granules. In passing upward from below, the immature granules come into contact with these elements and become partially surrounded by lunate osmiophil plaques. During the ripening process some granules acquire pigment, lipid, and iron by way of the Golgi apparatus. Many granules, however, contain none of these substances in large enough quantities to be demonstrated histochemically; ionic iron is present in the small yellow pigmented granules and only rarely is found in the large brown, apparently mature, granules. The Golgi apparatus in those cells that contain neither iron nor pigment

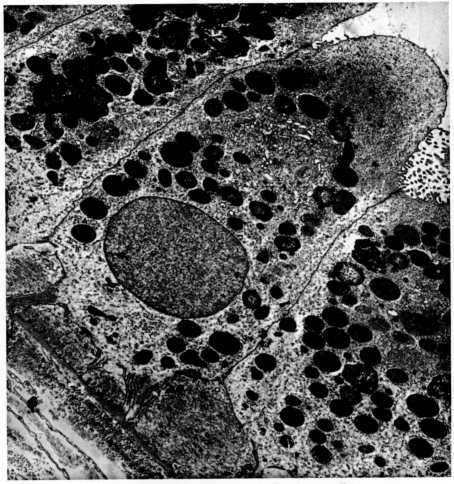

FIG. 10. Electron micrograph of secretory cells of an axillary apocrine sweat gland of a 30-year-old Negro. Both the collagenous and the amorphous parts of the basement membrane are evident at the bottom of the figure; the cells contain large mitochondria with few cristae, iron-containing granules and large, irregular pigmented granules. There is a prominent Golgi zone and a clear apical cap. The luminal border has numerous microvilli and very small clear vesicles. Magnification: × 80,000.

is as well-developed as that in cells rich in these substances. The Golgi apparatus, then, must perform some other function.

The size and shape of the Golgi apparatus change according to the activity of the cell. It contains lipid granules and PAS-reactive substances, which could be phospholipids, glycoproteins, or mucopolysaccharides. This is not the place to discuss the basic details and arguments for and against the existence of a Golgi apparatus, but the presence of a structure above the nucleus can be ascertained even in ordinary histological preparations, where its negative image is a typical morphologic feature of apocrine cells. The electron microscope also reveals a well-developed Golgi apparatus. Since cell structures cannot be considered mere ornaments, the Golgi apparatus must have a functional significance.

Under the electron microscope the Golgi apparatus consists of an aggregate of vacuoles and vesicles outlined by single smooth-surfaced membranes; there are no typical "Golgi lamellae" (see Dalton and Felix, 1956). Most of the vesicles and vacuoles are spherical, but some are pleomorphic; all contain a pale-staining material. The content of these vacuoles is similar to that in the many small vesicles in the "clear" apical cytoplasm of the cells (Yasuda and Ellis, 1961). Scattered through the ground substance of the Golgi area, which has a density similar to that of the cytoplasm, are sparse, fine granules (Fig. 10). The entire Golgi region is surrounded by granules and mitochondria.

Lipids

In frozen sections colored with Sudan black, the cytoplasm of all secretory cells shows a diffuse gray color. Some of the large, darkly pigmented globules are colored gray, others black, and some are not sudanophilic. The small yellow granules remain uniformly colored by Sudan black (Fig. 11A). None of the acidophilic, nonpigmented granules contains sudanophilic lipids. Immersion overnight in acetone does not diminish appreciably the sudanophilia of these cells. Immersion in acetone for 1 hour and in pyridine at 60°C for 18 hours removes only a small part of the sudanophil lipid in the cytoplasm; that in the pigmented globules and in the myoepithelial cells remains practically unchanged. When treated with the acid hematein test for the demonstration of phospholipids, reactive granules in the myoid cells are arranged in parallel rows and correspond to the sudanophilic granules. In unstained frozen sections viewed under near ultraviolet light, the large pigment droplets emit an orange-yellow light. The Schultz test for unsaturated steroids is consistently negative. None of the glands shows

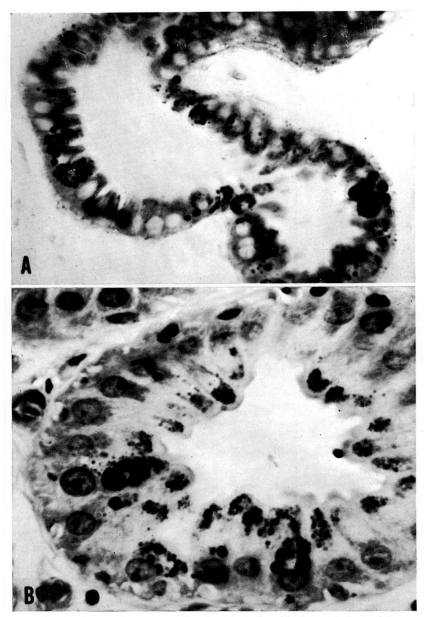

Fig. 11. (A) Frozen section colored with Sudan black B. (B) Acid-fast pigmented granules in a gland stained with Verhoeff's carbol fuchsin.

birefringent lipids, even in tissues which were left a long time in the fixative.

When paraffin sections of tissues fixed in Helly's fluid are colored with Sudan black, the large, darkly pigmented droplets become gray or black, but the small yellow granules are not sudanophilic. No other cytoplasmic element is sudanophilic. We have never encountered sudanophilic globules in the lumen of the glands. In some individual cases, the cells contain only unpigmented, nonsudanophilic granules. When stained with carbol-fuchsin and differentiated with hydrochloric acid, most of the large, darkly pigmented droplets are acid-fast (Fig. 11B).

Four "distinct" lipids have been described within the secretory cells of apocrine glands: (a) a sudanophil stippling in the cytoplasm, probably associated with the mitochondria; (b) numerous sudanophilic droplets which give a "plasmal" reaction, and are insoluble in acetone but soluble in pyridine at $60°C$; (c) a natural yellow pigment, which emits a yellow or orange fluorescence under ultraviolet light, is dissolved in sudanophilic droplets, and is soluble in acetone; and (d) "a great abundance of birefringent, acetone-soluble material." Actually only the first observation seems valid. The large lipid droplets are not wholly extractable with lipid solvents and remain sudanophilic even in paraffin sections. Similarly, most of the pigment contained in these globules is extremely resistant to extraction. Even in paraffin sections pigment is clearly yellow or brown and shows abundant autofluorescence. In agreement with Pinkus, we have not found birefringent lipids in the apocrine glands of the axilla, the external auditory meatus, or the mons pubis. Discrepancies in observations could be explained by a knowledge of the history of the material used. It is possible that under certain pathologic conditions anisotropic lipids might be present.

The secretory cells of axillary glands are said to contain neutral fat, fatty acids, and cholesterol. These substances are extractable with chloroform, and since most of the lipids in these glands normally resist extraction with lipid solvents, we question that they are present in demonstrable amounts. Moreover, the Schultz test for unsaturated steroids is consistently negative.

Iron

The presence of intraepithelial ionic iron, demonstrated with any of the standard cytochemical techniques, is a distinctive feature of apocrine axillary glands (Fig. 12). Of the other cutaneous glands of the body, only active mammary glands contain greater amounts of iron.

Homma (1925) and Manca (1934) found iron in the glands of the majority of specimens they studied. Some specimens abound in iron; others have little or none. Even separate coils of the same glandular unit may show some disparity in their content of iron, and whereas some cells may abound in it, morphologically identical cells may possess none. Usually, when present, iron is found in all tubules. Iron is said to be more abundant in specimens from middle-aged subjects and to increase in disproportionate amounts in subjects with pulmonary tuberculosis (Manca, 1934). The cells of the excretory duct show no iron. Connective tissue macrophages around iron-rich tubules often contain iron.

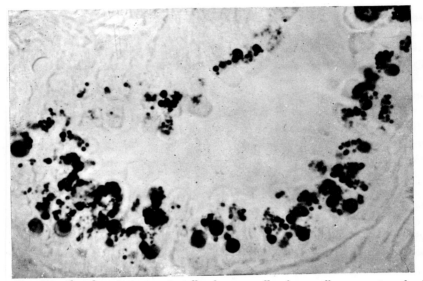

Fig. 12. Abundant ionic iron in tall columnar cells of an axillary apocrine gland.

The granules that contain iron are found in the cytoplasm alongside and above the nucleus. More precisely, they are clustered around the clear, supranuclear negative image of the Golgi apparatus. In well-fixed biopsy specimens, iron is nearly always seen in the form of small granules. The large iron granules described by other authors are very rare. Iron may be present in the tall cells, as well as in the low cuboidal ones. Ionic iron has been reported within the lumen of the tubules in a large number of biopsy specimens, but this happens only when the lumen is full of relatively intact, discarded epithelial cells. Regardless of the amount of iron in the epithelium, when the content of the lumen contains no cell particulates and is clear or flocculent we have never found iron there. This is consistent with chemical analyses of apocrine sweat, which contains no great quantities of iron.

There is some relation between the pigmented granules and the distribution of iron. When present, iron is associated with the small yellow pigment granules. The large dark brown granules rarely contain it. When they do, only a thin film at the periphery is reactive, and the brown pigment shows through unchanged. Most of the large pigment masses remain completely unreactive. Although the amount of pigment, yellow or brown, in the cells is no index to its presence, iron is found only in pigmented cells, and found in the small yellow granules only if the large brown ones are also present in the same cells. Manca (1934) also observed that only one of the pigments contains iron, and deduced that two pigments are present in apocrine glands: one, hemosiderin, which contains iron; the other, wear-and-tear pigment, which does not. Zorzoli (1950) failed to see an association between iron and pigment, and concluded that pigment is free of iron, although a distinct but intimately associated substance does contain it.

From a morphological standpoint it is difficult to assess the significance of iron. Since iron is not always present in the small yellow pigment granules, the pigment cannot properly be called hemosiderin. Perhaps an additional iron-containing substance is associated with the yellow pigment (Zorzoli, 1950). The presence of a thin covering of iron around the large brown granules suggests that the yellow pigment granules might grow into the brown ones, and that during this transformation either the iron is lost or the inorganic form is gradually transformed to organic iron. This speculation, however, cannot be confirmed by either the tests for bound iron, or by microincineration, both tests showing results similar to those of ionic iron. Thus, there is no clue to the fate of iron; even the electron microscope has been little help. Iron has not been found in any form in the terminal cytoplasm of the cells. Similarly, if the cells secrete by a sloughing off of the apical cytoplasm, would it not be reasonable to assume that in glands rich in iron the cell debris in the lumen should also contain it? Yet, we have not found a single case of ionic iron in the lumen, except in those cases where the large part of the epithelium of the tubule seemed to be collapsing.

Iron can be demonstrated easily with the Hale technique in apocrine glands in tissues fixed with osmium tetroxide embedded in methacrylates. As already observed under the light microscope, iron is restricted to the small, round granules, which under the electron microscope have a dense cortex. These granules also show tiny dense particles arranged in a pattern characteristic of ferritin (Fig. 13).

It has been postulated that skin, and particularly the sweat glands, are important organs for the excretion of iron (Mitchell and Hamilton, 1949). These conclusions were drawn from chemical analyses of sweat

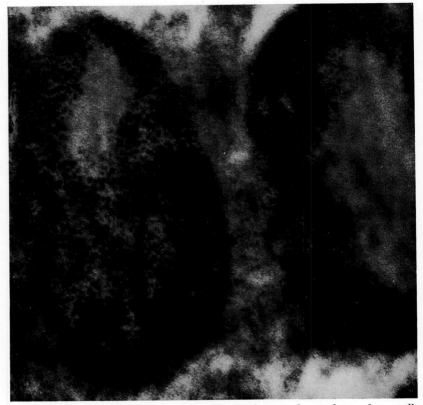

FIG. 13. Electron micrograph of granules in the apical cytoplasm of an axillary apocrine sweat gland of a Caucasian. The cortex of the granules contains small dense particles that are similar to ferritin in dimension and spacing. Magnification: × 68,000.

samples of skin washings of human subjects. Such pooled sweat samples are composed largely of eccrine sweat, and only a negligible part is contributed by the apocrine glands. When sweat samples are collected in a glove from the hand and forearm, where apocrine glands are unlikely to occur, the sweat can be separated into samples rich in cells and samples poor in cells. The "cell-poor" part contains negligible amounts of iron, but the "cell-rich" part contains a considerable amount of it (Adams *et al.*, 1950). The conclusion that loss of iron is associated with epidermal cell desquamation rather than sweating is inescapable.

Secretion Granules

Most accounts that deal with axillary apocrine glands give the impression that the only index of secretory activity in a gland is the

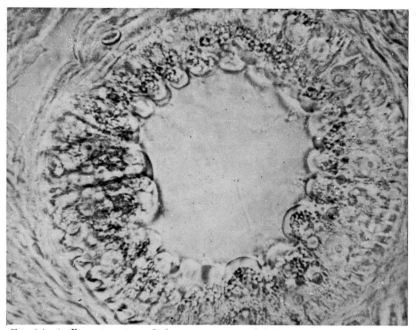

Fig. 14. Axillary apocrine tubule, in an unstained frozen section, showing pigment in the secretory cells.

presence of intracellular lipoidal and/or pigmented granules (Fig. 14). Yet, the cells in the glands of some individuals, and particularly those blonds of Nordic origin, may possess only traces of pigmented or lipoidal granules, or even none.

When stained with toluidine blue, thionine, or other basic dyes, the supranuclear cytoplasm appears to be riddled with tiny vacuoles. The "vacuoles" are actually chromophobe secretion spherules. Some of the larger spherules are slightly basophil. In some subjects, notably blond ones, these spherules are the only secretory elements present; in others the chromophobe spherules may be admixed with pigmented ones. In some cells these vacuoles may extend alongside and below the nucleus. The small "vacuoles" are eosinophil, when stained with eosin-methylene blue or with Giemsa, but some of the very large ones are basophil. The acidophil, small spherules are surrounded by cytoplasm that stains orthochromatically or delicately metachromatically with toluidine blue. The granules stain a clear blue-black with Heidenhain's hematoxylin (Fig. 15). When tissues are stained for mitochondria, many of the smaller granules are stained like mitochondria. All of the nonpigmented granules are strongly PAS-reactive, but since the reaction is not pre-

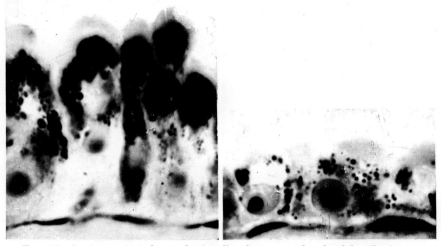

FIG. 15. Secretion granules in both tall columnar and cuboidal cells from two segments of the same axillary apocrine tubule.

vented by previous digestion with diastase or saliva, they contain no glycogen. The spherules probably contain 1,2-glycol groups.

The acidophil granules are said to be immature secretion granules that become large and pigmented as they mature. If this were the case, every ripe granule should be pigmented. But many mature secretion granules are free of pigment. Moreover, the glands in many subjects contain only unpigmented secretion granules.

The designation "secretion granules" implies that granules are secreted intact. However, the distal-most extension of the cytoplasm, which is the place where secretion must take place, is always free of granules. In preparations stained with the PAS method, which demonstrates even the smallest acidophil, nonpigmented granules, there are no visible granules in the free border of the cytoplasm, although this portion of the cytoplasm is PAS-reactive like the granules (Fig. 16). If apocrine secretion took place by a pinching off of the apical cytoplasmic extensions, more often than not the granules would remain in the cytoplasm left behind. It appears likely that the mature "secretory" granules become dissolved in the apical cytoplasm. Similarly, distinct

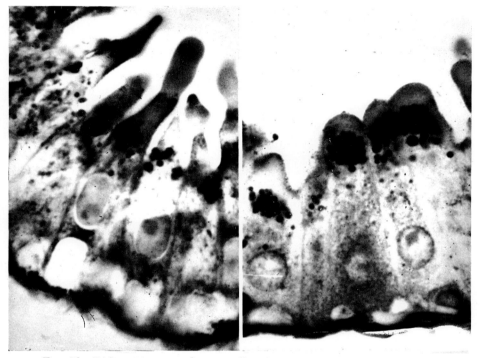

FIG. 16. PAS-positive granules in axillary apocrine glands. Both figures show some reaction in the apical, granule-free cytoplasm.

granules have not been found in the lumen of normal glands, although the luminal content is often PAS-reactive.

Under the electron microscope, two kinds of large granules can be recognized in the upper part of the cells (Fig. 10): large ones, measuring up to 2 μ in diameter (Kurosumi et al., 1959), called "smooth granules" by Charles (1959), and "light granules" (Kurosumi et al., 1959), with short cristae-like structures, of various shapes, sizes, and disposition. The "light granules," considered by Charles (1959) and Kurosumi et al. (1959) to originate from mitochondria, look like degenerating mitochondria and may correspond to the PAS-positive, chromophobe granules seen in ordinary microscopy. The large, dark granules in the apical cytoplasm also show wide variations in size and shape, and have a most heterogeneous nature. They are composed of dark particles of different intensities and sizes, of fine grain with high density, of irregularly shaped masses with less density, and of a pale area. Some granules are riddled with large vacuoles with a light core and a dark periphery. These are the pigmented granules that also contain lipid, pigment, and iron. The electron microscope shows no transitional forms between the two types of granules described here.

Miscellaneous Histochemical Observations

In contrast with eccrine glands, the apocrine glands of man have only a moderate amount of succinic dehydrogenase (Montagna and Formisano, 1955). Regardless of the size of the secretory cells the formazan crystals indicative of enzyme activity are inversely proportional to the amount of secretion material in the cytoplasm. Most frequently formazan crystals are clustered around the nucleus or above it; the basal part of the cells and the terminal cytoplasmic border are usually free of them. When a cell is full of secretion granules, a few formazan crystals are concentrated above the nucleus. The myoepithelial cells are consistently unreactive. In contrast with those of the secretory segment, the cells of the excretory duct have a relatively strong enzyme reaction.

In both apocrine and eccrine glands cytochrome oxidase activity is moderate in the duct and abundant in the secretory coil (technique of Burstone, 1959, 1960). In the gland the reaction is always strong, regardless of the height of the epithelium and the number of secretion granules in the cells.

There are great concentrations of monoamine oxidase in the duct and in the secretory epithelium (technique of Glenner et al., 1957). Although the secretory cells are full of coarse reactive granules, the myoepithelial cells have a scant reaction (Yasuda and Montagna, 1960) (Fig. 17A).

Amylophosphorylase activity is found only in the excretory duct, extending from the funnel-like dilatation that opens into the pilary canal to its junction with the secretory segment (Fig. 18A, B). The secretory coil, except for some scattered reaction in the myoepithelial cells, is unreactive (Ellis and Montagna, 1958; Yasuda et al., 1958). Even the glands of young children, which are small and contain glycogen, have very little phosphorylase in them (Montagna, 1959).

Although the eccrine glands of man contain only moderate amounts of

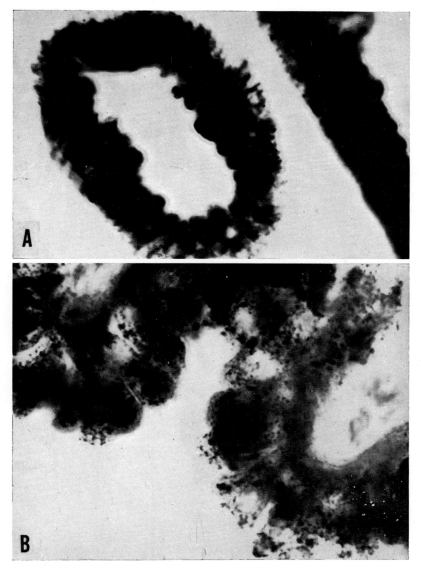

Fig. 17. (A) Monoamine oxidase and (B) β-glucuronidase in axillary apocrine cells.

esterases, the apocrine glands have relatively intense concentrations of these enzymes (Montagna and Ellis, 1958, 1959b). Regardless of the substrates used, the secretory cells are always replete with reactive granules. No other cutaneous appendage routinely contains so much esterase activity (Figs. 19 and 20).

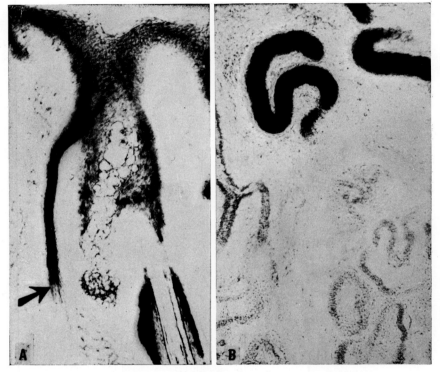

Fig. 18. (A) Amylophosphorylase in the duct, but not in the secretory segment of a ceruminous gland. The arrow indicates the abrupt transition from duct to secretory segment. (B) Amylophosphorylase in two coils of eccrine glands, above, but none in the apocrine axillary glands, below.

The apical border of the tall epithelial cells and the myoepithelial cells contains variable small amounts of alkaline phosphatase, although the duct is consistently unreactive. The endothelium of the vascular bed around the glands of man abounds in phosphatase and is clearly delineated in good preparations (Fig. 21). The coils of the glands are encircled by plexuses of capillaries, but only a few vessels accompany the duct (Ellis *et al.*, 1958). Even the dilated glands in the axillae of

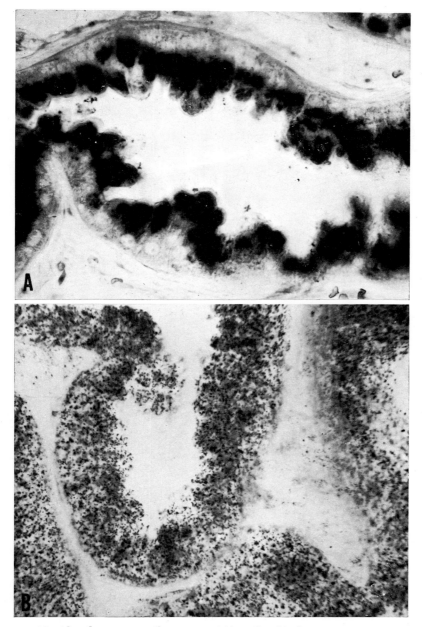

FIG. 19. Abundant nonspecific esterase (A) and indoxyl acetate esterase (B) in an axillary apocrine sweat gland.

older individuals have a fairly intact capillary supply around them (Montagna, 1959).

In man, the apocrine glands have very little acid phosphatase reactivity in the duct, but moderate reactivity in the apical portion of the secretory cells. The myoepithelial cells often show enzyme reaction. The glands abound in β-glucuronidase (Fig. 17B). It is interesting to find such disparity in the strength of the reaction of these two enzymes in the two types of glands, since both acid phosphatase and β-glucuronidase are said to abound in lysosomes (Allfrey, 1959).

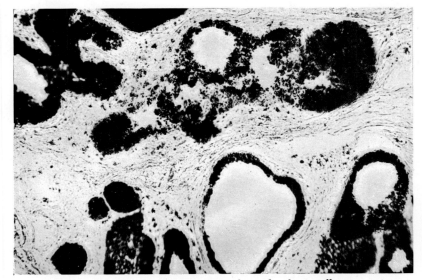

Fig. 20. Intense tween esterase activity in the coils of an axillary apocrine sweat gland.

The duct of apocrine sweat glands has practically no aminopeptidase activity, but the reaction is fairly strong in the secretory cells. This reaction is not so intense as that found in the eccrine glands (Adachi and Montagna, 1961).

Nerves around the apocrine sweat glands of man have not been demonstrated convincingly; if there are nerves there, it has been assumed that they contain neither specific nor pseudocholinesterases (Shelley and Hurley, 1953; Thies and Galente, 1957; Montagna and Ellis, 1958; Hurley and Shelley, 1960). Yet, the glands of Moll in the eyelids, which are apocrine glands, are surrounded by nerves that contain specific cholinesterase, and Aavik (1955) demonstrated nerves containing cholinesterase around the axillary apocrine glands of man. On the assumption that his technique was faulty, no one has paid much attention to his discovery. We now find that the axillary apocrine glands of the Negro have variable numbers of such nerves around them, but those of Caucasians do not (Montagna and Ellis, 1960a). These studies have thus far been confined to Negroes whose exact

FIG. 21. Alkaline phosphatase activity in the endothelium of the vessels around the coils of an axillary apocrine gland.

origin is not known, and it should be interesting to see what the glands of known ethnic groups will show. Since specific cholinesterase is found in both motor and sensory nerve fibers (Beckett *et al.*, 1956), its presence cannot be considered a characteristic feature of cholinergic nerve fibers. Regardless of the role of this enzyme in the conduction of nerve impulses, the important point here is that cholinesterase is present in the nerves around the apocrine glands of the Negro and not around those of Caucasians.

With some exceptions, the apocrine glands over the general body surface of the many primates we have studied have no cholinesterase-containing nerves around them (Montagna and Ellis, 1959a, 1960b, c). The apocrine glands in specialized skin areas, which have a more vigorous secretion than those over the general body surface, are often surrounded by cholinesterase-containing nerves (Fig. 22). The apocrine glands in the axilla of the chimpanzee and the gorilla are associated with such nerves, whereas the glands elsewhere on their bodies are not.

Axillary apocrine glands contain no glycogen (Montagna et al., 1953). However, the myoepithelial cells and the secretory cells in some dilated

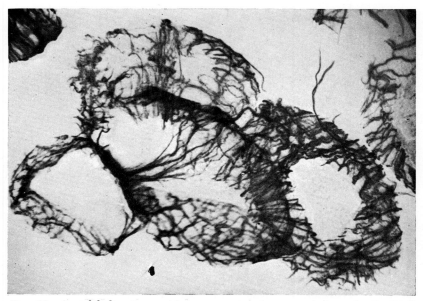

Fig. 22. Acetylcholinesterase-rich nerves around an apocrine gland of the brachial organ of the loris.

tubules may contain traces of glycogen, and their lumen is often full of flocculent, PAS-reactive substance. Apocrine glands in other regions of the body such as those in the mons pubis, often contain small amounts of glycogen (Montagna et al., 1951). The glands of children younger than seven years usually contain some glycogen (Montagna, 1959). Thus, vigorous assertions and denials of the presence or absence of glycogen are of doubtful value; glycogen is rarely present in appreciable amounts in apocrine glands, and its presence or absence may reflect the functional state of the organ. PAS-reactive substances, other than glycogen, are numerous in the apocrine cells, and have already been described. The cells of the ducts, particularly the basal ones, always have a certain amount of glycogen.

Axillary glands contain both sulfhydryl and disulfide groups distributed diffusely in the cytoplasm of the secretory cells, and are particularly concentrated in the myoepithelial cells. The apical borders of the cells, and often even the secretion of the lumen, contain disulfide groups. In the excretory ducts, disulfide groups are particularly concentrated in the cuticle (Montagna et al., 1954).

Myoepithelial Cells

Numerous, large, spindle-shaped myoepithelial cells are sandwiched between the single-layered secretory epithelium and the basement membrane (Figs. 5, 15, 16 and 23). Although there is some doubt that these are true muscle fibers, since they are believed to arise from the ectoderm, the cells resemble those of smooth muscle. They are approximately 5 to 10 μ in the widest diameter and 50 to 100 μ in length. In transverse sections of tubules the body of the cells appears to be triangular, between the bases of secretory cells. Myoepithelial cells, oriented roughly parallel to those of the tubule, and allowing parts of the secretory cells to rest against the basement membrane through the interstices that they form, are loosely dovetailed.

Myoepithelial cells are best developed in those tubules which are lined with the tallest epithelium. They are very delicate or sometimes impossible to demonstrate (Fig. 23B), in the dilated tubules, where the epithelial cells are flat and elongated. We do not know whether or not they are actually absent. Montes et al. (1960), who take exception to this statement, stating that "In enlarged tubules with atrophic epithelium, the myoepithelial cells were usually plump and prominent," support their objection with three photographs. All of these, however, show tubules lined with low cuboidal cells. In the excessively dilated tubules where the epithelial cells are reduced to long, flat squamae, myoepithelial cells are either absent or they lose their characteristic staining properties.

Myoepithelial cells have an acidophil cytoplasm. Delicate longitudinal fibrils in the cytoplasm can be stained with phosphotungstic acid-hematoxylin, with Regaud's and with Heidenhain's hematoxylin. These fibrils are more numerous and coarser than those in the smooth muscle fibers of the cutaneous arterioles and of the arrectores pilorum muscles (Bunting et al., 1948). Rows of lipid granules, probably phospholipids, are arranged parallel to the axis of the cell (Montagna et al.,

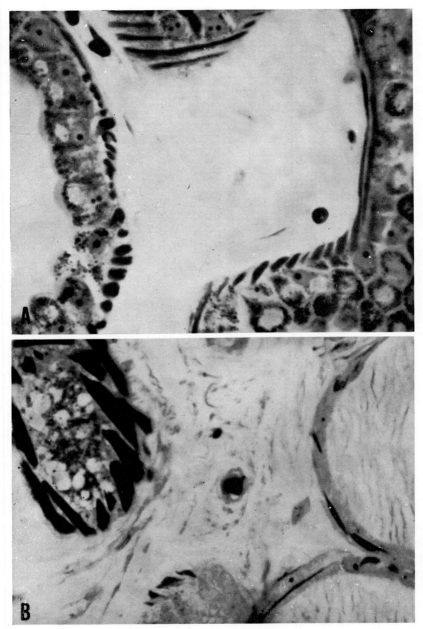

Fig. 23. (A) Myoepithelial cells cut in three planes: transversely (left), tangentially (lower right), and horizontally (upper right and top). (B) Contrast the large myoepithelial cells in the tubule to the left with the very small cells in the dilated segments on the right. Both figures (A) and (B) are stained with Heidenhain's hematoxylin.

1951). Under polarized light the cells show longitudinally oriented anisotropic striae similar to those in smooth muscle. Delicate granules of glycogen may also be found, longitudinally oriented in the cytoplasm. The cells contain very little cytochrome oxidase and practically no succinic dehydrogenase or monoamine oxidase. They consistently show some alkaline phosphatase, amylophosphorylase, and esterases. Thus, although some of their histochemical properties are similar to those of smooth muscle, others are different. In old age, the myoepithelial cells are said to become swollen, vacuolated, and laden with lipid and pigment (Ito et al., 1951). More often than not, however, the cells reflect the general state of the glands and may be in excellent condition even in very old subjects (Winkelmann and Hultin, 1958; Montagna, 1960).

Under the electron microscope, many "myofilaments" are aligned parallel to the long axis of the cells as in the myoepithelial cells of other organs (Chiquoine, 1958). Small mitochondria are arranged parallel to the myofilaments (Yasuda and Ellis, 1961). The basal part of the myoepithelial cells interdigitates slightly with the innermost layer of the basement membrane.

The much-debated function of myoepithelial cells during apocrine sweating seems to be fairly well settled. These cells, like muscle cells, have the ability to contract. Direct observation on axillary glands in situ, through an incision in the axillary skin, shows the myoepithelium contracting synchronously, and in peristaltic waves, with the appearance of a droplet of sweat upon the surface (Hurley and Shelley, 1954, 1960). Pharmacologic, mechanical, and electric stimuli, which normally initiate contraction in smooth muscle, also induce contraction in the myoepithelium and concurrently bring about apocrine sweating.

Secretory Process

The orifices of most apocrine sweat glands open inside the pilosebaceous canals or to the surface near the pilosebaceous orifice. Apocrine sweat is milky, viscid and pale gray, although it can be whitish, reddish, or yellowish. It fluoresces with a whitish or yellow light of moderate to low intensity. The secretion dries in glistening, glue-like granules. There are as many differences in the color, fluorescence, amount, and consistency of the secretion products as there are in the histological features of the glands. Secretion from the glands is usually slow and scanty, the total sweat in response to a given stimulus being considerably less than one milliliter. The glands do not secrete continuously, and there is a long latent period between active cycles (Shelley, 1951;

Hurley and Shelley, 1960). Here also, few appreciate the enormous amount of individual differences that exist.

The morphology of apocrine cells suggests that after the secretion granules have accumulated within the apical part of each cell, the free end is pinched off into the lumen. The basal part of the cell, which contains the nucleus, would, then, synthesize more secretion products and repeat the process. The cycle would begin in cuboidal cells, where a gradual accumulation of granules would take place above the nucleus. The granules would increase in size and in number and then become liquefied to form droplets. The cells would lose their cuticular borders, become cylindrical, and protrude into the lumen. Even the nucleus has been said to release particles into the terminal cytoplasm, which is said to be pinched off (Schiefferdecker, 1922; Hoepke, 1927; Schwenkenbecker, 1933). At the time of secretion, the myoepithelial cells are said to increase in volume; when they contract they squeeze the secretory cells, and under pressure the distal cytoplasm becomes detached. In addition to apocrine secretion, axillary glands are said to secrete also by eccrine and holocrine mechanisms (Holmgren, 1922; Ota, 1950). These assumptions do not completely survive scrutiny.

In histological preparations the long cytoplasmic extensions of the cells that protrude into the lumen suggest that they might break off. However, the content of the lumen of the nondilated tubules that are lined with tall cells is usually clear, with no apparent cell debris in it. On the other hand, numerous cell fragments may be found in dilated tubules. In some segments of tubules, much of the epithelium may slough off practically intact into the lumen. The cytoplasmic blebs that in histological sections appear to be free in the lumen are really attached to the subjacent cells; the pinched-off appearance is brought about by a dehydration and shrinking of the succulent cytoplasm. In frozen sections the terminal cytoplasm, however long, is turgid and gives no impression that it is pinching off. The free border of the tall apocrine cells terminates in a discrete brush that consists of large microvilli seen even with the light microscope (Montagna et al., 1953). The apex of the villi is globate, and the whole structure is PAS-reactive (Fig. 24). It seems likely that apocrine secretion occurs by a pinching off of the terminal globules of the microvilli or by an exudation of liquid substances through them. Occasionally, large, acidophil, PAS-reactive hyalin globules, or chromophobic ones at the apex of some of the large cytoplasmic blebs appear to be escaping through the intervillous spaces into the lumen. Since the lumen of normal apocrine tubules rarely contains visible granules and cell debris, the granules in each cell must dis-

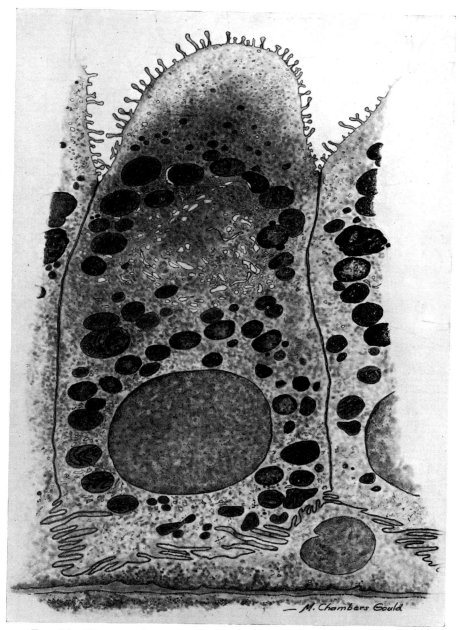

Fig. 24. Diagram of apocrine cells showing the various structural features described in this chapter.

solve in the terminal hyalin cytoplasm before secretion takes place. Secretion in these particular tubules could take place by either a fragmentation of the terminal part of the microvilli or by the oozing out of secretion products from them. Larger droplets may also escape directly from the terminal cytoplasm between the microvilli. True apocrine secretion cannot be verified in normal axillary apocrine sweat glands. These various suggested processes of secretion are supported by observations of the glands under the electron microscope (Yasuda and Ellis, 1961). Apocrine sweat is a mixture produced in a variety of ways mentioned above. It is not known whether some of these ways predominate over others under certain circumstances.

In nearly all specimens of skin obtained from the axilla, some tubules show various degrees of dilatation. The epithelium of these tubules consists of low cuboidal cells, but in the distended tubules the epithelium is reduced to squamous cells. The lumen of the tubules is often filled with a flocculent substance which may or may not contain visible cell debris. Unlike the content of normal tubules, which stains a pale blue with toluidine blue and is weakly PAS-reactive, the flocculent secretion often stains a strong metachromatic or orthochromatic color and is vigorously PAS-reactive. The flattened cells that line the lumen may also contain abundant metachromatic and PAS-reactive material. The characteristic staining properties of apocrine cells and their secretion, then, are markedly changed in the dilated tubules. Occasionally, the lumen of the dilated tubules is full of discarded epithelial cells rich in metachromatic and PAS-reactive substances. These cells may even contain granules of iron. Conflicting reports on the mode of secretion in apocrine glands might arise from the observations on such dilated tubules.

The dilatation of some segments of apocrine glands is a common phenomenon. In old age, some of the glands show a type of cystic dilatation (Fig. 25) and a change in the character of the secretion, which Winkelmann and Hultin (1958) call mucoid metaplasia. Changes similar to these may also occur in children and in young adults and are not characteristic of old age. Mucoid metaplasia and cystic dilatation are found predictably in women in the late 20's; they increase later in life and are common in people after 50. However, much of the axillary organ, even in the oldest subjects studied remains morphologically intact (Montagna, 1959). Although gonadal hormones may play an initial role in the development and the maintenance of these organs, once developed they seem to be relatively self-sufficient. Several observations support this. We found that the glands from two women ovariectomized 10 years were normal; this is in agreement with Klaar (1926) who made this observation in a larger number of specimens. The application of estrogens or androgens topically to the axilla, or the implantation of pellets of these hormones have no effect on the apocrine glands (Shelley and Cahn, 1955; Shelley and Hurley, 1953). The axillary organ of chronologically adult idiots, was infantile and undeveloped and the axilla had no hairs (Shelley and Butterworth, 1955). One of these subjects, a woman of 33, had a relatively normal menstrual cycle. This

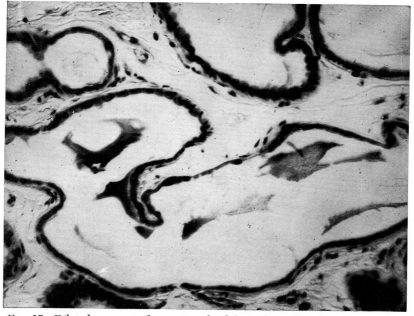

Fig. 25. Dilated segment of apocrine gland from the axilla of a woman 65 years old. The epithelium is flat, and nearly squamous. Stained with toluidine blue.

brings two facts into focus: (a) axillary hairs and apocrine glands differentiate at the same pace, and the agents which control one may, at least in part, control the other; (b) gonadal hormones, sufficient to maintain the menstrual cycle, may be inadequate to allow the development of normal axillary apocrine glands. If the apocrine sweat glands are a part of the complex of secondary sex characters, it is well to remember that they develop before puberty, and that they do not perish outright after the cessation of gonadal activity.

Apocrine glands undergo particular and interesting aging changes. Whether these changes are mucoid metaplasia, cystic dilatation, or atrophy (Ito *et al.*, 1951; Winkelmann and Hultin, 1958), the glands do not always change as units. In many cases, only some segments of a gland show changes, while the other parts of the same gland remain normal. In older subjects, whole glandular units may show such changes, but even in them many glands remain intact. Most of these are not specific changes and are of no greater magnitude than all of the other changes which take place in aging skin (Montagna, 1959).

The axillary apocrine glands of women are believed to undergo periods of greater or lesser activity that parallel the menstrual cycle and pregnancy. These concepts, based largely on histological material, have been accepted unquestioningly although there is good evidence to the contrary (Klaar, 1926; Montagna, 1956, 1959). The glands are said to be small and inactive during the intermenstruum, but swollen and active during the premenstruum and the menstruum (Loeschcke, 1925; Schaffer, 1926). Cavazzana (1947) states that during the premenstruum and menstruum the glands are actually larger than during the intermenstruum, their lumen is dilated and the secretory cells average taller. Cavazzana also observes that the myoepithelial cells are swollen and farther apart during the menstruum. During pregnancy the changes are supposed to be like those that occur during the menstruum but they are much more pronounced (Talke, 1903; Waelsch, 1912; Montes, *et al.*, 1960). A few authors (Loeschcke, 1925; Richter, 1932; Cornbleet, 1952), contrary to all others, believe that during pregnancy the axillary glands are in a resting state or at least their function is depressed. Unlike other authors, all of whom studied apocrine glands in autopsy material, or isolated biopsy material, those of us who have obtained biopsy specimens from the same women at weekly intervals during the menstrual cycle have found no changes in the axillary organ which correspond to the cyclic menstrual changes of normal women (Klaar, 1926; Montagna, 1956, 1959; Montes *et al.*, 1960). The functional activity, the thickness of the gland, the differences in the height of the epithelium and their content of granules, with or without pigment and iron in no way correspond to the menstrual cycle. The glands from specimens removed at monthly intervals during pregnancy and in puerperium exhibit a normal individual range of variation similar to that found in nonpregnant women (Montagna, 1956; Montes *et al.*, 1960).

The contradictions between these reports and those of others may be due to the use of improper and insufficient materials by the others. The most important point here is that most authors have failed to appreciate the enormous spectrum of variations which occur in the glands, even in one individual. It is so customary to believe in a cyclic activity that even such chemical data as increases in choline in the sweat during menstruation (Sieburg and Patzschke, 1923) is cited as proof of changes in the axillary glands. When one considers that only a small amount of the total sweat in the axilla is secreted by the apocrine glands, this "proof" becomes of little value. If cyclic differences occur in axillary apocrine glands, they do not seem to be reflected in their morphology.

The characteristic odor of the unclean axilla comes largely from the apocrine sweat. Sterile apocrine sweat, however, is odorless and the odor develops later, probably as a result of bacterial degradation (Shelley and Hurley, 1953; Hurley and Shelley, 1960). The axillary odor in Japanese subjects is said to diminish and disappear in old age, indicating a decrease and possible final cessation of axillary gland secretion (Ito et al., 1951). Sufficient data on Caucasian subjects, however, are not available. Hurley and Shelley (1960) found strong, normal axillary odor in 4 of 5 healthy men 65 to 70 years old.

Apocrine sweating is said to be largely a response to adrenergic stresses, such as fear, pain, sex, and systemic administrations of adrenergic compounds stimulate apocrine secretion. Secretion can be evoked also by local injections of epinephrine, as a result of which only those glands in the path of the spreading drug show secretions. Acetylcholine and pilocarpine, which induce profuse eccrine sweating, are said not to affect apocrine glands.

Pharmacological Responses of Apocrine Sweat Glands

Dr. T. Aoki, in our laboratory, has made preliminary studies of the pharmacological responses of the axillary apocrine glands in both Negroes and Caucasian subjects, and his results are particularly interesting. In these studies Aoki used the very sensitive iodine-starch method of Wada (1950) and Wada and Takagaki (1948). These are his results.

In agreement with Shelley and Hurley (1953) intradermal injection of adrenaline (l-adrenaline HCl, Parke, Davis and Co. 1:1000 commercial solution) in concentrations of 10^{-4} and 10^{-5} is effective in producing apocrine sweat response in all of the Negro and white subejcts tested. Although eccrine sweating also occurred, this was not so profuse and it was readily distinguished from apocrine sweating.

For cholinergic agents, Aoki used acetyl-β-methylcholine chloride (Mecholyl, Merck), acetylcholine chloride (Merck) and carbaminoylcholine chloride (Carcholin, Merck). These substances caused local eccrine sweating so profuse that it often prevented the exact identification of apocrine sweat spots in the pilary orifices. However, in four of nine Negro subjects tested, it was possible to see definitely the apocrine sweating response to Mecholyl used in concentrations of 10^{-4} or 10^{-5}; in the other five subjects the results were equivocal. Fortunately, in two of these four subjects, eccrine sweating in the axilla, spontaneous as well as in response to Mecholyl, was so weak and sparse that there was no difficulty in demonstrating apocrine sweating clearly (Fig. 26). In these two subjects injections of acetylcholine and Carcholin in concentrations of 10^{-4} and 10^{-5} also produced many clear apocrine sweat spots at the site of the injection. These responses, usually detectable one minute after the injection, were confined to the orifices of the hair follicles. Control injections with normal saline solution had no sudorific effects. This conflicts with the results of Shelley and Hurley (1953) and Hurley and Shelley (1960), who found cholinergic agents completely ineffective in producing apocrine sweating in the axilla. All of these four subjects were Negroes, and it is interesting that variable amounts of cholinesterase activity in the nerve fibers around the apocrine sweat glands are found only in the axilla of Negro subjects (Montagna and Ellis, 1960a).

After intradermal injections of Mecholyl, the sweat droplets that issued from the orifices of the follicles were collected separately with capillary tubes. The samples were turbid and slightly yellowish, similar to the apocrine sweat; samples collected from pores other than pilary orifices were always clear, and were eccrine sweat. This gives additional support to the conviction that the majority of the sweat spots that appeared at the pilary orifices in response to cholinergic stimulations are of apocrine origin. The secretion of sweat with similar characteristics after both adrenergic and cholinergic stimulations supports the belief that apocrine sweat glands are capable of producing only one type of secretion (Hurley and Shelley, 1954, 1960). The present study, however, is still too limited to completely deny the opinion that the apocrine sweat glands produce both apocrine and eccrine types of sweat (Sulzberger and Herrmann, 1954; Kuno, 1956; Rothman, 1954).

Atropine or dihydroergotamine (DHE) in a concentration of 10^{-4} were injected intradermally, and about 5 minutes later 10^{-4} Mecholyl was injected in the same site. There was almost complete absence of either apocrine or eccrine sweating at the site injected with atropine, but DHE failed to inhibit the effect of 10^{-4} Mecholyl on either apocrine or eccrine sweat response. In control experiments, previous injections of 0.9% NaCl also failed to inhibit the sweat response of Mecholyl. It is evident that the high doses used here are unphysiological, and that the apocrine sweat response caused by Mecholyl, acetylcholine, and Carcholin may not be due to cholinergic stimulations. Furthermore, we do

FIG. 26. Response of apocrine sweat glands to an intradermal injection of 10^{-4} Mecholyl in the axilla of a Negro. The large black spots at the base of each hair are apocrine sweat. The arrow indicates the site and the direction of the injection. (Courtesy of Dr. T. Aoki.)

not know whether these apocrine sweat responses are the result of simply squeezing out of sweat already pooled in the sweat gland by the contraction of the myoepithelium, or of true secretory activity.

When nicotine in 10^{-4} to 10^{-5} concentration was injected intradermally in the axillary skin of three Negroes who showed apocrine sweat response to cholinergic drugs, the subjects all gave positive results. The response was not so clear and did not spread as rapidly as in the case with the eccrine axon reflex sweating in the human forearm (Coon and Rothman, 1941; Wada *et al.*, 1952). Yet, some apocrine sweat spots did appear a distance from the injection wheal. In one trial in which a glass ring prevented the spread of the injected material, a solution of 10^{-5} nicotine injected in the skin area outside the ring induced apocrine sweat spots inside the ring. This observation, though limited to one subject, suggests the possibility of an apocrine sweat response by axon reflex mechanisms. Furthermore, Aoki has recently demonstrated a repeatable apocrine axon reflex sweating using nicotine and acetylcholine, in the general hairy skin of *Nycticebus*, a primitive primate.

The Phylogeny of Sweat Glands

It is not possible to reconstruct the phylogenetic history of any organ system by studying it in extant forms. It is fallacious to state that apocrine glands are more primitive than the eccrine glands, because eccrine glands seem to have developed gradually over the general body surface of primates, replacing apocrine glands. In assuming that the glands in the skin of "primitive" mammals are necessarily primitive, the histologist has been as arbitrary as the systematist. For example, the skin of the "primitive" *Ornithorhynchus* is not primitive at all, but beautifully adapted for an aquatic existence. Significantly, *Ornithorhynchus* has well-differentiated eccrine and apocrine glands (Montagna and Ellis, 1960d). Thus, who is to say which of these two types of glands is the more primitive? By stating that apocrine glands are more primitive than eccrine glands, we assume that the eccrine glands of primates have become progressively modified and specialized while the apocrine have stood still. This is unlikely to have happened. One can learn many things by studying the skin of primates systematically; we can infer from such studies that the sweat glands of man, eccrine and apocrine, are equally highly specialized and that they may have evolved from a common stem form. Such an archetypical gland probably resembled apocrine glands, but was as different from the modern apocrine gland as it was from the eccrine gland.

The primitive primates have generalized types of "apocrine" glands over the general body surface, and only somewhat specialized "eccrine" glands on the volar surface of the pes and manus. Neither of these two types of glands can be compared to the glands of man and of the higher primates. Furthermore, the two types of glands in the *Lorisidae* share many morphological and histochemical characteristics. The sweat glands of the *Lorisidae* usually grow one to a group of 4 to 20 or more hair follicles, the ratio of glands to hair follicles being small. Gradually the number of sweat glands over the general body surface has increased until there is practically a one-to-one ratio, and eventually in some parts of the human skin, more glands than hair follicles.

In spite of assertion to the contrary, the development of apocrine glands from hair follicles, and the opening of their ducts inside of a pilary canal seems to be a secondary event. The glands of the many primitive primates (the Prosimians) open directly onto the surface, often by a slightly coiled terminal segment and not inside the pilary canal. Even in the apes the apocrine glands may or may not open inside the pilary canals; only in man they nearly always do. This progressive shift of the orifice of the apocrine glands into the pilary canal can be verified phylogenetically in the extant primates.

The eccrine sweat glands of man have distinctive histochemical features, such as an abundance of glycogen, succinic dehydrogenase, amylophosphorylase, and the glands are surrounded by nerves that contain specific cholinesterase; the apocrine glands rarely share these characteristics. The eccrine and apocrine glands of the higher primates are essentially similar in these respects to those of man. This distinction, however, becomes meaningless in the lower forms. In the lorises, for instance, all sweat glands have these characteristics, even those that appear to be unmistakably apocrine.

The diameter of the duct of the eccrine sweat glands of man and of the higher primates is usually about one half to one third that of the secretory coil. The diameter of the duct of the apocrine glands is many times smaller than that of the secretory coil. In primitive primates the diameter of the duct of apparently eccrine glands is very narrow in contrast with that of the secretory coil, and thus the glands largely resemble apocrine glands. The duct of the eccrine glands of man and of the higher primates is very long and forms a sizeable part of the glomerate segment. This, however, is not the case in the glands of lower primates in which the glands have a straight, narrow duct directly attached to the coiled secretory segment.

One final consideration is that the scalp of man has a rich population of eccrine sweat glands, whereas that of the apes has only a few and that of most other primates has few or none. In the macaques, and the mangabeys, for example, eccrine glands are numerous on the brows, the lateral frontal, temporal and occipital (nuchal) regions, but few or none are found on the scalp proper. Thus, the acquisition of sweat glands on the scalp may be a recent event and must be considered one of the characteristic features of man.

In summary, then, the eccrine and apocrine glands of man are equally highly specialized and neither can be considered more primitive than the other. In the skin of man, the glands have attained a degree of specialization and development reached by no other mammal.

REFERENCES

Aavik, O. R. 1955. Cholinesterases in human skin. *J. Invest. Dermatol.* **24**: 103-106.

Adachi, K. and W. Montagna. 1961. Histology and cytochemistry of human skin. XXII. Sites of leucine aminopeptidase (LAP). *J. Invest. Dermatol.* (In press.)

Adams, W. S., A. Lesley and M. H. Levin. 1950. The dermal loss of iron. *Proc. Soc. Exptl. Biol. Med.* **74**: 46-48.

Allfrey, V. 1959. The isolation of subcellular components. *In* "The Cell" (J. Brachet and A. E. Mirsky, eds.), Vol. I, pp. 193-282. Academic Press, New York.

Beckett, E. B., G. H. Bourne and W. Montagna. 1956. Histology and cytochemistry of human skin. The distribution of cholinesterase in the finger of the embryo and the adult. *J. Physiol. (London)* **134**: 202-206.

Bergen, F. von. 1904. Zur Kenntnis gewisser Strukturbilder ("Netzapparate," "Saft-kanälchen," "Trophospongien") im Protoplasma verschiedener Zellenarten. *Arch. mikroskop. Anat. u. Entwicklungsmech.* **64**: 498-574.

Borsetto, P. L. 1951. Osservazioni sullo sviluppo delle ghiandole sudoripare nelle diverse regioni della cute umana. *Arch. ital. anat. e embriol.* **56**: 332-348.

Brinkmann, A. 1908. Die "Rückendrüsen von Dicotyles. *Z. Anat. Entwicklungs-geschichte* **36**: 281-307.

Bunting, H., G. B. Wislocki and E. W. Dempsey. 1948. The chemical histology of human eccrine and apocrine sweat glands. *Anat. Record* **100**: 61-77.

Burstone, M. S. 1959. New histochemical techniques for the demonstration of tissue oxidase (cytochrome oxidase). *J. Histochem. and Cytochem.* **7**: 112-122.

Burstone, M. S. 1960. Histochemical demonstration of cytochrome oxidase with new amine reagents. *J. Histochem. and Cytochem.* **8**: 63-70.

Carossini, G. 1912. Lo sviluppo delle ghiandole sudoripare, particolarmente ne' suoi rapporti collo sviluppo dell'apparato pilifero, nelle diverse regioni della pelle dell'uomo. *Arch. ital. anat. e embriol.* **11**: 545-603.

Cavazzana, P. 1947. Indagini sul comportamento morfo-funzionale delle ghiandole glomerulari apocrine della pelle e dell'ascella durante le fasi del ciclo mestruale e nella gravidanza. *Riv. ital. ginecol.* **30**: 114-134.

Charles, A. 1959. An electron microscopic study of the human axillary apocrine gland. *J. Anat.* **93**: 226-232.

Chiquoine, A. D. 1958. The identification and electron microscopy of myoepithelial cells in the Harderian gland. *Anat. Record* **132**: 569-583.

Coon, J. M. and S. Rothman. 1941. The sweat response to drugs with nicotine-like action. *J. Pharm. Exptl. Therap.* **73**: 1-11.

Combleet, T. 1952. Pregnancy and apocrine gland diseases: hidradenitis, Fox-Fordyce disease. *Arch. Dermatol. and Syphilol.* **65**: 12-19.

Dalton, A. J. and D. M. Felix. 1956. A comparative study of the Golgi complex. *J. Biophys. Biochem. Cytol.* **2** (Suppl.): 79-84.

Ellis, R. A. and W. Montagna. 1958. Histology and cytochemistry of human skin. XV. Sites of phosphorylase and amylo-1,6 glucosidase activity. *J. Histochem. and Cytochem.* **6**: 201-207.

Ellis, R. A., W. Montagna and H. Fanger. 1958. Histology and cytochemistry of human skin. XIV. The blood supply of the cutaneous glands. *J. Invest. Dermatol.* **30**: 137-145.

Glenner, G. G., H. J. Burtner and G. W. Brown. 1957. The histochemical demonstration of monoamine oxidase activity by tetrazolium salts. *J. Histochem. and Cytochem.* **5**: 591-600.

Hoepke, H. 1927. Die Drüsen der Haut. *In* "Handbuch der mikroskopischen Anatomie des Menschen" (W. von Möllendorff, ed.), Vol. 3, pp. 55-66. Springer, Berlin.

Holmgren, E. 1922. Die Achseldrüsen des Menschen. *Anat. Anz.* **55**: 553-565.

Homma, H. 1925. Über positive Eisenfunde in den Epithelien der apokrinen Schweissdrüsen menschlicher Axillarhaut. *Arch. Dermatol. u. Syphilis* **148**: 463-469.

Homma, H. 1926. On apocrine sweat glands in white and negro men and women. *Bull. Johns Hopkins Hosp.* **38**: 365-371.

Horn, G. 1935. Formentwicklung und Gestalt der Schweissdrüsen der Fusssohle des Menschen. *Z. mikroskop. anat. Forsch.* **38**: 318-329.

Horner, W. E. 1846. On the odoriferous glands of the negro. *Am. J. Med. Sci.* **21**: 13-16.

Hurley, H. J. and W. B. Shelley. 1954. The human apocrine sweat gland: two secretions? *Brit. J. Dermatol.* **66**: 43-48.

Hurley, H. J. and W. B. Shelley. 1930. "The Human Apocrine Sweat Gland in Health and Disease." C. C Thomas, Springfield, Illinois.

Ito, T. 1949. Histology and cytology of the sweat gland (in Japanese). *Igakuno-shimpo* **6**: 106-221.

Ito, T. and K. Iwashige. 1953. Zytologische und histologische Untersuchungen über die apokrinen Achselschweissdrüsen von gesunden Menschen höheren Alters (in Japanese). *Arch. histol. Japon.* **5**: 455-475.

Ito, T., K. Tsuchiya and K. Iwashige. 1951. Studien über die basophile Substanz (Ribonukleinsäure) in den Zellen der menschlichen Schweiss drüsen (in Japanese). *Arch. anat. Japon.* **2**: 279-287.

Klaar, J. 1926. Zur Kenntnis des weiblichen Axillarorgans beim Menschen. *Wien. klin. Wochschr.* **39**: 127-131.

Kölliker, A. 1853. *In* "Manual of Human Histology" (G. Busk and T. Huxley, eds. and translators), Vol. 1. Sydenham Society, London.

Krause, C. 1844. Haut. *Wagner's Handbook Physiol.* **2**: 108.

Kuno, Y. 1956. "Human Perspiration." C. C Thomas, Springfield, Illinois.

Kurosumi, K. and T. Kitamura. 1958. Occurrence of foldings of plasma membrane (β-cytomembrane) in cells of pig's carpal organ as revealed by electron microscopy. *Nature* **181**: 489.

Kurosumi, K., T. Kitamura and T. Iijima. 1959. Electron microscope studies on human axillary apocrine sweat glands. *Arch. histol. Japon.* **16**: 523-566.

Laden, E. L., I. H. Linden and J. O. Erickson. 1955. Study of normal skin with the electron microscope. *A.M.A. Dermatol.* **71**: 219-223.

Loeschcke, H. 1925. Über zyklische Vorgänge in den Drüsen des Achselhöhlenorgans und ihre Abhängigkeit vom Sexualzyklus des Weibes. *Virchow's Arch. pathol. Anat. u. Physiol.* **255**: 283-294.

Manca, P. V. 1934. Ricerche sulla struttura delle ghiandole apocrine. *Giorn. ital. dermatol. e. sifilol.* **75**: 187-193.

Melczer, N. 1935. Über das Golgi-Kopsche Binnennetz der menschlichen apokrinen Schweissdrüsenzellen. *Dermatol. Wochschr.* **100**: 337-342.

Minamitani, K. 1941a. Zytologische und histologische Untersuchungen der Schweiss-drüsen in menschlicher Achselhaut. Über das Vorkommen der besonderen Formen der apokrinen und ekkrinen Schweissdrüsen in Achselhaut von Japanern. *Okajimas Folia Anat. Japon.* **20**: 563-590.

Minamitani, K. 1941b. Zytologische und histologische Untersuchungen der Schweiss-drüsen in der menschlicher Achselhaut. Zur Zytologie der apokrinen Schweiss-drüsen in der menschlichen Achselhaut. *Okajimas Folia Anat. Japon.* **21**: 61-94.

Mitchell, H. H. and T. S. Hamilton. 1949. The dermal excretion under controlled environmental conditions of nitrogen and minerals in human subjects, with particular reference to calcium and iron. *J. Biol. Chem.* **178**: 345-361.

Montagna, W. 1956. Ageing of the axillary apocrine sweat glands in the human female. *In* "Ciba Foundation Colloquium on Ageing," Vol. II: Ageing in Transient Tissues, pp. 188-197. Churchill, London.

Montagna, W. 1959. Histology and cytochemistry of human skin. XIX. The development and fate of the axillary organ. *J. Invest. Dermatol.* **33**: 151-161.

Montagna, W. 1960. Cholinesterases in cutaneous nerves of man. *In* "Advances in the Biology of Skin," Vol. I: Cutaneous Innervation (W. Montagna, ed.) Pergamon Press, New York.

Montagna, W. and R. A. Ellis. 1958. L'histologie et la cytologie de la peau humaine. XVI. Repartition et concentration des esterases carboxyliques. *Ann. histochim.* **3**: 1-17.

Montagna, W. and R. A. Ellis. 1959a. The skin of primates. I. The skin of the potto (*Perodicticus potto*) Am. J. Phys. Anthropol. **17**: 137-162.

Montagna, W. and R. A. Ellis. 1959b. L'istochimica degli annessi cutanei. *Minerva dermatol.* **34**: 475-494.

Montagna, W. and R. A. Ellis. 1960a. Histology and cytochemistry of human skin. XXI. The nerves around the axillary apocrine glands. *Am. J. Phys. Anthropol.* **18**: 69-70.

Montagna, W. and R. A. Ellis. 1960b. The skin of primates. II. The skin of the slender loris (*Loris tardigradus*) Am. J. Phys. Anthropol. **18**: 19-44.

Montagna, W. and R. A. Ellis. 1960c. The skin of primates. III. The skin of the slow loris (*Nycticebus coucang*) Am. J. Phys. Anthropol. (In press.)

Montagna, W. and R. A. Ellis. 1960d. Sweat glands in the skin of *Ornithorhynchus paradoxus. Anat. Record* **137**: 271-278.

Montagna, W. and V. R. Formisano. 1955. Histology and cytochemistry of human skin. VII. The distribution of succinic dehydrogenase activity. *Anat. Record* **122**: 65-78.

Montagna, W., H. B. Chase and J. B. Hamilton. 1951. The distribution of glycogen and lipids in human skin. *J. Invest. Dermatol.* **17**: 147-157.

Montagna, W., H. B. Chase and W. C. Lobitz, Jr. 1953. Histology and cytochemistry of human skin. V. Axillary apocrine sweat glands. *Am. J. Anat.* **92**: 451-470.

Montagna, W., A. Z. Eisen, A. H. Rademacher and H. B. Chase. 1954. Histology and cytochemistry of human skin. VI. The distribution of sulfhydryl and disulfide groups. *J. Invest. Dermatol.* **23**: 23-32.

Montes, L. F., B. L. Baker and A. C. Curtis. 1960. The cytology of the large axillary sweat glands in man. *J. Invest. Dermatol.* **35**: 273-291.

Nicolas, J., C. Regaud and M. Favre. 1914. Sur la fine structure des glandes sudoripares de l'homme, particuliérement en cas que concerne les mitochondries et les phénomènes de sécrétion. *17th Intern. Congr. Med., Sect. 13, Dermatol. Syphilis,* pp. 105-109.

Ota, R. 1950. Zytologische und histologische Untersuchungen der apokrinen Schweissdrüsen in den normalen, keinen Achselgeruch (Osmidrosis axillae) gebenden Achselhaüten von Japanern. *Arch. anat. Japon.* **1**: 285-308.

Palade, G. E. 1952. A study of fixation for electron microscopy. *J. Exptl. Med.* **95**: 285-298.

Palade, G. E. 1955. A small particulate component of the cytoplasm. *J. Biophys. Biochem. Cytol.* **1**: 59-68.

Pinkus, H. 1958. Embryology of hair. *In* "The Biology of Hair Growth" (W. Montagna and R. A. Ellis, eds.), pp. 1-32. Academic Press, New York.

Richter, W. 1932. Beiträge zur normalen und pathologischen Anatomie der apokrinen Hautdrüsen des Menschen mit besonderer Berücksichtigung des Achselhöhlenorgans. *Virchow's Arch. pathol. Anat. u. Physiol.* **287**: 277-296.

Rolin, M. C. 1846. Sudoriparous glands of the axilla. *Am. J. Med. Sci.* **11**: 439.

Rothman, S. 1954. "Physiology and Biochemistry of the Skin." Univ. Chicago Press, Chicago, Illinois.

Schaffer, J. 1926. Über die Hautdrüsen. *Wien. klin. Wochschr.* **39**: 1-5.

Schiefferdecker, P. 1917. Die Hautdrüsen des Menschen und der Saügetiere, ihre biologische und rassenanatomische Bedeutung, sowie die Muscularis sexualis. *Biol. Zentr.* **37**: 534-562.

Schiefferdecker, P. 1922. Die Hautdrüsen des Menschen und des Säugetieres, ihre Bedeutung, sowie die Muscularis sexualis. *Zoologica* **72**: 1-154.

Schwenkenbecker, A. 1953. Cited from Comel (1933).

Shelley, W. B. 1951. Apocrine sweat. *J. Invest. Dermatol.* **17**: 255.

Shelley, W. B. and T. Butterworth. 1955. The absence of the apocrine glands and hair in the axilla in mongolism and idiocy. *J. Invest. Dermatol.* **25**: 165-167.

Shelley, W. B. and M. M. Cahn. 1955. Experimental studies on the effect of hormones on the human skin with reference to the axillary apocrine sweat gland. *J. Invest. Dermatol.* **25**: 127-131.

Shelley, W. B. and H. J. Hurley. 1953. The physiology of the human axillary apocrine sweat gland. *J. Invest. Dermatol.* **20**: 285-297.

Sieburg, E. and W. Patzschke. 1923. Menstruation und Cholinstoffwechsel. *Z. ges. exptl. Med.* **36**: 324-343.

Sperling, G. 1935. Die Form der apokrinen Haardrüsen des Menschen. *Z. mikroskop.-anat. Forsch.* **38**: 241-252.

Steiner, K. 1926. Über die Entwicklung der grossen Schweissdrüsen beim Menschen. *Z. Anat. Entwicklungsgeschichte* **78**: 83-97.

Sulzberger, M. B. and F. Herrmann. 1954. "The Clinical Significance of Disturbance in the Delivery of Sweat." C. C Thomas, Springfield, Illinois.

Talke, L. 1903. Ueber die grossen Drüsen der Achselhöhlenhaut des Menschen. *Arch. mikroskop. Anat. u. Entwicklungsmech.* **61**: 537-555.

Thies, W. and F. Galente. 1957. Zur histochemischen Darstellung der Cholinesterasen im vegetativen Nervensystem der Haut. *Hautarzt* **8**: 69-75.

Wada, M. 1950. Sudorific action of adrenaline on the human sweat glands and determination of their excitability. *Science* **111**: 376-377.

Wada, M. and T. Takagaki. 1948. A simple and accurate method for detecting the secretion of sweat. *Tôhoku J. Exptl. Med.* **49**: 284.

Wada, M., T. Arai, T. Takagaki and T. Nakagawa. 1952. Axon reflex mechanism in sweat responses to nicotine, acetylcholine and sodium chloride. *J. Appl. Physiol.* **4**: 745-752.

Waelsch, L. 1912. Über Veränderungen der Achselschweissdrüsen während der Gravidität. *Arch. Dermatol. u. Syphilis* **114**: 139-160.

Watson, M. L. 1955. The nuclear envelope, its structure and relation to cytoplasmic membranes. *J. Biophys. Biochem. Cytol.* **1**: 257-270.

Winkelmann, R. K. and J. V. Hultin. 1958. Mucinous metaplasia in normal apocrine glands. *A.M.A. Arch. Dermatol.* **78**: 309-313.

Woollard, H. H. 1930. The cutaneous glands of man. *J. Anal.* **64**: 415-421

Yasuda, K. and R. A. Ellis. 1961. Electron microscopy of human apocrine sweat glands. (Personal communication.)

Yasuda, K. and W. Montagna. 1960. Histology and cytochemistry of human skin. XX. The distribution of monoamine oxidase. *J. Histochem. and Cytochem.* **8**: 356-366.

Yasuda, K., H. Furusawa and N. Ogata. 1958. Histochemical investigation on the phosphorylase in the sweat glands of axilla. *Okajimas Folia Anat. Japon.* **31**: 161-169.

Zorzoli, G. 1950. Ricerche istochimiche sul pigmento intracellulare delle ghiandole axcellari dell'uomo. Nota I. *Boll. soc. ital. biol. sper.* **26**: 1-3.

CHAPTER 8

Reflections

Introduction

The aim of this book has been to present the microscopic anatomy of skin and to deduce functional significance from form and composition. In this last chapter, I am more reflective, and even speculative, in order to share with the reader some of my thoughts on the biology of skin which are not fully substantiated.

To avoid confusion, let us first define some of the terms that are used in this discussion. *Anlage* is a gathering of embryonic, or indifferent, cells from which an organ develops. An *indifferent*, or undifferentiated, cell is very difficult to define, but as used here denotes a cell that has not undergone visible specialization. *Differentiation* denotes the changes that take place in indifferent cells when they become specific, recognizable, functional adult cells. The cells of the epidermal system, regardless of their apparent differentiation, are equally capable of forming any part of the system and are *equipotential*. The changes that take place in adult, quasi-differentiated cells, into a type different from what would normally be expected, is referred to as *modulation*.

Although I have defined these terms rather dogmatically, I am aware of the grave difficulty in stating precisely the boundaries of each. For example, differentiation implies an advance of a cell from simplicity to complexity (Grobstein, 1959), but what are simplicity and complexity? It is convenient to think of the early embryo in terms of simplicity, homogeneity, and undifferentiation, but this must be understood in relative terms, since cells are neither simple nor homogeneous. Cells, regardless of their state of differentiation, have a highly organized cytoplasm, organelles, a nucleus, and numberless inherent patterns of developmental potentials. Unspecialized, or undifferentiated, cells are apparently uncomplicated only in so far as they are uncommitted in acquiring recognizable morphological and functional attributes which give them a final characteristic signature. We recognize differentiation in cells as a trend toward specialization and the attainment of greater complexity by undergoing changes in form and functions; these potential characteristics, however, must have been present in the cells all along. Some characteristic properties are expressed with such force that they mask others also present. Perhaps cells may also attain new characteristics in differentiation; some structural elements are modified,

425

as are also certain activities, special metabolism and molecular specificity (Grobstein, 1959). We distinguish at once highly differentiated cells from all others by their structural makeup and by their specific activities in the elaboration of specific end products.

It is very difficult to know what the boundaries of differentiation are in skin. For that matter, we do not know what is differentiation and what is modulation. Modulation changes are those which are expressed by cells only as long as the extrinsic factors that caused them persist (Weiss, 1939). When these factors are no longer effective, the cells revert to their normal structural and functional state. Differentiation, on the other hand, means stable, irreversible changes. In skin, then, how does one accurately separate modulation from differentiation? There are instances, as in the epidermis of the palms and soles, or the cornea of the eye, where the intrinsic bias of differentiation is stamped in the cells so indelibly that in spite of changes in extrinsic forces the tissues remain relatively unchanged; in nearly all other cases, however, the stamp of differentiation is carried lightly, and the intrinsic potentials seem to be at the constant mercy of the extrinsic factors.

Most of the skin appendages show constant change in growth and differentiation similar to that of embryonal systems. Unfortunately, we find only the differentiated states legible, and understand the developmental events *a posteriori* by the final product. The dynamism locked within the cells is still mysterious. With a few notable exceptions, then, adult skin, in spite of apparent specialization, remains largely uncommitted; it behaves in the adult as it did in the embryo. The patterns of growth and differentiation leave one with the basic impression that all of the cells of the cutaneous system are essentially *equipotential* and that true differentiation does not take place in skin, only *modulation* (see Weiss, 1939).

The histologist has insisted that the cells in adult skin are rigidly destined to produce only their own kinds. Yet, he has passed lightly over the fact that changes in the environment often induce great aberrations from the expected patterns of differentiation. We do not really know that such changes, or *metaplasias*, result from factors within the cells or within the stroma. A variety of agents, such as unnatural amounts of vitamin A, favor *in vitro* and, in some instances, *in vivo*, the differentiation of epidermal cells toward a mucoid, rather than a keratinous state (Fell and Mellanby, 1953; Weiss and James, 1955; Bern *et al.*, 1955a, b). In adult tissues, such mucoid metaplasia subsides and the epidermis returns to its normal state when the vitamin is withdrawn. Also, mucoid tumors of the skin, though not common, are found. This, clearly, is not the acquisition of a new characteristic by the cells, but rather an expression of one of its inherent potentials that is unmasked by proper extrinsic stimuli. I hesitate to call this metaplasia, since some cutaneous appendages often do the unexpected. Perhaps we should look upon such phenomena of metaplasia in skin as expressions of modulation. Even apparently differentiated cells, such as those from the outer root sheath of hair follicles and those of the ducts of sweat glands, under certain conditions, can regress into indifferent, equipotential cells; these later modulate into cells different from those which had characterized them before the change occurred.

During growth, the entire skin around each epidermal appendage shows correlated changes. Skin is an integrated organ. Unity of function and unity in response to stress are exhibited in both the dermis and the epidermis. Mechanisms which control the expression of differentiation of the indifferent epidermal cells probably reside within the dermis as well as within the epidermal structures themselves.

Equipotentiality and Modulation of Epidermal Cells

We recognize the different cutaneous appendages by their distinctive structural features and their specific end products. However, these features are visible only in the fully differentiated cells, and the pool of undifferentiated cells in any of them is practically indistinguishable. The indifferent cells are structurally and potentially similar, and the formation of strikingly dissimilar end products by them is brought about by specific inducing mechanisms.

It is remarkable that substances as dissimilar as sebum and keratin should be produced by cells basically so similar. Yet all epidermal cells form these different substances more readily than any other. All potential sebaceous cells normally show this bimodality. The innermost layer of cells in the ducts of sebaceous glands becomes progressively keratinized, as do the cells of the wall of the pilary canals and the surface epidermis; the undifferentiated cells elsewhere in the glands undergo sebaceous differentiation. Partial occlusion of the duct or other disturbances may induce nearly all of the indifferent, potential sebaceous cells to undergo only keratinous transformation (cf. Strauss and Kligman, 1958). When normal conditions are restored in such disturbed glands, keratinization becomes limited once again to the cells lining the excretory duct. Small keratin cysts may be found wherever sebaceous glands are numerous, such as in the face and the external auditory meatus. It is remarkable that both keratin and sebum can be formed by the cells anywhere in the hair follicles. Fragments of hair follicles stranded in the dermis of the skin of hairless mice give rise to sebaceous cysts, and these in turn become keratinized cysts. The indifferent cells in the pilosebaceous units, then, all share the ability to undergo sebaceous or keratinous transformation. Both sebaceous and keratinous cysts found in human skin, then, could originate from either sebaceous glands or hair follicles. In view of these facts, it seems unimportant to be so dogmatic on the precise origin of either sebaceous or keratinous cysts.

During wound healing the cells of the pilosebaceous units readily become epidermal cells. When the epidermis is destroyed, segments of injured hair follicles at the periphery of the wound flow radially and form a covering epithelium that undergoes normal keratinous differentiation. In the mouse, whole hair follicles at the edge of the wound can unfold and form epithelial tongues (Argyris, 1953). Sebaceous glands also participate in the formation of such epithelial tongues. Early in wound healing, partially or fully differentiated sebaceous cells can be found on the surface of the restored epidermis.

The ducts of sweat glands, long considered relatively passive structures for the transport of sweat to the surface of the skin, do remarkable things when they have been injured. When the epidermis and terminal ends of the ducts are removed experimentally, the basal cells of the stump of the sweat duct proliferate rapidly after a brief latent period (Lobitz et al., 1954). Some of these cells flow upward and form anew a spiraling terminal segment of the injured duct, even before the surrounding epidermis is restored. Other cells radiate laterally flowing over the surface of the wound. Cells from the epidermis at the periphery of the wound move centripetally over the denuded area until the two fields of new cells meet to restore an epidermis. The epithelium covering a repaired wound may thus be composed of cells derived from any or all of the cutaneous structures in the area. The restored epithelium is indistinguishable from normal epidermis. These changes in adult epithelial structures could not be achieved if these cells were rigidly differentiated.

In the mouse and rat, which are born practically naked, a few hair follicles continue to be formed from the epidermis for three or four days after birth. The ability to differentiate new hair follicles from the epidermis, however, seems to be lost after this epoch. Although much interest has focused on the formation of new hair follicles in the skin of man and other mammals, unquestioned proof is still lacking (Breedis, 1954; Billingham, 1958; Billingham, et al., 1959;

Kligman, 1959; Straile, 1959). One need not look at the newborn, or at wound healing, to find developmental patterns. In a sense, hair follicles undergo true morphogenetic changes with each cycle of growth. At the termination of every cycle, the lower portion of the hair follicle is dissipated, leaving only the short strand of cells of the hair germ. These cells comprise a true anlage; they remain relatively dormant until the follicle becomes active again, at which time the cells proliferate and reconstruct a hair follicle which is entirely new. The hair germ, or quiescent follicle, is an anlage. Some of the inductive mechanisms that bring about these changes seem to reside within, or be mediated by the dermal papilla. The papilla undergoes profound changes during the periods of growth and rest of hair follicles. During hair proliferation, it is large and contains abundant intercellular ground substance that strains metachromatically with toluidine blue, indicating the presence of acid mucopolysaccharides. When the hair follicles are quiescent, the small cells of the dermal papilla are crowded, and metachromatic substances are wanting. These changes may be the result of, or go together with, other more subtle changes in the dermal papilla, but they are predictable with every growth cycle of the follicle.

Much can be learned about the organization of hair follicles from observations of unusual circumstances. Early in life, genetically hairless mice lose their first pelage, and the hair follicle becomes fragmented in the dermis. The normal shortening of the follicle and the formation of the club and hair germ do not occur. The fragment that remains in contact with the dermal papilla becomes organized into a relatively well-formed, but small and disoriented, follicle. The hairs formed by these follicles do not emerge from the surface of the skin, but often grow parallel to it. Eventually these follicles become transformed into combined sebaceous and corneal cysts. The other fragments, which lose contact with the dermal papillae, develop directly into sebaceous cysts which later become keratinous. During normal catagen, or during catagen precipitated by X-irradiation, the bulb of the hair follicle degenerates and its base retreats up into the dermis. The receding base, however, never loses contact with the dermal papilla, which moves upward with it. The connective tissue sheath below the intact part of the follicle collapses and forms a flimsy trail below the dermal papilla which marks its path upward. If contact with the dermal papilla should be lost, the integrity of the follicles would also be lost.

The cells of the outer sheath in the upper portion of hair follicles demonstrates a variety of potentialities. When sebaceous glands are wiped out, they readily regenerate from the outer sheath (Montagna and Chase, 1950). During catagen, most, if not all, of the cells of the bulb flow up to become keratinized in the hair club or below it and the outer root sheath around the disappearing bulb collapses, forming a strand of cells below the club. The outer sheath, then, comprises the relatively permanent portion of the follicle and is, in fact, the potential hair germ, provided it does not lose contact with the dermal papilla (Montagna and Chase, 1954).

The bulb of a growing hair follicle demonstrates an orderly pattern of cell proliferation, flow, and differentiation. The indifferent cells that arise from the matrix move upward and laterally to form the three layers of the inner sheath and the hair. Growth and upward movement of the hair are accomplished by the addition of new cells from the matrix and by the increase in volume of each cell. The distribution of pigment in the cells of the hair bulb of colored hairs is very precise. The medulla and cortical cells of the hair acquire melanin, but the cuticle and all of the cells lateral to them normally have none. The distribution of dendritic pigment cells in the upper bulb around the dome of the papilla cavity and the extent of the dendritic processes are such that only the potential medullary and cortical cells are in contact with these dendritic processes in a particular stage of differentiation and can acquire pigment granules (Chase et al., 1951). In the damage that immediately follows X-irradiation, the cells of the cuticle of the cortex and those of the inner sheath also acquire melanin. During this time pigment is temporarily in excess, the cells are displaced, and the regular pattern is lost. Later, when a new hair is grown, the normal situation is restored; the pigment cells, if any are left, behave normally.

Role of the Stroma

In demonstrating equipotentiality, epidermal cells reflect their common origin. They are very different in the differentiated state, but the indifferent cells of the various appendages are the common form which share all of the inherent properties. Extrinsic factors or perhaps even intrinsic ones emphasize some of these potentialities while suppressing others. Some of the extrinsic factors apparently reside in the stroma, and there must be an intimate relationship and unity of function between the epidermal elements and their stroma.

The role of the connective tissue stroma in the maintenance of unity and in the guidance of the differentiation of epidermal appendages is not often properly emphasized. In the embryo, the mesenchyme always participates in the morphogenesis of organs (Grobstein, 1959); in some organs mesenchymal differentiation even precedes that of the parenchyma. Parenchymal anlagen require a well-prepared stromal field upon which to grow. The inductors may require for their action a specific organization of the responding system (Gianni, 1951). Perhaps they act by repatterning the system rather than by directly transforming its cells (Grobstein, 1952). Pure thyroid cells grown *in vitro*, for example, develop into typical thyroid tissue only when they are mixed with cultures of fibroblasts. The parenchyma of the submandibular gland of the mouse does not develop properly *in vitro* if the connective tissue capsule is removed (Borghese, 1950). Pure cultures of epidermal cells become organized into epidermis only when they are mixed with mesoderm (Fazzari, 1951).

Connective tissue, like the epidermis, shows a high degree of unity and lability of function and differentiation. Fibroblasts can transform into phagocytic cells. The three types of fibers are produced either by different types of cells or by the same cells. No one doubts that fibroblasts are associated with the formation of collagenous, and perhaps also reticular, fibers, but the formation of elastic fibers has received little thought. Since elastic fibers typically increase in tissues during ageing, there is a dyschrony in their formation in different organs (Fazzari, 1951). If specifically determined cells, "elastoblasts," exist, they seem to lie dormant until the time they become active in the formation of elastic fibers. If, however, there are no specific elastoblasts, what cells are responsible for the differentiation of elastic fibers? The elastic fibers in elastic cartilage present interesting possibilities. At least some of these fibers must be formed within the cartilage, and their development must be guided by the chondrocytes and/or chondroblasts. Elastic cartilage also contains collagenous fibers, and they must be formed under the influence of the same cells, there being no other cells in cartilage. Collagenous and elastic fibers, then, can be formed under the influence of the same cell. In connective tissue proper, elastic fibers are presumably formed by the fibroblast. Since chondroblasts are derived from fibroblast-like cells, fibroblasts, like epidermal cells, must be multipotential cells, the particular modulations of which are probably evoked by the specific physicochemical conditions of the environment.

The fibroblast in adult connective tissue need not be considered exactly the same type of cell at all times. Fibroblasts seem to regress to mesenchymal types, and the mesenchymal types in turn seem to differentiate into the different types of connective tissue cells. In the fibroblast we have the master cell of connective tissue; this cell must be delicately balanced and attuned to the biological demands of the organ. In maintaining this attunement, the fibroblast undergoes countless modulations which represent the imprints left upon it by the changes in the environment. Thus, the two principal component elements of skin, the dermis and epidermis, both exhibit lability and unity.

Unity and Integration

A series of different observations, some of them listed here, suggests that skin is a unified organ. After the skin of the guinea pig has been irradiated with 3000 r, sulfhydryl groups are said to diminish in the irradiated area as well as in the nonirradiated epidermis elsewhere in the animal. During the repair of the lesion, sulfhydryl groups increase in the regenerating epidermis, but the amount remains below that found in the nonirradiated epidemis of the same animal (Frederic, 1949). Since the amount of sulfhydryl groups in the nonirradiated epidermis is influenced by a lesion anywhere on the skin, perhaps a substance is secreted by the injured cells which modifies the metabolism of all the remaining intact epidermal cells. It has been claimed that wound healing in the skin of guinea pigs can be speeded up by painting the injured skin with one per cent ribonucleic acid (RNA) dissolved in physiological saline (Firket, 1951a, b). After such treatment, mitotic activity is said to increase in the treated side and also in a contralateral control wound that has either been treated with saline alone or left untreated. The number of mitoses on the control side painted with saline, however, is between that found in the epidermis of untreated intact animals and that found in wounds treated with RNA. When one wound is inflicted on the skin of a guinea pig, a large number of mitotic figures are encountered in it during repair. If a second wound has been inflicted simultaneously, the number of mitoses is reduced to less than half (Bassleer, 1953). Additional wounds have no significant further effects, and the number of mitoses remains approximately the same as with two wounds. When only one wound is present, the mitotic ratio in the intact epidermis is above normal. When two or more wounds are present, mitotic activity is suppressed. Pantothenic acid painted on wounds increases their regeneration rate. The untreated wounds and the intact, untreated epidermis in the same animal also show increased mitotic activity (Mouchette, 1953). To a greater or lesser extent, then, these observations point toward skin as an integrated, unified organ.

In the mouse the sebaceous glands destroyed with methylcholanthrene are readily reformed from the cells of the outer sheath of hair follicles. Regrowth is rapid in the hair follicles that are active, but in those that are resting, regrowth does not take place until much later, after the follicles become active (Montagna and Chase, 1950). Thus, the formation of new sebaceous glands is dependent on the state of activity of the whole follicle. One additional point is that the degree of damage that irritants inflict on skin depends upon the state of activity of the hair follicle (Chase and Montagna, 1951; Argyris, 1952). The local application of methylcholanthrene, vitamin A and its unsaturated ethers, polymers of chloroprene, etc., all cause various degrees of epilation and damage to the skin of the mouse, the rat, and the rabbit if the skin contains resting hair follicles. Skin with growing hairs, however, shows only minimal disturbance (Rademacher and Montagna, 1956). In both cases methylcholanthrene and vitamin A are shown by their fluorescences to be penetrating the skin. The physiological conditions prevailing in the skin during the two experimental treatments are different, and the conditions influence the nature and degree of the responses. This is an eloquent demonstration of organ integration.

The skin immediately around growing hair follicles undergoes profound changes which are related to the growth of these follicles (Chase et al., 1953). For example, during the early stages of anagen, the epidermis shows increased mitotic activity and a threefold increase in thickness. In middle anagen the epidermis becomes very thin, the dermis increases in thickness by about one-half, and the adipose layer by two to three times. During early anagen the peripheral acinar cells of sebaceous glands have increased mitotic activity, but in late anagen the sebaceous glands become smaller. These changes do not extend beyond the area immediately around active hair follicles. In man and the guinea pig hair growth is mosaic, i.e., each follicle goes through a cycle independent of neighboring ones, and changes can be observed on a reduced scale, or not at all.

Integration of skin in relation to the hair growth cycle is largely vertical; it is lateral only to a limited extent. In the skin of the mouse, rat, hamster, and rabbit, waves of hair growth move dorsally and posteriorly, adjacent follicles behaving synchronously. Hair follicles in these animals are so close together that there may be some "communication" among them. During the formation of the hair and the inner root sheath, some inhibiting substances could be accumulated within the follicle and associated structures (Chase, 1955); when such presumptive substances reach a certain level of concentration, hair growth ceases. When during the resting stage such a substance is dissipated the impetus to grow would again be expressed. Two facts point toward the existence of some such substance. Melanogenesis ceases shortly before hairs cease to grow, as if a high titer of this subtance were first detected by the pigment cells. When the stratum corneum is partially removed, the rate of mitotic activity in the basal layer of the epidermis increases roughly proportional to the amount of stratum corneum removed (Pinkus, 1952). A presumptive inhibiting substance could be held from escaping by the dead stratum corneum or be contained within the stratum corneum. Although there may be systemic, presumably blood-borne, effects on the skin, there must also be a local mechanism of control associated with the local sloughing of stratum corneum and the local hair cycles. Teleologically, a local system for maintenance and repair is more advantageous than a reaction of the whole skin to every local disturbance.

Summing up, skin is composed of very labile, equipotential cells, and the differentiation of epidermal appendages, or better, the modulation that precedes differentiation, is controlled by mechanisms that reside in both the dermis and the epidermis. The whole of skin, dermis and epidermis, is a unified, integrated system. If at times unity seems to be absent, perhaps we have failed to read its signs properly.

References

Argyris, T. S. 1952. Glycogen in the epidermis of mice painted with methylcholanthrene. *J. Natl. Cancer Inst.* **12**: 1159-1165.

Argyris, T. S. 1953. A study of the relationship between the hair growth cycle of the skin and wound healing in mice. Ph.D. Thesis. Brown University, Providence, Rhode Island.

Bassleer, R. 1953. Effets à distance d'un foyer cutané de nécrose et de régénération sur les mitoses de l'épiderme du cobaye. *Compt. rend. soc. biol.* **147**: 916-919.

Bern, H. A., J. J. Elias, P. B. Pickett, T. R. Powers and M. N. Harkness. 1955a. The influence of vitamin A on the epidermis. *Am. J. Anat.* **96**: 419-448.

Bern, H. A., D. R. Harkness and S. M. Blair. 1955b. Radioautographic studies of keratin formation. *Proc. Natl. Acad. Sci. U.S.* **41**: 55-60.

Billingham, R. E. 1958. A reconsideration of the phenomenon of hair neogenesis, with particular reference to the healing of cutaneous wounds in adult mammals. In "Biology of Hair Growth" (W. Montagna and R. A. Ellis, eds.), pp. 451-485. Academic Press, New York.

Billingham, R. E., R. Mangold and W. K. Silvers. 1959. The neogenesis of skin in the antlers of deer. *Ann. N.Y. Acad. Sci.* **83**: 491-498.

Borghese, E. 1950. Explantation experiments on the influence of the connective tissue capsule on the development of the epithelial part of the submandibular gland of Mus musculus. *J. Anat.* **84**: 303-318.

Breedis, C. 1954. Regeneration of hair follicles and sebaceous glands from the epithelium of scars in the rabbit. *Cancer Research* **14**: 575-579.

Chase, H. B. 1955. The physiology and histochemistry of hair growth. *J. Cosmet. Chem.* **6**: 9-14.

Chase, H. B. and W. Montagna. 1951. Relation of hair proliferation to damage induced in the mouse skin. *Proc. Soc. Exptl. Biol. Med.* **76**: 35-37.

Chase, H. B., H. Rauch and V. W. Smith. 1951. Critical stages of hair development and pigmentation in the mouse. *Physiol. Zoöl.* **24**: 1-8.

Chase, H. B., W. Montagna and J. D. Malone. 1953. Changes in the skin in relation to the hair growth cycle. *Anat. Record* **116**: 75-81.

Fazzari, I. 1951. Il problema dello stroma. *Rass. clin.-sci.* **27**: 355-361.

Fell, H. B. and E. Mellanby. 1953. Metaplasia produced in cultures of chick ectoderm by high vitamin A. *J. Physiol. (London)* **119**: 470-488.

Firket, H. 1951a. Action de l'acid ribonucléique sur la régénération de la peau. *Compt. rend. soc. biol.* **145**: 467-469.

Firket, H. 1951b. Recherches sur la régénération de la peau de Mammifère. Première partie: Introduction et étude histologique (evolution générale et analyse quantitative). *Arch. biol. (Liége)* **52**: 309-334.

Frederic, J. 1949. Étude histologique et histochimique de la peau du cobaye traitée par les rayons X. *Arch. biol. (Liége)* **60**: 79-101.

Gianni, A. 1951. Rapporti fra cellule epatiche e mesenchima attivo. *Boll. ist. sieroterap. milan.* **30**: 151-155.

Grobstein, C. 1952. Intra-ocular growth and differentiation of clusters of mouse embryonic shields cultured with and without primitive endoderm and in the presence of possible inductors. *J. Exptl. Zool.* **119**: 355-379.

Grobstein, C. 1959. Differentiation of vertebrate cells. *In* "The Cell" (J. Brachet and A. E. Mirsky, eds.), Vol. I, pp. 437-491. Academic Press, New York.

Kligman, A. M. 1959. The human hair cycle. *J. Invest. Dermatol.* **33**: 307-316.

Lobitz, W. C., Jr., J. B. Holyoke and W. Montagna. 1954. Responses of the human eccrine sweat duct to controlled injury. Growth center of the "epidermal sweat duct unit." *J. Invest. Dermatol.* **23**: 329-344.

Montagna, W. and H. B. Chase. 1950. Redifferentiation of sebaceous glands in the mouse after total extirpation with methylcholanthrene. *Anat. Record* **107**: 82-92.

Montagna, W. and H. B. Chase. 1954. A reappraisal of the formation of the hair germ in hair follicles (abstract). *Anat. Record.* **118**: 330-331.

Mouchette, R. 1953. Action de l'acide pantothénique sur la régénération de la peau de cobaye. *Compt. rend. soc. biol.* **147**: 1306-1309.

Pinkus, H. 1952. Examination of the epidermis by the strip method. II. Biometric data on regeneration of the human epidermis. *J. Invest. Dermatol.* **19**: 431-446.

Rademacher, A. H. and W. Montagna. 1956. Response of the skin of mice to methyl ether of vitamin A and vitamin A palmitate. *J. Invest. Dermatol.* **26**: 69-75.

Straile, W. E. 1959. A study on the neoformation of mammalian hair follicles. *Ann. N.Y. Acad. Sci.* **83**: 499-506.

Strauss, J. J. and A. M. Kligman. 1958. Pathologic patterns of the sebaceous gland. *J. Invest. Dermatol.* **30**: 51-61.

Weiss, P. 1939. "Principles of Development; a Textbook of Experimental Embryology." Henry Holt, New York.

Weiss, P. and R. James. 1955. Skin metaplasia *in vitro* induced by brief exposure to vitamin A. *Exptl. Cell Research Suppl.* **3**: 381-394.

Author Index

Numbers in italic show the page on which the complete reference is listed.

Subject Index

447